Milligan College Library
Milligan College, Tennessee

330

PRINCIPLES OF RURAL ECONOMICS

BY

THOMAS NIXON CARVER, Ph.D., LL.D.

DAVID A. WELLS PROFESSOR OF POLITICAL ECONOMY
IN HARVARD UNIVERSITY

GINN AND COMPANY
BOSTON · NEW YORK · CHICAGO · LONDON

4455

Milligan College Library
Milligan College, Tennessee

COPYRIGHT, 1911, BY THOMAS NIXON CARVER

ENTERED AT STATIONERS' HALL

ALL RIGHTS RESERVED

714.2

𝕿𝖍𝖊 𝕬𝖙𝖍𝖊𝖓𝖆𝖚𝖒 𝕻𝖗𝖊𝖘𝖘

GINN AND COMPANY · PRO-
PRIETORS · BOSTON · U.S.A.

He who sows the ground with care and diligence acquires a greater stock of religious merit than he could gain by the repetition of ten thousand prayers. — ZOROASTER

Milligan College Library
Milligan College, Tennessee

PREFACE

Though agriculture is our oldest and by far our largest and most important industry, it has only recently occurred to us in the United States that we had a rural problem. Nations, like individuals, are wont to prize the things they do not have rather than the things they have. Agriculture was so natural to our conditions, and established itself so easily, that we took it as a matter of course and gave our attention to the development of industries which did not show a disposition to grow naturally. Accordingly, during the first century of our national existence, our economic policy was framed mainly in the interest of the urban industries. The logical result of this artificial fostering of manufactures and commerce was the rapid building up of great overgrown cities and the creation of a group of urban social problems for which we were woefully unprepared. During the next twenty-five years these problems occupied the attention of economists and students of social science almost to the exclusion of everything else. It is only during the last decade that we have awakened to the fact that there is a rural as well as an urban problem. The agricultural colleges and the universities began offering courses on agricultural and rural economics, and there has been a remarkable development of interest in agriculture in the high schools of the country, which augurs well for the future of rural civilization in America.

The present treatise is written in the hope that it may direct attention toward some of the salient features of the rural problem. It emphasizes the public and social aspects of the problem somewhat more, and the business aspect somewhat less, than do most treatises on this subject. As a partial defense for his presumption in writing on so large and difficult a problem, with so little to guide him, the author may be allowed to mention that he grew up on a farm very near the center of the great agricultural region of the upper Mississippi Valley, that he later farmed independently on the Pacific coast, that he has made an effort to keep in touch with agriculture and rural life ever since, having, in addition to the ordinary methods of study, traveled a good many thousand miles on horseback and with a bicycle among the farms of this country and of Europe, and that he has been for several years teaching the subject of rural economics to classes varying in size from seventy-five to a hundred students in Harvard University.

The author desires to express his thanks to many of his former students for their helpful suggestions; to a brilliant group of young instructors in agricultural economics in several of our leading universities, particularly Professors H. C. Taylor of the University of Wisconsin, J. L. Coulter of the University of Minnesota, and George F. Warren of Cornell University; to Dr. L. G. Powers of the Bureau of the Census; to Sir Horace Plunkett, the leader in the economic regeneration of Ireland; to Dr. Howard L. Gray of Harvard University for valuable criticisms; to Miss A. E. Gardner of Cambridge, Massachusetts, for help in preparing manuscript; and, most of all, to his wife for her merciful but unerring criticism.

T. N. CARVER

CAMBRIDGE, MASSACHUSETTS

CONTENTS

I. WAYS OF GETTING A LIVING. The subject matter of economics, 1; War as a means of livelihood, 2; Economic and uneconomic methods, 2; Purpose of law and government, 3; Classification of economic methods, 4; The fundamental industries, 5; Changing the environment, 6; Why man dominates nature, 7; The pastoral stage, 8; Inefficiency of the hunting and fishing stage, 9; Transcendent importance of agriculture 10; Why agriculture is losing ground, 10; Extracting a living from other men, 11. II. FARMING AS A WAY OF GETTING A LIVING. Conditions of agricultural success, 13; Wherein the farmer is independent and wherein he is not, 14; Seasonal character of agriculture, 17; Domestic character of agriculture, 18; Farmers generally self-employed, 18; Reaction of business upon life, 20; Relation of the sexes in farming communities, 22; The rural districts the seed bed of the population, 25; Assumption of urban superiority, 26; Isolation the menace of farm life as congestion is of city life, 27.

I. THE EARLY STAGES. Hunting not universal, 29; Our own ancestors probably herdsmen, 30; Origin of the domestication of animals, 31; Reaction of the pastoral life upon character, 33; Reaction upon civilization, 33; Reaction upon family life, 34; Property in land, 35; Village communities, 35; Communal farming, 36; Private property in land, 38; The open-field system, 38; The two-field system, 39; The three-field system, 39; Lack of individual initiative, 40; Limited number of crops, 40; The manorial system, 41; Description of a manor, 41; Origin of the manor, 44; Inflexibility of the manorial system, 45; Decay of the manor, 45; Beginnings of commercial agriculture, 46; Inclosures, 46. II. THE BEGINNINGS OF MODERN ENGLISH AGRICULTURE. Our indebtedness to English agriculture, 48; Our indebtedness to other countries, 48; English indebtedness to the New World, 50; Transition to the modern system of rural economy, 51; The growth of tenancy, 52; New crops, 52;

I. LAND AS A FACTOR OF AGRICULTURAL PRODUCTION. Dependence
of agriculture upon area, 117; Law of diminishing returns, 118; An agricultural *vs.* a manufacturing and commercial policy, 119; Dependence
of manufactures upon markets, 120; Dependence of agriculture upon

BIBLIOGRAPHY

I. GENERAL WORKS

TAYLOR, H. C. Agricultural Economics (New York, 1905).

ANDREW, A. P. "The Influence of Crops upon Business in America," *Quar. Journ. Econ.* (May, 1906).

BAILEY, L. H. The Principles of Agriculture (New York, 1898); Cyclopedia of American Agriculture, Vol. IV (New York, 1909).

BERNARD, FRANÇOIS. Les systèmes de culture (Paris, 1898).

BRENTANO, LUDWIG JOSEPH. Agrar-Politik (Stuttgart, 1897).

BROOKS, WILLIAM P. Agriculture (Springfield, 1901).

BUCHENBERGER, ADOLPH. Agrarwesen und Agrarpolitik (Leipzig, 1892).

BURKETT, C. W. Agriculture for Beginners (Boston, 1904).

CATO. De Agri Cultura.

COLUMELLA. Husbandry (translated, London, 1744).

CARVER, T. N., and others. "Agricultural Economics," *Am. Econ. Assoc. Quar.* (April, 1908).

COOKE, SAMUEL. The Foundations of Scientific Agriculture (London, 1897).

CRONBACH, ELSE. Das landwirtschaftliche Betriebsproblem in der deutschen Nationalökonomie bis zur Mitte des XIX. Jahrhunderts (Wien, 1907).

DAVENPORT, EUGENE. The Principles of Animal Breeding: Thremmatology (Boston, 1900); Domesticated Animals and Plants (Boston, 1910).

DICKSON, ADAM. A Treatise of Agriculture (Edinburgh, 1875).

GOLTZ, THEODOR, FREIHERR VON DER. Vorlesungen über Agrarwesen und Agrarpolitik (Jena, 1899).

HATCH, K. L. Simple Exercises illustrating Some Applications of Chemistry to Agriculture (Washington, 1908).

HILGARD, E. W. Soils (New York, 1908).

HOPKINS, C. G. Soil Fertility and Permanent Agriculture (Boston, 1910).

JAMES, C. C. Practical Agriculture (New York, 1902).

JOUZIER, E. Économie rurale (Paris, 1903).

MEITZEN, A. Agrar-Politik.

PHILIPPOVICH, EUGÈNE VON. La politique agraire (translated from the German, Paris, 1904).

QUAINTANCE, H. W. The Influence of Farm Machinery on Production and Labor (New York, 1904).

ROBERTS, I. P. The Farmstead (New York, 1900).

ROSCHER, WILHELM. Nationalökonomik des Ackerbaues (Stuttgart, 1876).

THAER, ALBRECHT. The Principles·of Agriculture (translated, New York, 1846).

THÜNEN, J. H. VON. Der isolirte Staat in Beziehung auf Landwirtschaft und Nationalökonomie (Rostock, 1842).

VARRO. De Re Rustica.

WEST, SIR EDWARD. On the Application of Capital to Land (Reprint, Baltimore, 1903).

II. AGRICULTURAL GEOGRAPHY, RESOURCES, AND PRODUCTS

BRUCE, ROBERT. Food Supply (London, 1898).

COBURN, F. D. The Book of Alfalfa (Chicago, 1909).

CROOKES, SIR WILLIAM. The Wheat Problem (London, 1899).

DIETRICH, WILLIAM. Swine (Chicago, 1910).

DONDLINGER, P. T. The Book of Wheat (New York, 1908).

EDGAR, W. C. The Story of a Grain of Wheat (New York, 1903).

FISHER, JOSEPH. Where shall we get Meat?

GOODWIN, W. Wheat Growing in the Argentine Republic (Liverpool, 1895).

GRENÉDAN, J. DU PLESSIS DE. Géographie agricole de la France et du monde (Paris, 1903).

JOHNSTONE, J. H. S. The Horse Book (Chicago, 1908).

MAVOR, J. Report . . . on the North-west of Canada, with Special Reference to Wheat Production for Export (London, 1904).

MYRICK, HERBERT. The Book of Corn (New York and Chicago, 1904).

PLUMB, C. S. Indian Corn Culture (Chicago, 1908).

SANDERS, ALVIN H. Shorthorn Cattle (Chicago, 1900).

SERING, MAX. Die landwirtschaftliche Konkurrenz Nordamerikas in Gegenwart und Zukunft (Leipzig, 1887).

SHALER, N. S. The United States of America, Vol. I, chaps. vii and ix.

THOMPSON, G. S. The Dairying Industry (London, 1907).

WERNER, H. Die Rinderzucht (Berlin, 1902).

WING, JOSEPH E. Sheep Farming in America (Chicago, 1908); Alfalfa in America (Chicago, 1910).

WOODS, A. F. " The Present Status of the Nitrogen Problem," Yearbook of the Department of Agriculture, p. 125 (1906).

III. AGRICULTURAL HISTORY

A. GENERAL

PROTHERO, R. E. Pioneers and Progress of English Farming (London, 1888).

ALLEN, W. F. Agriculture in the Middle Ages.

ASHLEY, W. J. An Introduction to English Economic History, Book I, chap. i; Book II, chap. iv. (New York, 1893.) Surveys, Historic and Economic, pp. 39–166 (London, 1900).

CAIRD, SIR JAMES. English Agriculture in 1850–1851 (London, 1852).

CHEYNEY, EDWARD P. Social Changes in England in the Sixteenth Century (Philadelphia, 1895).

COLMAN, HENRY. European Agriculture and Rural Economy (Boston and London, 1846).

CUNNINGHAM, W. Outlines of English Industrial History, chap viii (New York and London, 1895).

CURTLER, W. H. R. A Short History of English Agriculture (Oxford, 1909).

DAUBENY, CHARLES. Lectures on Roman Husbandry (Oxford, 1857).

GARNIER, RUSSELL M. History of the English Landed Interest (Early Period) (London and New York, 1892); The same (Modern Period).

GAY, EDWIN F. Inclosures in England in the Sixteenth Century, *Quar. Journ. of Econ.* (August, 1903).

McDONALD, JAMES, and SINCLAIR, JAMES. A History of Hereford Cattle (London, 1910).

MAYO-SMITH. Statistics and Economics, chap. vii.

ROGERS, J. E. T. History of Agriculture and Prices in England.

SEEBOHM, FREDERICK. The English Village Community (London, 1883).

SIMONDE DE SISMONDI, J. C. L. Études sur l'économie politique (Paris, 1837); Essays 4, 5, and 6 on Conditions in Scotland, Ireland, and Tuscany.

SINCLAIR, JAMES. A History of Shorthorn Cattle (London, 1909).

YOUNG, ARTHUR. Annals of Agriculture and Other Useful Arts (London, 1784); The Farmer's Letters to the People of England (London, 1786); The Farmer's Tour through the East of England (London, 1771); A Six Weeks' Tour through the North of England (London, 1770); A Six Weeks' Tour through the Southern Counties of England and Wales (London, 1772); Tour in Ireland (Bohn's Library); Travels in France (Bohn's Library).

B. AMERICAN

FLINT, CHARLES H. "Progress in Agriculture, 1780–1860," in Eighty Years' Progress of the United States (New York and Chicago, 1864).

ARNOLD, B. W. History of the Tobacco Industry in Virginia from 1860 to 1894 (Baltimore, 1897).

BOGART, E. L. Economic History of the United States, chaps. i, v, ix, xvii, xviii, xxi (New York, 1908).

BRUCE, PHILIP A. Economic History of Virginia in the Seventeenth Century, Vol. I, chaps. iv–vii (New York, 1896).

COMAN, KATHARINE. The Industrial History of the United States, pp. 32–38, 47–62, 154–171, 243–255 (New York, 1905).

HAMMOND, M. B. "The Cotton Industry," *Pub. Am. Econ. Assoc.*, New Series, Vol. I, No. 1.

HART, A. B. "The Disposition of our Public Lands," *Quar. Journ. Econ.*, Vol. I, pp. 169, 251.

HIBBARD, B. H. History of Agriculture in Dane County, Wisconsin (Madison, 1904).

McCOY, C. F. "Cultivation of Cotton," in Eighty Years' Progress of the United States (New York and Chicago, 1864).

NIMMO, JOSEPH. Report in regard to the Range and Ranch Cattle Business of the United States (Washington, 1885).

OLMSTED, FREDERICK LAW. A Journey through the Back Country (New York, 1860); A Journey in the Seaboard Slave States (New York, 1856); A Journey through Texas (New York, 1857); Journeys and Explorations in the Cotton Kingdom (London, 1861).

PIERSON, C. W. "Rise and Fall of the Granger Movement," *Popular Science Monthly* (December, 1887).

RAND, BENJAMIN. Economic History since 1763, pp. 98–109, 207–242 (New York, 1903).

SATO, S. History of the Land Question in the United States (Baltimore, 1886).

WEEDEN, WILLIAM B. Economic and Social History of New England, 1620–1789, Vol. I, pp. 53–89; Vol. II, pp. 492–507. (Boston, 1890.)

IV. PRESENT AGRICULTURAL CONDITIONS AND TENDENCIES

PRATT, E. A. The Organization of Agriculture (New York, 1904).

ALFASSA, G. La crise agraire en Russie (Paris, 1905).

ALVORD, HENRY E. " Dairying at Home and Abroad," Yearbook of the Department of Agriculture, p. 145 (1902).

BASTABLE, C. F. " Some Features of the Economic Movement in Ireland," *Econ. Journ.*, Vol. XI.

BEAR, WILLIAM E. The British Farmer and his Competitors (London (Cobden Club), 1888).

BÉCHAUX, E. La question agraire en Irlande (Paris, 1905).

BRINKMANN, TH. Die dänische Landwirtschaft und ihre Entwickelung unter dem Einfluss der internationalen Konkurrenz (Jena, 1908).

CARL, ALFRED. Die Organisation der landwirtschaftlichen Tierproduktion unter Berücksichtigung der Arbeitsteilung und Specialisierung (Halle, 1898).

CHANNING, FRANCIS A. Truth about Agricultural Depression (London, 1897).

CLOTHIER, GEORGE L. " Forest Planting and Farm Management," Yearbook of the Department of Agriculture, p. 255 (1904).

DE FOVILLE, ALFRED. Le morcellement (Paris, 1885).

DUCLAUX, MME. The Fields of France (London, 1904).

DUN, FINLAY. American Farming and Food (London, 1881).

FAY, C. R. Coöperation at Home and Abroad (New York, 1908).

HAGGARD, H. RIDER. Rural England (London, 1902); Rural Denmark (London, 1911).

HOLMES, GEORGE K. " Causes affecting Farm Values," Yearbook of the Department of Agriculture, p. 511 (1905).

IMBART DE LATOUR, J. J. B. La crise agricole en France et à l'étranger (Nevers, 1900).

LEGOYT, ALFRED. Du morcellement de la propriété en France et dans les principaux États de l'Europe (Marseille, 1866).

LESLIE, CLIFFE. Land Systems and Industrial Economy of Ireland, England, and Continental Countries.

MOUNIER, L. De l'agriculture en France (Paris, 1846).

NICHOLSON, J. S. The Relations of Rents, Wages, and Profits in Agriculture, and their Bearing on Rural Depopulation (London, 1906).

PLUNKETT, SIR HORACE. Ireland in the New Century (London, 1905).

Report of the United States Industrial Commission, Vol. XI.
SAINT-GENIS, FLOUR DE. La propriété rurale en France (Paris, 1902).
TAYLOR, H. C. Decline of Land-owning Farmers in England (Madison, 1904).
VANDERVELDE, E. La question agraire en Belgique (Paris, 1905).
WILLIAMS, E. E. The Foreigner in the Farmyard (London, 1897).
WINFREY. "Progress of the Small Holdings Movement," *Econ. Journ.*, Vol. XVI.

V. AGRICULTURAL PROBLEMS

A. PROBLEMS OF FARM MANAGEMENT

CARD, F. W. Farm Management (New York, 1909).
ADAMS, EDWARD F. The Modern Farmer in his Business Relations (San Francisco, 1899).
ALDRICH, WILBUR. Farming Corporations (New York, 1892).
BAGOT, ALAN. The Principles of Civil Engineering as applied to Agriculture and Estate Management (London, 1885).
Certain Ancient Tracts concerning the Management of Landed Property (London, 1767).
COTTON, J. S. "Range Management," Yearbook of the Department of Agriculture, p. 225 (1906).
HALE, J. H. The Business Side of Agriculture. Massachusetts Public Documents (New York, 1898).
HUNT, T. F. How to choose a Farm (New York, 1906).
Report of the United States Industrial Commission, Vol. X, pp. ix and lxiv; and Vol. VI, pp. 5–19.
ROGERS, ARTHUR G. L. The Business Side of Agriculture (London, 1904).
SPILLMAN, W. J. "Cropping Systems for Stock Farms," Yearbook of the Department of Agriculture, p. 385 (1907); "Systems of Farm Management in the United States," Yearbook of the Department of Agriculture, p. 343 (1902).

B. PROBLEMS OF RURAL LIFE IN GENERAL

BUTTERFIELD, KENYON L. Chapters in Rural Progress (Chicago, 1908); The Country Church and the Rural Problem (New York, 1910).
ANDERSON, WILBERT L. The Country Town.
BOLTON, B. M. "Hygienic Water Supplies for Farms," Yearbook of the Department of Agriculture, p. 399 (1907).

EMERICK, C. F. "Agricultural Discontent," *Pol. Sci. Quar.*, Vol. IX, p. 436.

FAIRCHILD, GEORGE T. Rural Wealth and Welfare (New York, 1900).

HAGGARD, H. RIDER. A Farmer's Year (London, 1899).

KELSEY, CARL. The Negro Farmer.

MICHIGAN POLITICAL SCIENCE ASSOCIATION. Social Problems of the Farmer,— papers read at a joint meeting of the Mich. Pol. Sci. Assoc. and the Mich. Farmers' Institutes, February, 1902.

PLUNKETT, SIR HORACE. The Problem of Rural Life in America (New York, 1911).

STREETER, J. W. The Fat of the Land (New York, 1904).

C. PROBLEMS OF AGRICULTURAL POLICY. THE RELATION OF THE STATE TO AGRICULTURE

BAILEY, L. H. The State and the Farmer.

ANDREWS, FRANK. "Freight Costs and Market Values," Yearbook of the Department of Agriculture, p. 371 (1906).

BANKS, E. M. "The Economics of Land Tenure in Georgia," in *Columbia Univ. Studies* (New York, 1905).

BONSTEEL, J. A. "The Use of Soil Surveys," Yearbook of the Department of Agriculture, p. 281 (1906).

BRENTANO, L. "Agrarian Reform in Prussia," *Econ. Journ.*, Vol. VII.

CAIRD, SIR JAMES. The Landed Interest and the Supply of Food (London, 1878).

CHEYNEY, E. P. Recent Tendencies in Reform of Land Tenure.

COLLINGS, JESSE. Land Reform (London, 1908).

DARÁNYI, I. The State and Agriculture in Hungary, 1896–1903 (London, 1905).

FAWCETT, HENRY. State Socialism and Nationalization of Land.

GEORGE, HENRY. Our Land and Land Policy (New York, 1901).

KAUTSKY, KARL. Die Agrarfrage (Stuttgart, 1899).

LEVY, J. H. (Ed.). Symposium on the Land Question.

LAMBERT, EM. L'industrie agricole et l'industrie des transports (Paris, 1908).

MARLATT, G. L. "The Annual Losses occasioned by Destructive Insects in the United States," Yearbook of the Department of Agriculture, p. 461 (1904).

MEAD, ELWOOD. Irrigation Institutions (New York, 1903); "The Relation of Irrigation to Dry Farming," Yearbook of the Department of Agriculture, p. 423 (1905); Report of Irrigation Investigation in California (Washington, 1901).

PROBYN, J. W., and others. Systems of Land Tenure in Various Countries (London, 1876).

RUTTER, F. R. "Foreign Restrictions on American Meat," Yearbook
of the Department of Agriculture, p. 247 (1906).

WALKER, C. S. "Is there a Distinct Agricultural Problem?" *Pub. Amer.
Econ. Assoc.*, p. 56 (1897).

WALLACE, A. R. Land Nationalization (London, 1883).

VI. NEW OR SPECIAL OPPORTUNITIES IN AGRICULTURE

HARWOOD, W. S. The New Earth (New York, 1906).

CHILCOT, E. C. "Dry Land Farming in the Great Plains Area," Yearbook
of the Department of Agriculture, p. 451 (1907).

COLLINS, T. B. The New Agriculture (New York, 1906).

CONN, H. W. Agricultural Bacteriology (Philadelphia, 1901).

HALL, BOLTON. A Little Land and a Living (New York, 1908); Three
Acres and Liberty (New York, 1907).

KROPOTKIN, P. Fields, Factories, and Workshops (Boston, 1899).

MAXWELL, G. H. The Homecrofters.

MOORE, H. E. Back to the Land (London, 1893).

NEWELL, F. H. Irrigation in the United States (New York, 1902); The
Reclamation of the West (Washington, 1903).

SPILLMAN, W. J. "Diversified Farming in the Cotton Belt," Yearbook of
the Department of Agriculture, p. 193 (1905); "Opportunities in Agriculture," Yearbook of the Department of Agriculture, p. 181 (1904).

TERRY, T. B. Our Farming, or how we made a Rundown Farm bring
both Profit and Pleasure (Philadelphia, 1893).

WHITTAKER, GEORGE M. "Opportunities for Dairying in New England,"
Yearbook of the Department of Agriculture, p. 408 (1906).

WAYS OF GETTING A LIVING

- **I. Uneconomical**
  - **1. Destructive**
    - War
    - Piracy
    - Plunder
    - Swindling
    - Counterfeiting
    - Adulteration of goods
    - Monopolizing
  - **2. Neutral**
    - Marrying wealth
    - Inheriting wealth
    - Benefiting through a rise in land values
- **II. Economical**
  - **1. Primary industries**
    - Farming
    - Mining
    - Hunting
    - Fishing
    - Lumbering
  - **2. Secondary industries**
    - Manufacturing
    - Transporting
    - Storing
    - Merchandising
  - **3. Personal or professional service**
    - Healing
    - Teaching
    - Inspiring
    - Governing
    - Amusing
    - etc.

PRINCIPLES OF RURAL ECONOMICS

CHAPTER I

GENERAL PRINCIPLES

I. Ways of getting a Living

The subject matter of economics. The study of man's efforts
to get a living, which is the subject matter of economics, may
well be considered one of the most serious and important
topics which can possibly engage the attention of the student.
We may begin this study with the rather commonplace observation that the race must get its living out of the material world
which surrounds it; that is, its living must ultimately come
out of the soil and the water. But when we consider man as
an individual rather than as a race, we find that he sometimes
makes his living directly out of other individuals, and not
invariably out of the soil and the water. In a primitive or
savage state, unrestrained by a sense of justice or by a code of
laws, he usually followed the method which promised the largest
returns for the least effort. If war and plunder offered much
more attractive opportunities he resorted to war and plunder.
If hunting animals rather than men offered an equally good
opportunity, he hunted animals. But when neither of these
methods proved profitable enough, he resorted to the herding
of animals, sometimes to the herding of men under the form
of slavery, sometimes to the cultivation of the soil and the
selection, planting, and harvesting of desirable crops.

War as a means of livelihood. The terms "war" and "plunder" are usually applied to efforts of one nation, tribe, or community as a whole to get land, wealth, or some other economic advantage from another community as a whole. Where the same methods are practiced by the members of a nation, tribe, or community against their own fellow citizens they are called murder, robbery, and theft. Cannibalism and slavery have seldom been practiced except against members of outside communities,—against people to whom one did not feel any of the obligations of a common citizenship. It is obvious that such methods of getting a living are destructive rather than productive. The world as a whole could obviously never be enriched by war and plunder, for example, though the successful party may be enriched if the plunder is rich enough to more than balance the cost of the war.

Even within the same nation, tribe, or community there are sometimes practices which enrich one man or group of men at the expense of others. Such practices are always the mark of a weak and inefficient or of a corrupt government, and are growing less and less in proportion as governments become efficient and honest. There are also practices by means of which men get a living by serving other people or the community as a whole. These include the commoner industrial and business practices and the leading forms of professional and personal service. The fewer there are in any nation who get their living at the expense of others, and the more there are who get their living by productive and serviceable practices, the better it is for that nation, and the more it will prosper.

Economic and uneconomic methods. Accordingly the first and fundamental distinction to be made among different ways of getting a living is that between the uneconomic or unproductive methods and the economic or productive methods. The uneconomic methods of getting a living are sometimes destructive, and include all those occupations in which one's success depends upon one's power to destroy, to injure, or to deceive. War, plunder, robbery, and fraud of all kinds are included in this class. These methods are called "uneconomic," because when one individual secures something by any of these methods no one else is benefited and some one is sure to be injured. Other methods are not positively destructive, but are nevertheless unproductive in the sense of returning to society no real advantage for the living received. Getting rich by marrying or inheriting wealth, or through a rise in land values, would come in this class. The economic or productive methods of getting a living are those in which one's success depends upon one's power to produce or to serve. All productive industries and all useful trades and professions belong in this class. They are called economic because, when one individual gets something by any of these methods, no one else is injured and some one is always certain to be benefited. People who make their living by these methods do not impoverish other people, but tend to enrich them. The richer a man gets by any of the productive methods the richer he makes the rest of the world, and in proportion as the whole community or the whole world adopts these methods, in that proportion will the whole community or the whole world prosper, whereas the opposite is true of the uneconomic methods.

Purpose of law and government. With the progress of civilization, with the growth of a sense of justice and a perception of what is good and what is bad for a people, with the development of systems of law and governmental control, there is a tendency more and more to prohibit the uneconomic methods and to leave only the economic methods open to individuals. A government may be said to be just and efficient in proportion as it distinguishes sharply between these methods and as it succeeds in suppressing all uneconomic methods. No government has yet attained perfection in either of these particulars, but some are making continuous progress. However, every government is first concerned with the repression of the uneconomic methods within its own territory. They sometimes allow and even organize uneconomic methods in other territories, that is, they sometimes engage in wars of conquest. Progress in the direction of suppressing this particular uneconomic method comes very slowly.

Even within their own territory various forms of deception are frequently allowed by modern governments, but these methods need not be considered at any great length. The sturdy beggar who disguises himself as a cripple in order to appeal to the sympathy of the passers-by, the counterfeiter and the confidence man who take advantage of the ignorance and the cupidity of their victims, and the gambler who takes advantage of their inexperience and their inability to grasp the laws of probability, are well-recognized types which the laws of most civilized countries are trying to suppress. But the manufacturer and seller of worthless nostrums under the name of medicine, of shoddy or adulterated goods under the name of pure goods, the writer and the publisher of sensational falsehoods under the name of news, the teacher of irrational superstitions under the name of religion, — every one, in fact, who profits by deception, — belong in the same class. Needless to say, activities of this description tend to the impoverishment rather than the prosperity of all except those who practice them; they are uneconomic, and the more men there are practicing these methods upon their fellow citizens, the worse it is for the country as a whole and the poorer it will become.

Classification of economic methods. The economic ways of getting a living may be divided into three principal classes, called primary industries, secondary industries, and personal and professional service. The primary industries, sometimes called extractive industries, are those which are engaged in extracting useful material from the earth, the soil, or the water. They are hunting, fishing, farming and stock raising, lumbering, and mining. The secondary industries are those which handle and make over the materials furnished by the primary industries and bring them to a place where they can be used, or change them into a form which is more desirable, or store them till a time when they are more needed. They are transporting, manufacturing, and merchandising. Personal and professional services are all services which, though of the highest utility, are not engaged directly in producing or handling material commodities. The barber, the physician, the teacher, the musician, and a great many others are performing services of this class.

The fundamental industries. Those industries which extract useful materials from the physical world are always the fundamental, as they were the original, sources of subsistence. We know very little about the primitive state of man, but it is reasonable to suppose that he got his living by gathering such edible fruits and herbs as grew spontaneously without cultivation, by hunting wild animals, or by fishing. In this stage the economic life of man did not differ greatly from that of the lower animals. His success depended, as did theirs, upon his finding enough of these natural products for his nourishment. But while the animals have continued to take the natural world as they find it, and to live or die according as they find or fail to find natural products ready for their use, men have assumed the active rôle and have transformed their environment to suit their own needs. With the exception of such elementary processes as the digging of burrows, the building of nests, and, in the case of the beavers, the construction of somewhat elaborate shelters, animals have made no attempts to improve their natural surroundings. Whatever primitive man may have done, the lowest races known to-day do more than the animals in this direction. They not only construct shelters, they fashion tools and weapons, they build fires, and, with few and doubtful exceptions, they manufacture some form of clothing ; while higher races have all succeeded in modifying their natural surroundings to such a degree as to have created for themselves a new and better environment.

Changing the environment. It has been a favorite literary device to represent some one as falling into a Rip Van Winkle sleep on the eve of a social or political revolution and awaking after the revolution is accomplished, to find himself in a new world, though in the old place. For the purpose of showing how far our civilized life has changed from that of primitive man, we may get along with a much simpler device. Let us imagine that a philosophical savage has been whisked through space and set down at one of those points where modern civilization has taken on an acute form. Let us imagine him on the busy corner of a great city, where pavements have displaced the native turf, where the ground beneath is honeycombed with cellars, subways, sewers, conduits, etc., where many-storied buildings rise into the air on every hand, and the sky is obscured by elevated railways, and wires, poles, and other obstacles. Or imagine him in a law court, where the notorious John Doe and Richard Roe are having one of their interminable disputes adjudicated amid much learned disputation of counsel and the citing of many ancient precedents and modern instances. Or picture him in a stock exchange where men in every stage of corpulency and physical unfitness are furiously buying and selling intangible rights to give or receive intangible evidences of ownership in intangible forms of property, and all the while deceiving themselves into thinking that the world is fed and clothed by such operations as these. In the effort to imagine the surprise and perplexity of our philosophic savage we may ourselves arrive at a conception of the extreme complexity and artificiality of that which we call civilized life. Moreover, we shall see that it is all connected, directly or indirectly, with the work of getting a living.

In his pursuit of a living, man has changed the surface of the earth and made it over to suit his own needs.

Why man dominates nature. Man, as a race, has succeeded in achieving this result by virtue of the fact that he has known how to control and direct the forces of nature. He has observed the sequence of cause and effect, he has seen that certain desirable results followed certain preceding conditions, and has therefore taken measures to create those conditions in order that the results might follow. He has been able to utilize certain mechanical principles, like the elasticity of the bow, the cutting power of the ax, the lifting power of the lever, etc.; and these have given him the beginnings of a mastery over nature which he has followed up by a more and more complete domination, until now he is beginning to realize that he can live in a world almost of his own making. At least he can remake the world in which he lives, creating for himself a new and better home, where more and better food grows than grew before, where artificial shelters, with artificial heat and light, take the place of bushes and caves, and where clothing protects the body from cold and heat, thorns and insects ; a world also from which dangerous beasts have been, and dangerous insects and microbes doubtless soon will be, exterminated, and where artificial means of locomotion supplement, if they do not displace, the natural means.

There is a philosophy, to which the student of economics ought easily to incline, which regards this task of subduing the earth and making it a better and more comfortable home for himself as the first and greatest duty of man on earth. This philosophy would test the soundness of all conduct, of all social institutions, and even of all moral codes, by this question : Do they help in the great task which the human race has before it, or do they hinder? If they help, they are good and sound. If they hinder, they are unsound and bad. But this work of subduing the earth is only the larger aspect of the work of getting a living; for getting a living means, as indicated above, extracting the means of subsistence, of comfort, and of happiness out of the material world which surrounds us.

The pastoral stage. Among those peoples who originally got their living by hunting, and who therefore subsisted largely upon animal food, the next stage of industrial development was usually the pastoral. This was a stage in which men got their living principally by herding and breeding animals which they had tamed and domesticated. This was more economical than hunting, for several reasons. In the first place, the people protected their useful animals from beasts of prey; again, they drove away the wild and less useful animals which might consume the grass needed by their own animals. By these methods larger numbers of useful animals were enabled to live in a given territory, and thus more ample subsistence was secured. Not only was the subsistence more ample; it was also more regular in its supply and more easily accessible.

The pastoral industry consisted, as already indicated, in giving a preference to certain selected types of animals and in excluding other animals which would interfere with their multiplication and growth. It was eventually found, however, that certain plants were more useful than others, either as forage for the animals or as food for man, and that these plants could only be increased by waging war against other plants, now called weeds, which contended against the useful ones for the possession of the soil. When men began to give the preference to these useful plants, to prepare the soil for them, and to destroy the useless ones in order that the useful might multiply and grow, agriculture was born. That is what agriculture consists of to this day. This was an improvement over the mere herding of animals, as herding had been over hunting. By enabling more useful plants to grow than had grown before, subsistence was greatly increased, and the limit is not yet reached. Peoples who never made their living by hunting wild animals, but by gathering wild herbs and fruits, probably developed into the agricultural stage directly without having passed through the pastoral stage.

Inefficiency of the hunting and fishing stage. That the barbarous method of getting a living by hunting and fishing is very inefficient as compared with agriculture may be shown by the following considerations. It is the opinion of those most competent to judge, that there were never more than 500,000 Indians in that part of the present territory of the United States which lies east of the Mississippi and the Missouri rivers. By their methods of getting a living, which consisted mainly of hunting and fishing, even this small number could eke out only a meager existence. Each tribe was forced to be on its guard lest its hunting grounds be invaded by other tribes and its source of subsistence thereby cut off. But this same territory now supports about 60,000,000 people, and most of their food and a good part of the materials for their clothing are produced on its farms. No country of equal area, however rich by nature, is capable of supporting a population such as this by hunting and fishing alone.

Of all the extractive industries farming has become, in all civilized countries, vastly the most important. In certain small communities lumbering and mining may, for a brief period, overshadow farming; but for large areas, and over long periods of time, none of the other extractive industries can even rival farming. Moreover, lumbering — as distinct from forestry, which is a kind of farming — and mining tend to exhaust, once and for all, the store of natural resources which they are engaged in extracting. On the other hand, farming may last for indefinite periods, by reason of the fact that if wisely managed the soil may be conserved and renewed, and even improved. For this reason agricultural communities are usually characterized by their stability, whereas lumbering and mining communities, usually called camps in this country, are characterized by their instability.

Transcendent importance of agriculture. As compared with the secondary industries, agriculture is still overwhelmingly the most important, if we consider the world at large, or any considerable section of it which is self-supporting. But agriculture is gradually losing this position, relatively at least, for reasons which will be noticed later. Even now there are certain sections, and even whole countries, which manufacture a great deal more, and produce on farms a great deal less, than they consume, exchanging their surplus manufactures for the surplus agricultural products of other sections or countries where land is more abundant and population less abundant. In such places agriculture may be, for a time, forced into a subordinate position.

Why agriculture is losing ground. Again, as civilization advances and men come to demand finer and still finer products for their use, the tendency seems to be for manufactures, trade, and transportation to gain in magnitude and importance as compared with the extractive industries. In order that there may be a supply of the finer products which the world is coming to demand, the raw materials which the extractive industries furnish must be worked over more and more and brought to a higher degree of refinement. This is, in general, though not wholly, the work of the secondary industries, and thus the magnitude of their work grows in comparison with that of the extractive industries. However, this demand for finer products tends also to stimulate certain high types of farming, such as market gardening, fruit growing, milk production, etc. It takes more work, for example, to produce the very best quality of milk than a poor quality; and when the market comes to demand a higher grade of milk, *and is willing to pay for it*, there will be more men employed in dairying, and that industry will then grow in magnitude and importance, even though no more milk is produced per capita than now. Thus the gain resulting from a higher civilization and a higher standard of living is not exclusively, though it is mainly, on the side of the secondary industries. There are other causes, however, which tend to stimulate the growth of the secondary industries at the expense of the primary. Among these may be mentioned the invention of farm machinery, which is manufactured in the cities, and by means of which labor is saved on the farms, thus tending to reduce, relatively to the city population at least, the number of people living on the farms. But whatever may happen in the very distant future, it still remains true, taking the world over, that agriculture is the greatest industry.

Extracting a living from other men. It was remarked at the beginning of this chapter that when we consider man as a race we find that he must get his living out of the material world. As an individual, however, we shall find that, even when he is following an economic method of getting a living, he does not always get it out of the material world, and that his individual success does not always depend upon his ability to control or direct the forces of physical nature. It sometimes depends upon his power to direct and control other men, and sometimes upon his ability to please them. Controlling other men in the sense of governing them, persuading them, leading them *in the right direction*, and stimulating them to higher endeavor, is of the greatest possible assistance in the task of subjugating nature and remaking the earth, and they who are able to do this are among the greatest of men. Even though such men frequently have little knowledge of the natural world and little aptitude for the actual work of controlling and directing physical forces, nevertheless they know men, they understand the human heart, and they are experts in directing the forces which govern human society. The work of pleasing men, even of amusing them, may also help in this great task if it enables the workers to return to it with new vigor and enthusiasm.

It would not be possible, however, to draw any sharp dividing line between those occupations where individual success depends upon skill in controlling physical forces and material things, and those where it depends upon skill in controlling social forces and men. The success of almost every person, unless it be that of the pioneer in an uninhabited wilderness, depends, in some slight degree at least, upon his ability to adapt himself to social as well as physical conditions, — upon his ability to deal successfully with other men as well as with things. And there is scarcely any one, unless it be the politician, whose success does not depend in some slight degree at least upon knowledge of physical forces and the properties of things, together with some skill in applying that knowledge. Nevertheless, there are certain occupations where success depends *primarily* upon power over things, and to a slight degree upon power over men, and vice versa. The farmer, the sailor, the mechanic, the engineer, and the experimental scientist may all be put in the former class. In the latter we should probably put, in addition to the politician, who is the example *par excellence*, the lawyer, the actor, the preacher, the teacher, and the salesman, — every one, in fact, whose active work consists mainly in talking, or whose success depends mainly upon being keen judges of human nature.

Upon this topic the words of Thomas Carlyle are not only instructive but inspiring as well.

Two men I honor, and no third. First, the toilworn Craftsman that with earth-made Implement laboriously conquers the Earth, and makes her man's. Venerable to me is the hard Hand; crooked, coarse; wherein notwithstanding lies a cunning virtue, indefeasibly royal, as of the Scepter of this Planet.

Venerable too is the rugged face, all weather-tanned, besoiled, with its rude intelligence; for it is the face of a Man living manlike. O, but the more venerable for thy rudeness, and even because we must pity as well as love thee! Hardly-entreated Brother! For us was thy back so bent, for us were thy straight limbs and fingers so deformed: thou wert our Conscript, on whom the lot fell, and fighting our battles wert so marred. . . .

. A second man I honor, and still more highly: Him who is seen toiling for the spiritually indispensable; not daily bread, but the bread of Life. Is not he too in his duty; endeavoring towards inward Harmony; revealing this, by act or by word, through all his outward endeavors, be they high or low? Highest of all, when his outward and his inward endeavor are one: when we can name him Artist; not earthly Craftsman only, but inspired Thinker, who with heaven-made Implement conquers Heaven for us! If the poor and humble toil that we have Food, must not the high and glorious toil for him in return, that he have Light, have Guidance, Freedom, Immortality? — These two, in all their degrees, I honor: all else is chaff and dust, which let the wind blow whither it listeth.

From *Sartor Resartus*

II. FARMING AS A WAY OF GETTING A LIVING

Conditions of agricultural success. Of all the leading occupations in a civilized country, there is none in which success depends so little upon social, and so much upon physical, knowledge and adaptability as farming. And there is none where life is lived and work is done in such intimate and direct contact with nature and so little in contact with other men. One result of this kind of life and work is that the farmer acquires less of what are sometimes called the social graces, — less adroitness in the amenities of social intercourse, less expertness in the intricacies of drawing-room etiquette, — than the members of almost any other large class. Those who get their living out of other men must of necessity be skillful in the arts of pleasing other men. It is part of their business. But they who get their living out of the soil must concentrate their attention upon the soil and the things pertaining to it; and the skill and knowledge which they acquire must relate to these things rather than to social intercourse. It is for this reason, and for this reason only, that urban people have generally found occasion to reproach rural people for their lack of urbanity.

This characteristic, however, is becoming less noticeable in the case of the modern commercial farmer than it was in that of the self-sufficing farmer. The self-sufficing farmer made his farm produce nearly everything which he and his family consumed. Having little to buy or sell, and few occasions for travel, he had few points of contact with other men ; therefore he had little to gain by social polish, and few opportunities for acquiring it. The tendency is, however, toward greater and greater specialization in agriculture, toward a system under which each farm produces only those crops for which it is best suited. Under this system each farmer of course produces a great deal more of these special crops than he can possibly consume. He must therefore sell all or the greater part of what he produces, and with the proceeds buy the other goods which he needs. This calls for a great deal of buying and selling ; it brings him more and more into contact with the world of men, as well as with the world of material things ; and it is forcing him to become more and more familiar with its movements, its manners and customs, its markets, its political and commercial policies, and its scientific discoveries. Therefore this old distinction between rural and urban people, based upon the farmer's lack of social polish, is tending to disappear, and may possibly disappear altogether with the lapse of time.

Wherein the farmer is independent and wherein he is not. These considerations bring us to the question of the so-called independence of the farmer. In the days of the self-sufficing system of agriculture the farmers were less dependent than any other class upon commercial, social, and political conditions, — conditions existing in the world of men. Industrial disturbances, financial panics, commercial depressions, and all such happenings were of little moment to those who got their living out of the soil. Viewed from this standpoint, the farmer led an independent life. But, on the other hand, happenings in the physical world were of the utmost concern to him, and he was, in fact, more dependent upon these than any other class. Floods, droughts, storms, untimely frosts, backward seasons, and a multitude of such conditions continually threatened to render his labor of no avail or to destroy the fruits of it. Continual watching of weather signs made the farmer, with the possible exception of the sailor, the most expert of all judges of weather, and made that subject, together with crops, the two perennial themes of rural conversation. Rural people need not feel sensitive upon this point. These are topics of vastly more weight and interest than those which commonly form the basis of conversation among urban people. Aside from the work of guarding against loss by bad weather, the farmer had to wage continuous warfare against weeds, vermin, predatory beasts and birds, various forms of blight upon his crops, and disease among his animals. Thus it will be seen that the farmer's was a one-sided independence ; he was independent of those things which the business man of the city most dreaded, — such as changes of fashion, loss of good will or credit, new competitors, financial panics, and a multitude of other changes which might force him into bankruptcy, — all of them changes in the world of men, many of them mere psychological changes. The business man of the city, thinking only of his own peculiar cares and trials, has often envied the farmer his independence. But, on the other hand, the business man concerned himself very little about ordinary changes of weather and such things as worried the farmer. Nothing short of a tornado or a flood severe enough to destroy property ever interfered with the regularity of his work. The farmer, thinking only of his own peculiar cares and trials, often envied the city man his independence.

But the farmer's independence is not so one-sided when he ceases to be a self-sufficing farmer and becomes a commercial farmer; that is, when he ceases to live directly upon the products of his farm and begins to live upon the profits of farming. To be sure he is still compelled to watch the weather. Wet and dry seasons continue to affect his crops; disease, blight, and pests still attack them, and storms still destroy them; but he is now learning how to reduce their power to do him injury. He is learning to drain his land and to adapt his methods of cultivation to the character of the season, to spray and use other means of preventing injury by pests; but he is still, and must continue to be, in more direct and immediate contact with the varying and uncertain manifestations of nature's power than the members of any other class. On the other hand, the fact that the farmer is coming to live upon the profits of farming, rather than upon the products themselves, increases his dependence upon the markets and market conditions. Anything, therefore, which affects his customers and their power to purchase, affects him also.

At the same time, even merchants and manufacturers are coming to realize, as the railroads and financial interests have long realized, a vital dependence upon those weather conditions which affect farm crops. In our interlocking industrial system no large interest can be seriously affected without also affecting many others in some degree. A financial writer in one of our leading reviews wrote, a few years ago, as follows:

That estimates of the outturn of home and foreign harvests should at this season of the year be awaited with interest is perfectly natural. Harvest results provide the one essential factor in economic and industrial progress which is wholly beyond the control of man. Human sagacity may insure wise currency legislation; it may increase the output of gold; it may avoid political complications; it may develop existing trade at home; it may create new trade abroad; but it cannot create abundant harvests or prevent a crop failure, upon which alternative, at certain junctures, nearly all of the five other influences cited above depend. With all the increase, during the three past generations, of other factors going to make up prosperity or adversity, it is almost as true to-day as it was a century ago that the average nation's industrial welfare depends chiefly on the raising of an abundant crop and its sale at fair prices.[1]

Seasonal character of agriculture. The mention of the dependence of the farmer on weather and other climatic conditions suggests another important characteristic of agriculture as a way of getting a living, — that is, its seasonal character. This applies not only to the changing of the seasons from spring to summer, from summer to autumn, and from autumn to winter; but even during the same day the nature of the work changes from hour to hour. It is never possible, in the temperate zone, to work day in and day out, week in and week out, at one simple operation repeated indefinitely, as is commonly done in almost every mechanical industry. On a farm there are things which have to be done at certain hours of the day, and quite different things at other hours; and so from day to day, from week to week, from month to month, and from season to season the work is constantly changing. These are normal changes such as can be predicted in advance. On any ordinary farm there are a multitude of operations, widely different in their nature, requiring the use of different powers or different kinds of skill. On account of its seasonal character, therefore, the work of the farmer is more diversified than that of any other large class of workers.

In addition to these normal seasonal changes, necessitating regular changes in the farmer's work, there are always to be expected a certain number of abnormal or unforeseeable changes or interruptions in the regular work. A sudden change of the weather, for example, may necessitate a complete change in the farmer's plans for the day, and force him to do a kind of work

[1] The *Nation* (New York), Vol. 72 (1876), p. 464.

which he had not planned to do at all. The work of the farmer, more than that of any other class, calls for versatility and resourcefulness. He must always be ready to decide what is to be done next, when these numerous interruptions occur. The worker in a factory, on the other hand, has fewer interruptions of this kind. He learns one particular kind of work and may keep at it for months, and even years, without any abrupt change. This requires neither versatility nor resourcefulness, but merely patience and dexterity.

Domestic character of agriculture. Again, the work of the farmer is carried on in direct connection with the home and the family. In this particular it differs widely from all the other large industries, such as mining, manufacturing, etc. There are still a few small shops and stores where the business and the home are united, and the work of the household is not sharply separated from the " business " of getting a living; but these are survivals of an older system and are not now characteristic of these industries as a whole. But it is quite the common thing, especially in this country, for the farmer to live on the farm, and for different members of the family to participate more or less in the common work of the farm or of supporting the home and the family. There is, therefore, no such sharp distinction between "business " and the home, or between " business " ideals and the ideals of private life in the country as there is in the city. When, however, the farmer turns trader, he frequently imitates the practices which urban traders too generally follow, and departs from the ideals of private life. In such cases he is very much inclined to justify himself with the remark, " That 's business." Those who make this remark virtually admit that the standards of business are different from those of ordinary life.

Farmers generally self-employed. Mention has already been made of the so-called independence of the farming class. There is another sense in which the farmers as a class are, in a very real sense, more independent than any other large class. They are the most independent in the sense that, in all highly civilized countries, the vast majority of them are their own employers. Perhaps the most important distinction of all between agriculture and other large industries is that agriculture is still, and will probably continue to be, an industry of small units; whereas other large industries, such as manufacturing, mining, and transportation, as well as commercial and banking enterprises, seem to be tending at the present time toward larger and larger establishments. There is, it is true, also a counter-tendency, too frequently overlooked in these other industries; but, in spite of this, the large establishments, especially in our great cities, seem generally to have the advantage over the smaller ones. But no such tendency is showing itself as yet in agriculture, and it is not likely to unless something at present unforeseeable should occur to give the mammoth farm an advantage which it does not now possess over the small farm. According to the census of 1910 it appears that the very large farms are diminishing in number. This indicates that they are less productive than those of medium size. This characteristic of agriculture is a matter of great importance, because it means that a large proportion of the men engaged in this industry are their own masters and the heads of independent concerns. In an industry of large-scale production, or where large establishments are the prevailing type, the opposite is true, a very small proportion of those engaged being their own masters or heads of independent concerns.

According to the census of 1850 there was one farm for 14 rural residents, that is, persons not living in cities of more than 8000 inhabitants; but according to the census of 1900 there was one farm for every 9 such persons. The difference may be accounted for in part by the larger families of that earlier period; but these figures signify at least that there is as yet no tendency toward such a concentration in agriculture as has taken place in manufacturing, trade, and transportation. That these farms were generally of respectable size is shown by the fact that in 1900 there was one farm of fifty acres or more for every 13.4 rural residents. When we consider that living in towns and villages of less than 8000 inhabitants there are vast numbers of people who are not farmers at all, we shall see how generally true it is that agriculture is still an industry of small units. Moreover, as shown by the above figures, the size of the unit is certainly not increasing, but appears to be decreasing slightly, though this may be only temporary or accidental. One is therefore safe in saying, on the basis of these figures, that there is no other large industry where the individual has so good a chance of becoming his own employer, or of being the head of an independent business unit, as in agriculture. Certainly there is no other large industry where so large a proportion of the men engaged are actually self-employed, and where so small a proportion are in the position of employees. For high-spirited men and for men of independence and initiative this will always be an attractive feature of the agricultural industry. But there is little in this industry to attract two other classes of people. Those with a liking for speculative risks, who are willing to risk everything for large prizes, will find little here to attract them. It is not a field for vast enterprise, nor are vast fortunes made in it. Again, they who have little initiative — they to whom the question of what to do next is always a painful one — will always prefer industries where questions of this kind are solved for them them by bosses, foremen, and superintendents.

Reaction of business upon life. The two last-named characteristics of the agricultural industry combine to produce a most profound reaction upon the life and character of rural people.

The fact that agriculture is still a family industry where the work and the home life are not divorced, and where all members of the family participate in the common toil for the support of the home, gives a natural basis for a type of family life which it is very difficult to maintain in the city. Educators will generally agree that one of the greatest weaknesses of the city home is the lack of a common business interest among all the members of the family. City parents who are wise will always recognize this weakness and take pains to overcome it. But the typical farmer's family requires no artificial methods to bring its various members together on the basis of a common interest. When the breadwinner of a city family is not self-employed, but an employee, as the majority of them are, this weakness is still further emphasized. There is, then, nothing in the way of a business interest to be handed from father to son. The sons are deprived of the priceless advantage of learning to work along with the father, under his direction and in imitation of him. This advantage the country boy usually has, partly because of the fact, already mentioned, that agriculture is an industry of small units, which means that a large proportion of those engaged in it — a vast majority of them in this country — are self-employed.

As a result of this, there are business problems, aside from the perennial one of household expenditures, to be discussed in the family council, — questions of selling as well as of buying, of investing for production as well as buying for consumption. All these things add to the strength of the bonds which hold the rural family together. One result is that the rural family is a stable institution, whereas the city family has become a relatively unstable one. This relative instability is shown in several ways. In the first place, the divorce rate is much higher in the cities than in the country districts. In the second place, the city families tend to die out through celibacy, sterility, and various other agencies, whereas the rural families persist. The farms not only feed the cities with their material products, but they also furnish the cities with men and women.

Relation of the sexes in farming communities. One of the most important of all the characteristics which distinguish rural from urban life is the greater interdependence of the sexes in the former. Most of our present notions as to what is " proper work " for men and women have been handed down to us from our rural ancestors. The idea that the " proper work " of women lies mainly within the walls of the dwelling, while that of men lies without, is a natural result of rural conditions. Though there is a great deal of light work to be done about a farm, there are always kinds of work which require the somewhat higher average muscular development of masculine workers. Where there is live stock to be handled, there are also kinds of work which require masculine courage and resourcefulness as well as muscularity. There are very few farms, in fact, where all the outdoor work could be carried on profitably by women alone. It is true that on farms where highly specialized agriculture is practiced there is room for the use of considerable female labor out of doors, but these farms are exceptional. Again, on the small peasant farms of Europe, and on a few of the small negro farms of our Southern states, a great deal of work is done by women. But peasant farming is a low type of farming, usually carried on by very inefficient methods, the purpose being to make as good a living as possible from a tract of land too small to permit of an efficient application of labor and tools. Such farming is usually accompanied by a low standard of living on the part of the farmer and his family. One result of this necessity for masculine labor in the country is that there are relatively few opportunities, certainly much fewer than in the city, for a woman to make an independent living for herself outside of the household. An unmarried woman is therefore at a much greater disadvantage in the country than in the towns and cities.

At the same time an unmarried farmer is at a still greater disadvantage. In most cases he must live on his farm, — in all cases it is to his advantage to do so. The sparseness of the agricultural population makes it impossible to depend upon boarding houses. The geometrical as well as the social conditions of farm life dictate that there shall be an independent household on every farm. No such set of conditions exists in the city. The unmarried business man and the unmarried business woman may suffer moral and social loss, but they can scarcely be said to be under the slightest disadvantage in a purely business sense. The farmer needs a wife as a part of his business equipment because, on the farm, the home is a part of the business and the business a part of the home. Accordingly there are, in the country, very few of those old unmarried males who infest the business and professional circles of our cities. The sexes need one another in the work as well as in the life of the country. Partly for this reason, and partly because of the more wholesome and normal style of living in the country, there is a more wholesome attitude of the sexes toward one another than is found in the city, particularly in certain business and professional circles, where the artificialities of life are most abnormally developed.

Finally, farming is almost the only occupation left where the child can, under wholesome conditions, contribute a share of the work necessary to the support of the family of which he is a part. Where children work at other occupations the conditions are usually so abnormal, and so morally or physically unwholesome, that a strong prejudice has arisen against child labor as such. There are stronger objections to child idleness than to child labor. A certain amount of work *under wholesome conditions* is necessary for the physical, mental, and moral development of the average child. The farm furnishes those conditions. In the first place the child can work with the parents, learning from and being guided by them. In the second place, the work of the farm or the farm household includes many desultory operations, commonly known as chores, which do not require long hours or continuous and sustained attention. For this kind of work the child is physically and mentally adapted, since he is what might be called a desultory creature, whereas he is unadapted for any work which requires continuous attention to the same operation hour after hour and day after day. Again, a part at least of the farm work is done out of doors, and children do not suffer from close confinement as they do in stores, mines, and factories.

Because of the help which children can, without harm to themselves, render in the work of the farm, they can pay, in part at least, the cost of their upbringing. This is another reason why marriages are, as a rule, earlier and families larger in the country than in the city. It is sometimes insinuated that such motives ought to have no place in the problems of marriage and of family life. Such insinuations, however, are based upon an idealism which is not only impractical but vicious. No one need apologize for this admixture of economic and romantic motives when he understands that all sound romance has an economic foundation. No pure form of social or domestic life, no high type of morality, has ever been developed among any people except where it has been organized around some kind of productive work. The ideal of production for a common family purpose, — of building a family and perpetuating a prosperous, productive family estate,— instead of subtracting from the dignity of family life, is really one of the greatest factors in adding dignity to it. Where there is no purpose of this kind there is nothing to deserve the name of marriage. However, when the economic motive becomes perverted, as it sometimes does, and the children are looked upon as financial resources for the benefit of the parent alone, and the income is devoted mainly to his own selfish gratification, it is quite a different thing.

The deliberate determination to found a family, or to perpetuate one already honorably established, and to preserve its traditions, is not as general as it ought to be either in the country or the city. Such a motive appeals only to men and women of mental and moral substance, — to such men and women as will always be the natural leaders of their communities until civilization begins to decline through moral decay. But the opportunities for the carrying out of that determination are better in the country than in the city. The reason is found primarily in the greater economic solidarity of the rural as compared with the urban family, — to the fact that the rural home is part and parcel of the rural business and the rural estate.

The rural districts the seed bed of the population. It has been said that the greatest social distinction is not that between laborers and employers, but that between the people who dwell in the city and those who dwell in the country. There is no doubt that the tendencies of city life are quite different from those of the country. City life tends to develop ideals, standards, sentiments, and manners different from those of rural life, and thus to separate city people from rural people. If this tendency could go on unimpeded for a great many generations, it might produce wider differences than it does; but it is checked by the fact that the cities have to be continually replenished from the country. In any modern city it will be found that many of the most prominent people come from the country, and that the great majority of them are descended from parents or grandparents who lived in the country. While this continues there can never be so wide a distinction between city people and country people as would otherwise occur, for the reason that city people are themselves mostly country people recently come to town, that is, within two, three, or, at the most, four generations.

Assumption of urban superiority. If we look at the matter historically, however, we find that there have been times when this distinction was a very real one. It is surprising how many opprobrious terms there are, doubtless coined by city people, which at one time meant merely "countryman." "Heathen," "pagan," "boor," "villain," and even "peasant," as that word is frequently used, all having originally about the same meaning in different languages, are examples which show in what poor esteem the countryman was held at one time or another by his cousins from the city. But this low esteem has frequently been merely the result of a failure on the part of those who get their living out of other men to appreciate the men who get their living out of the soil.

This failure is sometimes due to a lack of appreciation of the real virtues and the many excellent qualities of those who till the soil. An ancient occupation, pursued by countless generations, accumulates a vast fund of wisdom and skill, much of which escapes the pages of the written book, being transmitted from father to son on the thin air of oral tradition or of living example. Such an occupation is agriculture. Working in flint has been called the oldest trade in the world, but tilling the soil has first claim to that distinction, unless the word "trade" is to be applied to special mechanical occupations only. In consequence of its antiquity and its universality there has developed a body of rural lore and technic, which has no counterpart anywhere else, but which is entirely underestimated by, if not absolutely unknown to, the urbanite. But because so much of it is learned outside of schools, by the actual process of doing rural work, father and son working together generation after generation, it does not commonly go under the name of "learning." Moreover, the marvelous technic of rural work is acquired in such a commonplace way that we frequently regard it as a matter of course, and do not appreciate that it is real technic. There are probably no instruments known to any craft which are more perfect in their adaptation, with more fine points upon which excellence in their form and construction depends, than some of the simpler implements of modern husbandry. The common plow is an example. The shaping of the moldboard so as to give the maximum efficiency with the minimum resistance is a problem of the utmost nicety. It is a problem to which Thomas Jefferson himself gave years of thought and calculation. Though this part of his work has not attracted so much of the world's attention as that which he devoted to the problem of the best form of government, it is not quite certain that it was less important.

These considerations should combine to give character and dignity to rural life and work, at least in the minds of those who see deeper than mere superficial culture, or manners, or arts of expression, and are able to appreciate the relative value to the world of various ways of getting a living.

Isolation the menace of farm life as congestion is of city life. At the same time these considerations should call our attention to some of the real dangers of rural life. The sheer isolation of farm life has a depressing effect upon the intellectual life of those who require the stimulus of excitement and contact with other men to keep their minds active. Such people frequently sink into a state of mental inactivity and moral torpor which helps to justify some of the epithets which have been applied to them. This is a danger to which a new country such as ours is peculiarly open. Where the conditions of life are as easy as they have been in this country up to the present time, even very inefficient specimens of humanity have been able to hold their own against competition. If they are fortunate enough to get possession of land which does not attract more progressive farmers, they may live unmolested for generations. Accordingly one finds, in out-of-the-way places in different sections of our

Milligan College Library
Milligan College, Tennessee

country, a degree of ignorance, inefficiency, and moral degeneracy which it would probably be impossible to find in any of the countries of western Europe. The stern competition of those old and thickly populated countries makes short work of all such incapables and sends them speedily to the almshouse, or drives them to crime, and thence to prison or the gallows. We must look forward in this country, as our population increases and land comes to be in greater and greater demand, and the conditions of life become harder and harder, as they inevitably will for weaklings, to the unpleasant prospect of a century or so of weeding out.

These country slums seem to be, so far as conditions outside the individual are concerned, the product of isolation, just as the city slums are, in the same sense, the product of overcrowding. Though the fundamental conditions in both cases are personal and not environmental, yet the environment has its influence in one case as well as in the other. The effect of isolation upon weak characters is to destroy all respect for tradition, authority, or social convention. Society tends to break up into its atomic elements, and each individual to become a law unto himself, following his weak and vacillating will, sometimes toward amiable nonmorality, sometimes toward vicious lawlessness. The weak character, without any of the restraints which society furnishes to strengthen it, loses its sense of social obligation and is governed by whim and caprice, or becomes suspicious, morose, and impatient of restraint or interference.

CHAPTER II

HISTORICAL SKETCH OF MODERN AGRICULTURE

I. The Early Stages

Hunting not universal. In different times and places there have probably been savages who never depended upon the hunting of animals and the catching of fish for their food supply, subsisting rather upon fruits, nuts, and edible roots. Many writers have been in the habit of saying that such people are exceptional, and that the first stage of development in man's struggle to get a living is the hunting and fishing stage. However, some recent writers have challenged that conclusion and contended that the hunting and fishing stage has been confined to certain localities where conditions are unfavorable to agriculture and where game and fish have been relatively abundant. But even in those localities where vegetable food was relatively abundant, it is probable that men lived by gathering the fruits, nuts, roots, etc., which grew wild before they began cultivating them systematically. Again, it has been too frequently assumed that the second stage is always the pastoral stage, that is, the stage in which men get their living by domesticating, herding, and breeding animals whose flesh and milk furnish a supply of food and whose skins and fleeces supply clothing and tents. On the contrary, it is certain that, in some cases at least, the tilling of the soil followed immediately after the hunting stage even where men had lived mainly by hunting and fishing ; while it has generally been the case that those tribes and peoples who formerly lived on wild fruits, vegetables, etc., passed into the agricultural stage without having known anything resembling a pastoral industry. It is not improbable that, in a few cases, such as the ancient Phœnicians, commerce developed directly out of fishing. The Indians of North America, before the coming of the white man, had never domesticated any animals except the turkey and the dog. The domesticated turkey played such an insignificant part in the Indian economy, and in so few places, that, so far as the present discussion is concerned, it may be ignored altogether. The dog was used chiefly in the chase, though occasionally for food, and therefore belongs to the economy of the hunting rather than to that of the pastoral stage. We do not find in these two cases even the semblance of a pastoral economy; that is to say, there were no Indians in North America who ever derived any appreciable part of their subsistence from the herding and breeding of domesticated animals. Even after the coming of the white man the horse was for many years the only domestic animal added to the wealth of the Indians, and he, like the dog, was used mainly in war and the chase, and therefore belonged also to the hunting economy. On the other hand, agriculture was everywhere practiced except in the far north, where it was impracticable. Among some tribes, such as the Pueblos and the nations in Mexico, the art of cultivating the soil had reached a tolerably high state of development. Therefore we may safely say that the Indians of that part of North America now comprised within the territory of the United States were passing directly from the hunting and fishing into the agricultural stage without passing through the pastoral stage at all. According to another view they had formerly been agriculturists, but had taken to a hunting life because of the abundance of game, especially after the relatively late increase of the bison.

Our own ancestors probably herdsmen. However, it seems to be well established that our own ancestors, the peoples of western

Asia and Europe, generally passed through a pastoral stage of development before they became tillers of the soil. Therefore the study of the development of agriculture as *we* know it must include a study of the pastoral life and economy. The life of the early Hebrew patriarchs, as described in the book of Genesis, was distinctly pastoral. When Abraham left Ur of the Chaldees and migrated westward into the country now called Palestine, he was a herdsman, a cattle rancher, differing from the cattle ranchers of our Far West in several particulars, but mainly in that he had no settled abode, but dwelt in tents and moved about with his flocks and herds seeking pasturage. In this respect his life resembled very closely that of the modern Bedouins, who are still in the pastoral stage. It was not until the sojourn in Egypt that the Hebrews became, perforce, tillers of the soil.

The colder climate of Europe would not have permitted the precise style of life led by the Hebrew patriarchs and the modern Bedouins. Nevertheless, it is generally agreed that the European races in their early home, before the dawn of recorded history, were primarily herdsmen. The earliest Greek and Italian settlers in their respective peninsulas were probably migrating herdsmen seeking pasturage for their flocks and herds. They came driving their cattle before them, and bringing their women, children, and such household goods as they possessed, in rude carts drawn by oxen. At a much later date the people of northern Europe were still subsisting on the products of their herds, though in the time of Tacitus the Germans were beginning to practice a rude type of agriculture, as were the Britons at the time of Cæsar's invasion. It is almost certain that Ireland remained a pastoral country until toward the seventh century of our era.

Origin of the domestication of animals. It is probable that the practice of domesticating animals began with the keeping of pets. Having captured a young animal, it occurred to some savage to amuse himself by playing with it. If food was sufficiently abundant, he might easily prefer to keep it as a permanent pet rather than to sacrifice it to his own appetite. When a number of pets were kept in the same village, they would soon form the nucleus of a herd, and in the course of years would multiply. Then it would not require very great intelligence to see the advantage of having a herd of this kind to fall back upon in times when game was scarce. A great many individual animals from these herds would undoubtedly escape and take to their natural wild life. Only the tamest animals, or those most attached to their human masters, would remain in domestication. Again, we may well believe that when it became necessary to slaughter any of these pets for food, it would be the least tamable which would be sacrificed, rather than those with milder dispositions. This process of selection going on generation after generation — that is, the elimination of the less tamable and the preservation of the more tamable — would eventually result in the breeding of a tame or domestic variety of the animals in question, differing in many respects from their wild cousins.

It is worthy of remark that our branch of the human race has not reduced a single new animal to domestication since the beginning of recorded history, every one of our farm animals having been domesticated so long ago that we have no historical record of the time, place, or circumstances under which it was accomplished.[1] This ought to give us a new respect for our prehistoric ancestors, even though they were ignorant of many things which have been discovered since, and which we, therefore, have had an opportunity to learn.

[1] The zebra may be a possible exception to this statement, individual animals of that species having been tamed. But it can scarcely be said that it has yet become a domestic animal in general use. Pet sea lions, wolves, rats, etc., are not really domesticated animals. Their wild nature has not been bred out.

Reaction of the pastoral life upon character. While this transformation in the character of our domestic animals was taking place, similar transformations were taking place in the character of their masters. Those individuals or those tribes who were first to perceive the advantage of possessing flocks and herds, and to avail themselves of that advantage, would prosper out of proportion to their less astute neighbors. In the intense struggle for existence which always took place among savage tribes, the advantage would be on the side of those who availed themselves of this more abundant and more permanent source of food. Those who were too lazy or too stupid to profit by this advantage would be exterminated, or, what amounted to the same thing, would be driven from their lands by their more prosperous and more powerful neighbors. Thus the land would come to be peopled entirely by men of this more advanced and more intelligent type, by a process of selection similar in some respects to that which produced a domestic variety of animal. Even at the present time there are, even in the most civilized communities, reversions to the wild type of man. Criminals of the more brutal type, anarchists, and even a certain bellicose type of socialist, — the whole underworld of revolt in fact, — are in rebellion against the restraints and institutions of civilized society. They are the untamable animals of the human herd.

Reaction upon civilization. But the transformation was not limited to the character of the individual men ; it affected also their laws and institutions, their religion, and their ideas of morality. One of the first of these changes to occur was the development of a new concept of property. When men began to prize their herds as a source of income and to live off the produce of them, the concept of capital was born. By the concept of capital is meant the idea of a fund of wealth as a source of income, — a fund which had to be guarded and preserved for the sake of the income, and whose preservation required some self-control and foresight, otherwise it would be eaten up in times of hunger and thus the future source of income cut off. When one man or one group of men had succeeded in building up a herd, we may be very sure that neither would be willing to share the fruits of labor peaceably with others. Whereas, under the economy of the hunting and fishing stage, there was very little private property and practically no private capital, the transition of the pastoral economy brought with it the institution of private capital and gave it great prominence. Wealth came to be estimated in terms of cattle, and the possession of large wealth, as well as prowess in battle or the hunt, became the basis of distinction.

Reaction upon family life. With the perception of the desirability of capital and the profit to be derived therefrom, came also a perception of the value of labor on the one hand, and the desirability of being attached to a wealthy flock owner on the other. Particularly was it seen that women and children were valuable aids to the herdsman ; and women saw the advantage of being attached to a herdsman who was capable of supplying them with food, clothing, and shelter, rather than to a hunter who at best was able to provide only an uncertain living. This situation gave rise to what is known as the patriarchal family, which took the place of the somewhat loose and indefinite type of family life which existed in the hunting stage. Under the patriarchal family the flock owner was the supreme head, his wives were virtually his slaves,— were usually purchased from their fathers, — while his children, even his married sons, were subject to him so long as he lived, except that he might sell his daughters as wives to other herdsmen, in which case they became subject to their new masters. The whole household frequently numbered many individuals,— children, grandchildren, and great-grandchildren. They were all attached to the herd and under the authority of the herdsman, their oldest living male ancestor.

Out of the patriarchal family developed the tribe, a large group of related families claiming descent from a common male ancestor. One significant fact regarding patriarchal society is that it was based upon kinship rather than upon neighborhood or residence in a given geographical area. It would never have occurred to a member of such a society or tribe that you were entitled to a share in his government or his religion merely because you happened to be his neighbor or to live in the same territory. Unless you were born a kinsman of his, you were not a member of his tribe, and you could not have his religion unless you were made a make-believe kinsman by the process of adoption.

Property in land. While private capital came to play an important part in the pastoral economy, there were only the beginnings of property in land. The idea that one man had a better right than another to pasture his flocks upon a given piece of land would at first have seemed monstrous indeed. However, by mutual agreement it came to be understood in some cases that each herdsman or the head of each pastoral group was to restrict his cattle to certain lands. Thus in Genesis XIII we are told how Abraham and Lot agreed to separate, and each to restrict himself to a given territory, because land was getting scarce, or rather because their herds and herdsmen were getting so numerous as to invite quarrels. This was a beginning of the idea of property in land, for whenever men begin to think in terms of " mine and thine " they are beginning to think in terms of property. However, in this case it was not strictly private property, but rather group or tribal property, for the patriarchal family was a considerable group, of which the patriarch was the head.

Village communities. As this process went on and families grew into tribes, and tribes increased in numbers, each tribe would be more and more restricted in its area. When a definite area with definite boundaries came to be the domain of each tribe, the wandering life gave way to settled life, generally in small villages surrounded by woodland and pasture. For many years the property remained tribal rather than individual. As members within the village still further increased, and the expansion of the area of pasture land became impossible, some more productive method of securing food became an absolute necessity. This was found in the growing of crops. It has been estimated that an area of land sufficient for the support of one hundred people by pasturing animals will, when brought under ordinary tillage, support from three to four times as many. In the beginning tillage was confined to small fields of specially fertile land, usually near the village, the outlying lands remaining in pasture and woodland. At first these fields may have been cultivated in common and the produce shared in common, but before the beginning of recorded history the system of *pure* communism had been given up in some parts of Europe, and soon after in other parts, though a modified type of communal farming persisted until well within the historical period. This was a type of farming in which the lands were the common property of the village community, but in which each family was allotted a share upon which to grow crops for its own subsistence.

Communal farming. After the pastoral tribe had lived a settled village life for a few generations, gradually the old idea of kinship as the basis of organization began to give way, and territoriality — that is, residence within a given territory — began to be the basis. The village broke up into families somewhat resembling the modern family. This change was helped on by the growing interest in tillage. The idea that he that will not work shall not eat is very deep-rooted. So long as all the cattle of the village were herded by the common labor on the common land, it was not easy to distinguish the product of one man's labor from that of another. But when ground began to be cleared and crops to be sown and harvested, it easily became possible to make this distinction. They who had been most diligent and most intelligent in their work would secure the most abundant crops, and they would naturally be unwilling to share their harvests with their less industrious neighbors. Thus it came about early in the historical period in Europe, particularly in England, that there was no communistic sharing of crops, though the land was still held in common.

Either before or soon after the development of the system of individual crops, — it is not known which, — the system of common property in herds gave way to that of private property, so that the modified form of communal farming which was coming into use at the beginning of the historical period was after the following description.[1] At some favorable spot in the township would be located the village. Near this village would be located the cultivated fields and the meadowland, and outside was the pasture and woodland. From this common forest the villagers were allowed to cut wood for their individual use, and upon the common pasture they were allowed to pasture the cattle which they owned as individuals. The cattle were usually herded in common by persons appointed especially for that purpose. The cultivated fields had formerly been reallotted frequently, each family being given an approximately equal area, usually thirty acres, of approximately equal fertility. Sometimes these allotments were in small scattered patches, so that each family might have, as nearly as possible, its share of each grade of land. Thus, while there was communal property in land there was private property in the herds and the produce thereof, and in the crops harvested from the cultivated fields. After the crops were harvested the cattle of all the villagers were allowed to

[1] Cf. Sir Henry Sumner Maine, Village Communities in the East and West (London, 1871).

pasture on the stubble, the individual family having exclusive use of its allotment only for the purpose of growing a crop.

Private property in land. Generally it came about that the same families would be allotted the same portions of the cultivated fields year after year, and eventually generation after generation, until each one began to regard itself as having a right to its permanent allotment. Thus was private property in land established within the cultivated fields long before communal property in the pasture and woodland was given up. This latter form of communal property has persisted in some places down to the present time under the name of " rights of common." But long after the institution of private property in the cultivated fields was definitely established, it generally remained a limited form of property ; that is to say, the family owned its fields only for the purpose of growing crops. After the crops were harvested the villagers still had the right to turn their stock upon the stubble as upon a common pasture. The meadowland, for the cutting of hay for the winter forage, was reallotted annually for a long time after the arable land had ceased to be reallotted, — after it had, in fact, become private property. After the hay harvest this meadowland was thrown open, like the stubble, to the herds of the village.

The open-field system. As a system of land ownership this is sometimes called the *mark system*, but as a system of agriculture it is usually called the open-field system. Even after the arable land had become the private property of the different families of the village, it was not separately fenced but held in great open fields. These fields were subdivided after a most ingenious and interesting system. While each family might own a considerable acreage, its land did not lie in a body but in a great many small strips, usually of one acre each. These acre strips were usually, though not always, a furlong (furrow long) in length, and four rods wide, being the amount which one plow team was supposed, on the average, to be able to plow in a day. The acre strips belonging to the different families lay side by side, separated from one another only by narrow grass paths called balks. At the ends of a group of these acre strips were unplowed strips called headlands, where the plow teams turned. Thus in the same furlong, or group of acre strips, every family in the village might own its strip, while each family would own similar strips in a great many different furlongs. As suggested above, this arrangement was probably for the purpose, originally, of equalizing things by giving each family a share in land of every grade or quality.

The two-field system. Farmers everywhere discovered very early that continuous cropping tends to wear out the soil and cause it to decline in productiveness. This would lead them, after a few years of cropping, to abandon one field and clear another for cultivation. After a time it was discovered that when a field had been idle for a few years, a part at least of its original fertility was restored. Thus one of the great laws of agricultural production was discovered before the beginning of the historical period, namely, that though continuous cropping will wear out the soil, yet an interval of rest tends to restore its fertility. At first it is probable that there was no system in the practice of cultivating land until it was worn out and then abandoning it. The villagers would cultivate a piece of land until they made up their minds that it would be better to abandon it and clear another piece for the plow. Eventually, however, a regular system was adopted. This is known as the "two-field system." This simply consisted in dividing the plow-land into two parts and growing crops on each part in alternate years, allowing each to lie fallow during the off years.

The three-field system. This was followed by another discovery, namely, that a change of crops does not exhaust the soil quite so rapidly as a continuous repetition of the same crop.

After this was discovered it was found possible to grow crops for two years on the same field and let the land lie fallow the third year and still preserve its fertility. This gave rise to what is known as the "three-field system." Under this arrangement the plowland was divided into three parts. A fall grain (wheat or rye) would be sown on the land which had lain fallow during the previous summer. In the following spring the stubble of the previous year's crop of fall grain would be plowed and sown to spring grain (oats or barley), and the land which had grown spring grain the year before would be allowed to lie fallow. Thus each field in turn would be sown one year with a fall crop, the next year with a spring crop, and the third year would lie fallow. This system, being somewhat more productive than the two-field system, tended to displace it, though very slowly in some parts.

Lack of individual initiative. Under either of these systems the individual family, while owning its land and its crops, had comparatively little independence. It was compelled to follow the rotation prescribed by the community, to have its crop harvested by a prescribed date in order that the cattle might be turned out to pasture on the stubble, and in a multitude of other ways was bound by the laws and customs of the village. Some historians tell us that the plowing was done coöperatively, with large teams consisting of eight oxen, to which each family contributed one or two oxen, though it is probable that no uniform rule existed on this point, certainly not as to the size of the teams.

Limited number of crops. The crops grown were mainly grain, — that is, wheat, rye, oats, or barley. Very few fruits or garden vegetables were grown by or known to the common farming class. Their food was necessarily limited in variety, consisting mainly of bread, porridge, milk, butter, cheese, and salted meats, with eggs and poultry occasionally. Sugar was a rare luxury, but nearly every farmer kept bees, and honey was therefore almost the only form of sweetening in common use. Though this diet lacked variety, it seems to have been fairly abundant. The coarse and monotonous food was generally washed down with home-brewed ale or beer, at least in the more well-to-do families.

The manorial system. The communal form of rural organization under which these developments of the agricultural industry took place was gradually replaced by a new form known as the manorial system. This was a change in the form of land ownership rather than in the system of farming. The manorial system succeeded the mark system of ownership, but the open-field system of farming accompanied both. It is not possible to fix upon any date as marking the end of the communal or mark system, and the beginning of the manorial system. In England, the country in whose agricultural history we in this country are most interested, it probably began about two centuries before the Norman Conquest (1066 A.D.). The practical completion of the movement followed speedily after that event, for the Normans found the manorial system a convenient basis for the reorganization of the kingdom. Not only were the existing manors granted to the followers of William the Conqueror, but the entire kingdom was surveyed and divided up in the same way. In the winter of 1085–1086 a general survey of the kingdom was ordered, and was carried out during the following year. This is known as the Domesday Survey, and the results were recorded in what is known as Domesday Book. This is the first recorded agricultural survey on a thoroughly comprehensive scale, and is probably the most complete survey ever made of the agricultural resources of any nation.

Description of a manor. If we will imagine one of the village communities as having become the private property of an over-lord, and the villagers as having become his hereditary tenants under the name of "villeins," farming the land very much as they had been doing under the communal or the mark system, but paying rent in kind or in service to the lord, we shall have a general idea as to what the manor was like. However, the lord of the manor was not simply the owner of the land ; he was also the ruler of the local community, holding courts and enforcing the laws. He was also responsible to the king for certain duties and services. From one point of view he may be looked upon as an officer of the local government under the king, receiving, instead of a salary from the king, a grant of the land with the right to collect rents therefrom. In many cases, however, his function as an officer of the local government was assumed by himself without any authority from the king. Being the most powerful man in the neighborhood, in a time of turbulency or of inefficient administration of law, he assumed a position of leadership or of authority. The rents which the tenants had to pay may therefore, from the same point of view, be looked upon as their taxes for the support of the local government or the local ruler. Sometimes, however, one manor included many villages, especially after the Norman Conquest. These tenants were of various classes, most numerous of which were the villeins.[1] Each villein held a tract of arable land, usually about thirty acres, besides a share of the meadowland, and had the right of pasturing his stock upon the commons and of cutting wood in the forest, very much as he had done under the communal system. He was, however, by no means a freeman. He was attached to the land he tilled, and could not leave it without the lord's consent. He could be sold with the land, but not apart from the land like a common slave. At the same time he was compelled to pay certain rents in kind,

[1] The word "villein" meant a villager, or one who lived in the vill, or village, and went out from this survivor of the old village community to till his allotment of land or to work for the lord on the demesne lands.

but in England he paid his rent principally by performing labor for the lord.[1]

The land of the manor was not all let to tenants. Certain portions, called the demesne lands, were held and farmed directly by the lord himself or under his general management, and they were cultivated by the labor of the villeins and smaller tenants. These smaller tenants were called bordars, crofters, cotters, etc., and held very small tracts, usually about five acres. Upon the demesne land kept by the lord for his own use crops were sown, harvested, and threshed by the labor of these tenants. Each villein was compelled to work two or three days a week throughout the year for his lord, besides certain special days in harvest time. There were a number of other duties enforced upon the villeins, all of which were more or less profitable to the lord. The villein was obliged, for example, to take his grain to the lord's mill to be ground, to take his cows to the lord's bull, to allow his sheep to lie a part of the time on the lord's land for the sake of the manure. Sometimes special contributions of honey, — one of the most important articles of luxury of that

---

[1] The following description (from Ashley's English Economic History, Part I, p. 6) gives an excellent picture of an English manor:

There was a village street, and along each side of it the houses of the cultivators of the soil, with little yards around them : as yet there were no scattered farmhouses, such as were to appear later. Stretching away from the village was the arable land, divided usually into three fields, sown one with wheat or rye, one with oats or barley, while one was left fallow. The fields were again subdivided into what were usually called "furlongs," and each furlong into acre or half-acre strips, separated, not by hedges, but by "balks" of unploughed turf; and these strips were distributed among the cultivators in such a way that each man's holding was made up of strips scattered up and down the three fields, and no man held two adjoining pieces. Each individual holder was bound to cultivate his strips in accordance with the rotation of crops observed by his neighbors. Besides the arable fields there were also meadows, inclosed for hay harvest, and divided into portions by lot or rotation or custom, and after hay harvest thrown open again for the cattle to pasture upon. In most cases there was also some permanent pasture or wood, into which the cattle were turned, either "without stint" or in numbers proportioned to the extent of each man's holding. . . .

Supposing such fields and meadows were owned in common by a group of freemen, the condition of things would be what is called the *mark system*. But the manorial system was something very different; for in a manor the land was regarded as the property, not of the cultivators, but of a lord.

period, — of eggs, poultry, or ale were required. The land held by the villein remained intact generation after generation. Upon his death it went to one son; the others sought positions elsewhere, — as craftsmen in the towns, servants in the lord's household, and sometimes as soldiers. Under the manorial system there were considerable numbers of freeholders occupying a position somewhat above that of the villein, but as time went on the difference between these two classes became an uncertain one and tended to disappear.

Origin of the manor. The process by which this transformation of a village community into a manor came about is somewhat complicated. In a general way it may be said to have been the result of three practices: (1) Even under the community system the king had certain rights in the way of taxation or services from the village. He sometimes granted these rights to a monastery as a convenient way of endowing it, or to a private individual as a mark of favor. (2) In those turbulent times it was not always easy for a plain tiller of the soil, untrained in the profession of arms, to protect himself against marauders or more formidable invaders. His safest plan was frequently to put himself under the protection of some expert fighter or powerful leader, agreeing to pay him certain services or rents in return for his protection. (3) It became the practice for a time to buy off, by gifts of money, the Danes who were harassing the country. It was necessary to raise this money by taxation, under the name of Danegeld. It was useless to try to collect it directly from the common villagers; it was collected rather from the monasteries and the lords, who in turn found ways of getting it out of the men under them, being, in fact, given considerable authority in the matter. Thus the power and authority of the lords grew, and the liberty of the villagers dwindled until we find them in the position of the villeins, as just described.

Inflexibility of the manorial system. As suggested above, the open-field system prevailed on the manors, as it had within the village communities. There grew up a great many special offices, such as cowherd, shepherd, swineherd, etc., whose duties consisted in looking after the live stock of the entire village while it was out on the common pasture. All of these offices tended to become hereditary, being handed down from father to son, as a matter of legal right, generation after generation. The same rigid customs prevailed with respect to the rotation of different crops and the time and manner of harvesting them. Thus there was very little room for private initiative except on the part of the lords, and the art of agriculture made very little advancement. Even the change from the two-field to the three-field system, obvious as the advantages of the change must have been, came about very slowly. It could not come about in a village until the majority could be convinced that it was desirable, and it is difficult to convince the average man by words alone that there is a better way of doing a thing than the way he has always been doing it. Under a more individualistic system the change could have been made by one man as soon as there was one man wise enough to see the advantage of it. His success, if it proved a success, would have convinced his neighbors much sooner than argumentation and arithmetic could have convinced them. Accordingly, it is no accident that the next stage in the progress of English agriculture was delayed until after the break-up of the manorial system.

Decay of the manor. The transition from the manorial to the modern individualistic system of rural economy was a long and complicated process, which need not be described in detail. In fact, historians are not agreed as to many of these details. Two practices which grew up in England after the thirteenth century may be said to have been chiefly instrumental in bringing the manorial system to an end. These are called commutation, or the substitution of money rents for services rendered by the villeins to the lords; and inclosure, or the fencing in of tracts of land comprising either the old open fields or the common pasture. These practices, in turn, accompanied, if they were not brought about by, a change from a self-sufficing system of agriculture to a commercial system.

Beginnings of commercial agriculture. In the early days of the manor it was a self-sufficing unit, producing practically everything it consumed and buying practically nothing from the outside world. But with the general progress of trade and industry which followed upon the restoration of settled political conditions, this self-sufficiency gave way to a certain degree of interdependency, — to the custom of selling produce from the manor and buying goods from the outside world. Roads were being built, towns where craftsmen plied their trades were growing up, and money was beginning to circulate. Thus it happened that certain villeins, more successful or more intelligent than their neighbors, began to make bargains with the lord, agreeing to pay him a certain sum of money every year if he would relieve them of the necessity of working for him on his land. With the money thus received the lord would then hire laborers to work on his land in place of the villeins whom he had released. Wherever this change was possible it was found to work better for all concerned. The villeins were free to put all their time on their own land, and the lord could employ a permanent force of laborers upon his land. This enabled both sides to work more systematically and regularly, and freed them from the continuous interferences of the older system, which must have proved not only unprofitable but exceedingly vexatious besides.

Inclosures. But when crops began to be sold for money, or when farmers began to think in terms of money, the concepts of profit and loss became much more definite and concrete, and the motive for reducing cost of production became much sharper. Then it began to appear, as it had never appeared before, how wasteful the old open-field system was, where each family cultivated a large number of acre and half-acre strips scattered about over the open fields. The movement began to make headway toward the consolidation of these scattered holdings into more compact forms. At first this was probably done by mutual consent, though the lords seem to have been the leaders in the movement. The demesne lands cultivated by the lords were the first to be consolidated and inclosed, but, since they were sometimes scattered about also in acre strips among the holdings of the villeins, these consolidations involved considerable rearrangement of all the holdings. Again, the villeins were sometimes persuaded to accept additional arable land, or some other advantage, in place of their rights in the common pasture. Thus the lords were enabled to convert portions of the pastureland into arable land and to inclose the rest. In these and other ways the process of inclosure went on, and the old open-field system gradually disappeared. This change did not take place, however, without a great deal of opposition, especially in the later stages, and a certain amount of political and social controversy was waged over the policy of inclosures. It is not improbable that many injustices were done, and it is certain that evils frequently resulted from this change; but there is not the slightest doubt that the change was in the direction of a more efficient agriculture, and that it prepared the way for the improvements which were to follow. Modern agriculture could have developed only on consolidated farms, and not on scattered acre and half-acre strips. It was now possible to vary the size of the holding according to the capacity of the tenant and the needs of agriculture. It was also possible for superior farmers to profit by their own intelligence, since they were no longer bound by the fixed rules of the community, and for new crops to be introduced instead of following the rigid system of rotation prescribed under the two-field or the three-field system. In short, it made possible the individualistic system of agricultural economy.

II. The Beginnings of Modern English Agriculture

Our indebtedness to English agriculture. Our own agricultural history is more closely related to that of Great Britain than to that of any other part of the world. Not only did the American colonists bring with them the rural customs and practices of the mother country, but they continued for a long time, even down almost to the present, to look mainly to England for improvements in almost everything agricultural except farm machinery, in which we have led the rest of the world. New and improved varieties of fruits, grains, and vegetables, and, more especially, superior breeds of live stock, have generally come from England and Scotland; in fact, it has not been uncommon in some parts of this country to designate improved and cultivated varieties of our garden and field crops and of our live stock by the general name of "English." Thus English hay meant anything but wild hay; English fruit, almost any kind of grafted fruit; English cattle, horses, etc., almost anything except common scrub stock. While this was not always a strictly accurate use of terms, it indicated in a general way our indebtedness to the more highly developed agriculture of the mother country, especially during our pioneer period, when our energies were devoted less to improving our crops and herds than to the gigantic task of subduing the continent and bringing it under cultivation.

Our indebtedness to other countries. Though France helped us to win our political independence and gave us some of our best political ideals, she contributed little to our agriculture except the Percheron horse; the French coach horse, which is really not yet an established breed, and owes its best qualities to the

Milligan College, Tennessee

English Thoroughbred; and the Rambouillet variety of the Merino sheep, which had in turn been borrowed from Spain. Though the Dutch laid the foundations of our largest city and gave us some of the best features of our system of popular education, their most valuable contributions to our agriculture are buckwheat, white clover, and the Holstein cow. Spain gave us our monetary unit, the dollar, but contributed nothing special to the improvement of our agriculture except the Merino sheep and some of the progenitors of the American mule. Germany and the Scandinavian countries have given us a great many sturdy farmers, and every country is indebted to Germany for many scientific discoveries which have indirectly benefited agriculture as well as other industries; but, aside from the Oldenburg coach horse and a few special varieties of grain and fruit, she has made no significant contributions toward the direct improvement of our agriculture. We have borrowed from many nations in fact, but all of them together have scarcely contributed as much as Great Britain to our agricultural development. From that country we have imported every one of our leading breeds of cattle except the Holstein and the Brown Swiss,[1] all our leading breeds of sheep except the Merino in its different varieties, several of our leading breeds of swine, and a few breeds of poultry. To her we owe the Shire, the Clydesdale, and the Suffolk among draft horses, and the Thoroughbred, which is the foundation of all our saddle and driving horses. In addition we have brought from Great Britain most of the common garden and field crops except those which were indigenous, such as corn, potatoes, and tobacco, and also cotton, which obviously could not have come from so cold a country as England, the common cultivated varieties being imported from the eastern hemisphere, though certain species are native to

[1] Since the islands of Jersey and Guernsey are under the British flag, the Jersey and Geurnsey cattle are included under British breeds.

4 + 5 5
Milligan College Library
Milligan College, Tennessee

America. Because of this direct relationship between British agriculture and our own, it is important that we know something about the development of agriculture in the mother country, especially during the period immediately preceding and contemporaneous with our colonial era.

English indebtedness to the New World. The manorial system having fallen into decay, as described in the preceding section, and the open-field system having begun to give way before the consolidation of holdings and the growth of inclosures, English agriculture was just entering upon a new period of development at the time of the founding of the first English colonies in America. It is probable, however, that the New World itself had indirectly contributed something to that awakening. The vast quantities of silver and gold, particularly silver, which flowed into Europe as the result of the Spanish conquest and exploitation of Mexico and various South American countries, greatly increased the circulating medium of the civilized world and brought on a period of rising prices. The English managed to get a share of this treasure not only by the peaceful methods of trade and commerce, but by the methods of war and piracy. A period of rising prices is generally an advantage to the farming class, particularly at a time when farmers buy little and sell much, though sometimes a corresponding disadvantage to other classes. This period of rising prices, following the greater abundance of money, doubtless contributed its share to the progress of English agriculture during the seventeenth and eighteenth centuries.

Besides having increased the world's supply of the precious metals, the New World contributed several new agricultural products to the Old World during this period, particularly Indian corn, the potato, and tobacco. Neither corn nor tobacco have ever been largely cultivated in England, the climate being too cool and the season too short. But the potato eventually became a valuable crop. For a long time, however, it was regarded as a mere agricultural novelty, later as a garden vegetable, and not till about the middle of the seventeenth century as a field crop. But this was about the time of one of the greatest agricultural expansions which England has known, and was contemporaneous with the most active period of American colonization.

Transition to the modern system of rural economy. Much earlier than this, however, the Black Death (1348–1349, 1361–1362, 1368–1369) had nearly depopulated some parts of rural England and greatly reduced the supply of agricultural labor. The owners of many estates found their profits or rents greatly reduced as a result of this scarcity of labor, and began to cast about for new ways of utilizing their land. Bread being the chief article of diet of the English people in those days, the arable land was devoted almost exclusively to the growing of grain. But the difficulty of securing labor enough to sow and harvest the grain crop led many landlords to change the arable land into pasture and resort to the raising of sheep and cattle, especially sheep. Like every period of reorganization, this change was attended by many evils and much bitter feeling. A great deal of the political agitation of the ensuing period grew out of the economic changes that were taking place. On the one side there were many complaints that England was being ruined by the growth of inclosures, and also by the conversion of arable land into pasture; and a great many attempts were made to stop these practices by legislation. On the other side there were complaints from the landlords and the larger tenant farmers that farm laborers were demanding unusual and, from the standpoint of the employing class, exorbitant wages. Many attempts were made to fix wages by law and to punish with the severest penalties any agricultural laborer who would demand more.

The growth of tenancy. Another result of the difficulty which the lords of the manors had in getting laborers to cultivate their demesne lands was the growth of leases. By leasing their lands in large holdings to some of the more successful farmers, sometimes to their own bailiffs, the lords were relieved of the difficulty and vexation of dealing with the irritating labor problem. Soon afterwards, therefore, it may be said that large-scale farming by tenant farmers began, and has continued down to the present time as the characteristic English system.

The Statutes of Laborers (1351 and later) failed to keep wages down, and the condition of hired laborers continued to improve. This sometimes led villeins to abandon their holdings — literally to run away — and seek employment as hired laborers on other manors. If they could evade recapture for a period of years, they remained freemen thereafter. Again, the growth of towns opened opportunities for villeins to escape and seek employment as town craftsmen. Seeing that so many of their fellows had become freemen, many of the villeins, together with many town craftsmen, rose in revolt under one Wat Tyler in 1381, for the purpose partly of throwing off the last remnants of villein service which were being exacted, and partly as a general protest against the political and economic inequalities of the time. Though the revolt was mercilessly put down, it is the belief of some students of the problem that it had some influence in hastening the break-up of the manorial system and bringing on the system of agriculture whereby free farmers leased lands from landlords. This is the system of fixed money payments in place of services. Under this new arrangement the position of the tenant as well as that of the agricultural laborer continued to improve.

New crops. Following this series of changes there were many minor changes and improvements in agricultural methods and products. New crops, such as hops, began to be cultivated, and many fruits and vegetables which had formerly been confined to the gardens attached to the manor houses began to be cultivated by tenant farmers. But the great expansion came in the middle of the seventeenth century, and it was due primarily to the introduction of clover and turnips. Cutler, in his " Short History of English Agriculture," speaks of this as the greatest agricultural event of the century. The turnip had long been known in England as a garden root, and perhaps to some slight extent as a field crop, but its cultivation did not begin on a large scale until Sir Richard Weston began, about 1645, urging its cultivation after the Dutch method. From this time on, these two crops — turnips and clover — increased steadily though slowly.

Clover and turnips. The advantages of these two crops were that the clover greatly increased the farmer's yield of hay, and the turnips enabled him to dispense with the fallow and to utilize all his land every year. Moreover, the clover tended to enrich the soil, as we now know, by restoring nitrogen to it; and both crops enabled the farmer to keep more cattle on his land and thus increased his supply of manure. Again, it had formerly been necessary for the farmer to kill his supply of meat in the fall, while the animals were fat, and then the country had to eat salt meat during the rest of the year. With clover and turnips the farmer could keep his cattle fat during the winter and supply the country with fresh meat the year round. The persistence of the open-field system in many parts of England probably accounts, in large part, for the fact that the cultivation of these crops did not increase more rapidly. Nevertheless, the progress made was sufficiently rapid to mark an epoch in English rural economy.

Great rural enterprises. This period was one of general agricultural enterprise in several other directions. In the fens of the eastern counties, great drainage schemes were begun which have made this one of the richest farming regions of England.

A number of great agricultural writers began to publish books on various branches of husbandry. Fruit growing increased in the southern counties. The practice of applying lime and marl, seaweed, oyster shells, etc., to the land increased generally. But none of these other improvements approached in importance the the introduction, already mentioned, of clover and root crops. This prepared the way for the still greater improvements which were to take place in the eighteenth century.

Parallel development in other industries. The eighteenth century was a period of wonderful awakening in manufacturing as well as in agriculture in England. In fact it is doubtful if any quarter of a century, either before or since, has seen more rapid and far-reaching changes in the manufacturing industries than that which elapsed between the years 1760 and 1785. At about the former year began the era of canal building under the leadership of the great engineer Brindley, whose dictum that "the natural use of rivers is to feed navigable canals" became historic, though the more recent development of the railway has destroyed its original importance. At that time the building of canals greatly cheapened transportation within the kingdom. In 1765 Watt discovered the principle which was to make the steam engine a commercial success. The way was prepared for the enlarged use of the steam engine and of machinery by Roebuck's blast furnace (1760) and the substitution of coke for charcoal in smelting, followed by Cort's method of puddling and rolling in 1784, by means of which the production of iron was greatly cheapened. Then came in rapid succession a series of epoch-making inventions in the textile industries, — the flying shuttle in 1760, Hargreave's spinning jenny in 1767, Arkwright's spinning roller in 1769, Crompton's mule spinner in 1779, and Cartwright's power loom in 1785. A cotton factory was driven by steam for the first time in 1785. Wedgewood gave a great impetus to the pottery industry, and a number of other improvements combined to accelerate the industrial revolution which was taking place.

Agricultural improvement; Jethro Tull. Somewhat earlier than this, however, began a series of rapid agricultural improvements which were even more important for the economic development and prosperity of the kingdom. About 1701 Jethro Tull began to drill wheat and other crops, having invented a drill for that purpose; and a little later to cultivate growing crops by horse power, the process being called horse hoeing. In 1731 appeared his work entitled " Horse-Hoeing Husbandry," which is regarded as one of the most important agricultural works ever published. Some of his theories are now regarded as imperfect, but the practices which he based upon those theories have not yet been materially improved upon. Thorough and deep pulverization of the soil was the central idea of his system. For this purpose he not only drilled the wheat, but actually cultivated between the rows, either by hand or horse power. While this particular practice of cultivating between the rows of wheat and other small grain has not been generally followed since, it has been continued with respect to turnips and other root crops, and is the usual method of growing Indian corn and cotton in the United States. This was a further step in the direction of the utilization of the fallow land, or rather of doing away with the necessity of fallowing. He even argued that the rotation of crops was less necessary under this system than under any other, and actually grew thirteen successive crops of wheat on the same land, without manure, getting better crops than his neighbors who followed the old methods.

"Turnip Townshend." About 1730 Lord Townshend began what came to be known as the Norfolk system. His two special interests were turnips and the rotation of crops, though he also introduced the practice of marling the light sandy land. He grew turnips and talked turnips so incessantly that he won for himself the nickname of " Turnip Townshend." In growing turnips he

followed Tull's system of drilling and horse hoeing. His system of rotation covered four years, and included (1) turnips,
(2) barley, (3) clover and rye grass, (4) wheat. It was said
that when he began this system much of his estate was barren
heath, but by 1760 it was brought to a high state of cultivation
and had increased in value tenfold.

Coke of Holkham. The work begun by Tull and Townshend
was carried on with even more striking results by Coke of Holkham, who began, about 1776, the reclamation of a body of
semibarren land which was described as little better than a
rabbit warren. Like his predecessors, he grew clover and turnips
and improved the rotation of crops, with the result that the
productivity of his land was more than doubled. He found
that most of the farmers were using too many horses in their
plow teams, the custom being to use from three to five. He
found that two were enough. It is said that he succeeded in
maintaining 2500 well-bred sheep on land which had formerly
supported only 800 worthless scrubs. He also became an ad-
mirer and breeder of Devon cattle. His estate achieved a world-
wide reputation ; his annual sheep shearings became great events,
men journeying from America to attend them, and Lafayette
expressed it as one of the regrets of his life that he had never
witnessed one. His influence did a great deal to bring about
improvements in agriculture all over England, and it is even
said that but for him and his influence England would not
have been able to produce food enough to sustain her during
the wars with Napoleon, and must therefore have succumbed.[1]

Gentlemen farmers. These three men — Tull, Townshend,
and Coke — did more for English agriculture than merely to re-
claim barren land and teach better farming to the rural class.
They raised agriculture to the rank of a learned profession, and

[1] See Curtler, A Short History of English Agriculture (Oxford, 1909),
pp. 227–228.

made it an attractive and honorable career for gentlemen and scholars. Their work, and more particularly their example, inspired that long line of gentlemen farmers, — men of means and education who have devoted themselves to agriculture with all the zeal and enthusiasm of the artist for his art or a professional man for his profession, and who have done so much to keep English agriculture in advance of the rest of the world from that day to this.

Arthur Young. The writings of Arthur Young and others contributed to the same end. Arthur Young, the best known of all English writers on agriculture, was a farmer of Suffolk, who began writing in this field in 1767 and continued for the next thirty-eight years, many of his writings being translated into French, German, and other languages. He traveled up and down England and other countries on horseback for months at a time, making careful observations, which he published in his series of "Tours." From 1773 to 1776 he made several tours in Ireland, and during the years 1787 to 1790 he made three extensive tours in France. His "Travels in France," published in 1792, is his best-known work, mainly because he described the condition of the people on the eve of the great revolution, and his account is still regarded as the best description of the actual state of the country and the people at the time of that great crisis. He is the author of the well-known phrase, "The magic of property turns sand into gold." Underdrainage of wet land began to be practiced in 1764 by Joseph Elkington in Warwickshire.

The breeding of live stock ; English breeds of cattle. While these advances were being made in general agriculture and the cultivation of field crops, equally striking results were being achieved in animal breeding. Accounts differ as to the character and quality of English live stock at the beginning of this period. The probabilities are that there was little uniformity, even in the same neighborhood. There was certainly much poor and unprepossessing stock. Bradley,[1] writing in 1726, divided the cattle of England into three classes according to color, — the blacks, whites, and reds. The blacks he described as the strongest for labor, though small, and found chiefly in the mountainous districts. They were, in all probability, the ancestors of the modern Welsh cattle, to which the description still applies. The whites were larger and were common in some of the eastern and southeastern counties. They were probably the basis upon which was built the modern breed of Shorthorns, through admixture with cattle imported from time to time from Holland. The reds were still larger, gave richer milk, were bred in Somerset, and were probably the ancestors of the modern Devons.

The French writer, Paul Diffloth,[2] classifies the Shorthorns as a variety of the Netherlandish race of cattle, of which the Holsteins, the Flemish, the Danish, the Oldenburghs, and others are continental varieties. The Devons he classifies as a variety of the Irish race, of which the Bretons, the Jerseys, the Guernseys, the Ayrshires, and the Kerrys are other varieties. The Herefords are, according to this writer, a variety of the Germanic race, of which the Norman cattle of northern France, and several German breeds, such as the Breitenburgs and the Mechlenburgs, are other varieties.

The evidence in favor of this classification is by no means conclusive. There are certain striking similarities between the cattle of the Netherlands and those of Durham, Yorkshire, and Lincolnshire, where the Shorthorns originated. Moreover, the evidence is fairly conclusive that the ancestors of the modern Shorthorns had, from time to time, been improved by importations of Dutch blood. Whether, as Diffloth suggests, the original cattle of these regions were united in a previous geological age, and

[1] Quoted in Curtler, A Short History of English Agriculture, p. 167.
[2] Encyclopédie Agricole, " Zootechnic : Bovidés " (Paris, 1904).

separated geographically by the formation of the North Sea, it is impossible to say. It is probable that the Herefords were built up by the process of careful breeding and selection of cattle from several different breeds. There are some points of resemblance between the Herefords and the Normans, and, more remotely, between these and certain German breeds, but whether there is any historical connection it is impossible at this distant time to say. It used to be claimed that there were importations from Normandy, and Curtler states that Lord Scudamore, in the latter half of the seventeenth century, introduced red cows with white faces from Flanders. Why such unlike breeds as the Devons, the Jerseys, the Bretons, the Kerrys (which latter three are very much alike except as to color), and the Ayrshire should be grouped together under the same race it is difficult to say, except that they occupy neighboring counties and are all precocious milkers except the Devons, which have been bred primarily for beef and for working oxen, although Devon cows, like most of the others of this group, give very rich milk.

Bakewell and the Longhorns. Whatever may have been the original breeds of English cattle, and however the modern breeds may be interrelated, it is well known that there was in the Midland counties, in the middle of the eighteenth century, a breed, more or less well established, known as the Longhorns. Robert Bakewell, the first great English breeder, began working with this breed about 1775. Though he wrought notable results, they were soon afterwards eclipsed by the still more remarkable results achieved by the brothers Charles and Robert Colling with the Durhams, or Shorthorns, as they came to be called in contradistinction to the Longhorns. This was not at all to the discredit of Bakewell or his methods, the undoubted fact being that the Collings had a better breed of cattle to work upon.

Bakewell's greatest success as a breeder was with sheep. Even less is known regarding the original breeds of sheep than of cattle in England, but they were said to be a nondescript, inferior, and unprepossessing lot until Bakewell began breeding them according to the principles of scientific selection. He virtually created a new breed, the Leicesters, which, according to Curtler, "in half a century spread over every part of the United Kingdom, as well as to Europe and America, and gave England two pounds of meat where she had one before." He set an example and a standard for a multitude of followers, who have made English mutton proverbial throughout the world. It is pleasant to be able to state that Bakewell's work was appreciated in his own day ; he was visited by royal personages and by men of distinction from all parts of the world. His breeding operations were highly profitable and his income from his animals became very large for that day ; yet he died a poor man, largely because of his unstinted hospitality and generosity. It was in 1760 that he began managing the estate at Dishley, where he spent the rest of his life, dying in 1795.

The Colling brothers and Shorthorn cattle. Next to Bakewell, the Colling brothers did more than any others for the breeding industry of Great Britain. Charles, the more successful of the two, was born in 1751, and began his operations about 1770 at Ketten, near Darlington, in the valley of the Tees, while his brother established himself at Brampton. The real origin of the modern Shorthorn is said to date from the purchase of the bull calf Hubback by Charles Colling in 1785. The exact ancestry of this remarkable animal is not definitely known, but it is pretty certain that he had some Dutch blood. However, the cattle of the valley of the Tees, sometimes called the Teeswater Durhams, had long been known for their superior qualities, particularly as milkers, but also for their size and beauty. Charles Colling noticed Hubback running in the common pasture at Hornby. He had been sold at the market, along with his mother, to a blacksmith of Darlington, who in turn gave them to his daughter as a wedding present when she was married at Hornby. The quick eye of Charles Colling appreciated the excellence of Hubback's conformation, from the standpoint of the beef producer, and with characteristic decisiveness he lost no time in purchasing him. Both Bakewell and the Collings reversed the common practice of the time of continually crossing different breeds and varieties, which was done in the mistaken belief that such frequent crossings were necessary to prevent inbreeding and deterioration. Such a method only produces mongrels. They bred from within a given race, and did not hesitate to inbreed where they saw that it was desirable to fix a certain type.

Benjamin Tompkins and the Herefords. About the same time, or a little earlier (1760), Benjamin Tompkins began improving the cattle of Herefordshire, and succeeded in establishing the magnificent breed of Hereford cattle, the only close rival of the Shorthorns in beef production, though distinctly inferior as milkers. About the same time the Duke of Bedford began improving the Devon cattle, though this is perhaps the oldest breed, or the breed whose distinct characteristics can be traced back the farthest of any in England. In spite of their many excellent qualities the Devons do not seem to have shown such adaptability to new conditions in different parts of the New World as have the Shorthorns and the Herefords. The enormous sales to the New World, including Australia, of breeding animals of these two popular breeds have been very important factors in English agricultural prosperity during the last century. In their own country, however, and in parts of New England where oxen are used, the Devons have retained their popularity.

The Thoroughbred. The early half of the eighteenth century was remarkable in the annals of horse breeding for the rapid development of the English Thoroughbred through the importation of Eastern blood. The Darley Arabian, a bay stallion from whom the best individuals are descended, was imported sometime between 1700 and 1706. The success of his progeny helped to remove the prejudice against Eastern blood, and the succeeding years saw many other importations, Prince George himself becoming active in the encouragement of importation. Next to the Darley Arabian, the most influential sire was the so-called Godolphin Arabian, who was almost certainly a Barb. He was a brown-bay stallion imported from France, where, as the story runs, he was so little appreciated that he had actually drawn a cart on the streets of Paris. He is believed to have been foaled in Barbary about 1724, and the first of his progeny in England was foaled in 1732.

Before this, however, there had been considerable interest in racing, and, by the process of selection, supplemented by frequent importation, there had been great improvement in the native stock. James I and Charles II had both been horse lovers and both had imported Eastern horses, the latter in particular having sent his master of horse abroad for the purchase of breeding animals. There was, therefore, by the beginning of the eighteenth century an excellent foundation stock to build upon. The two historic animals mentioned above doubtless owe their influence as much to that fact as to their own undoubted merit. But in spite of the interest in the subject, the annals of horse breeding show no such striking individual achievements in the building up of new and improved types as those of Bakewell with sheep and the Collings with cattle.

Draft horses. The modern British breeds of draft horses were built up mainly in the nineteenth century, though here, as in the case of the Thoroughbred, the native stock formed the foundation. The Shire is probably the direct descendant, with relatively few admixtures of foreign blood, of the old English cart horse, — a large, coarse, powerful animal, usually black in color, but not a very distinct breed. The Suffolk Punch, perhaps the first of the modern breeds to become an established type, is probably the result of crossing stallions from Normandy, relatives of the modern Percherons, upon the native mares. Arthur Young mentions them as early as 1775. The Clyde is said to have been the product of crossing Flemish or Belgian stallions upon native Scotch mares.

The English agriculture of the seventeenth and eighteenth centuries, as described in this section, was the type with which the colonists who came to America during our colonial period were familiar. The use they made of their knowledge and the new knowledge they acquired in adapting themselves to the conditions of the new continent is the subject of the following sections.

 ## III. BEGINNINGS OF AMERICAN AGRICULTURE [1]

The main periods. The agricultural as well as the political history of the United States is divided into two eras. The first is the colonial era, lasting from 1607 to 1776. The second is the era of national development, lasting from 1776 to the present time. This era of national development, however, is divisible into four distinct periods: first, from 1776 to 1833; second, from 1833 to 1864; third, from 1864 to 1888; and fourth, from 1888 to the present time. The first era, being contemporaneous with the colonial era of our political history, may be called the era of establishment. It was the time during which the colonists transplanted European methods of agriculture to American soil and readapted them to the new conditions. This readaptation consisted in learning how to live a wilderness life, and to clear wild land of trees, stumps, and stones. It consisted also in learning by experiment what crops were adapted to the soil and climate, and what methods of cultivation were best calculated to insure satisfactory returns.

[1] For a fuller and more detailed account see the author's "Historical Sketch of American Agriculture," in Bailey's Cyclopedia of American Agriculture, Vol. IV, pp. 39 ff. The Macmillan Company.

What we owe to the Indians. The first European settlers in America were not, however, thrown absolutely upon their own resources in learning to readapt their farming methods to the new conditions. They learned many of their first and, as it proved, most valuable lessons directly from the Indians. Rude as were the agricultural methods of the Indians, according to modern standards, we must not forget that they taught our ancestors how to grow two crops which were destined to play a large part in our national economy. These crops were tobacco and Indian corn, or maize. The former was the most important money crop in the Southern colonies during the entire colonial period, and remained in the lead until 1801, when it was outstripped by cotton. During our entire history corn has been the leading agricultural product of the country as a whole, and still retains that position with no other crop even a close second. There is no other crop which so distinguishes American agriculture, and it is doubtful if there is any other single product which confers such distinction on American industry.

How the colonists got land. In the agricultural history of any country one of the first and most important questions is that of the relation of the people to the land. In our early colonial history the land was supposed to be the property of the British crown, and all titles were ultimately derived from that source. There was considerable variety of procedure among the different colonies in the acquiring of a title to land. In Virginia the land was granted by the crown to the London Company, which in turn made grants to private individuals, that is, after a year or two of unsuccessful experimenting with a system of common ownership.

The land system of Virginia. There were three methods by which a private individual might acquire title to land in this colony. One was to buy a share of the stock of the London Company, known as a "bill of adventure." This was practically a certificate entitling one to a share of the profits of the Company and to one hundred acres of land, with a possible second hundred in addition. The second method of acquiring land was by meritorious service. Ministers of religion, physicians, and other public servants, including those who had performed manual labor, were sometimes granted tracts of land as a partial reward for their services to the people of the colony. The third method, and the one which, after the first four decades, became the most common, was known as "head right." Under this right any shareholder who transported to the colony at his own expense a person, bond or free, could secure fifty acres of land for every person so transported, provided such person remained in the colony three years or longer. This right was afterwards extended to settlers who were not shareholders, and finally came to be so laxly administered that any person could secure a patent by merely paying a fee to the secretary of the colony.

How the land was surveyed. After receiving a right to land, the next question was to get located, or to have the land surveyed and to get possession of it. The first step was to present one's certificate of "head right" to the surveyor and to select some unappropriated tract. It was customary to select land adjacent to the shore of the sea or of a river, so long as any such land remained. It was the practice of the surveyor to adopt the shore as a base and to measure off a line on this base whose length depended upon the size of the tract to be surveyed. From either end of this line, and at right angles to it, lines were run back to the distance of a mile. These two lines, together with the base and back lines, constituted the boundaries of the farm, which was thus rectangular in outline and one mile deep. The back lines of the tracts first surveyed formed a base line for a new series of tracts to be laid off when all the land adjacent to the waterways had been taken up and patented.[1]

[1] Cf. Bruce, Economic History of Virginia, Vol. I, pp. 531–532.

After the survey was made and the patent issued, the patentee was still required to build a house and settle on the land before the title was complete.

Land speculation. In the colonial period, especially after the first few years, a considerable volume of land speculation grew up. This usually took the form of securing a grant for a considerable tract and then organizing or otherwise inducing a group of colonists to settle upon it. After a part of the tract had been settled the remainder would command a higher price from later settlers, and thus would yield a profit to the promoters. This method, so familiar even in our own day in the Far West, began very early in our colonial history and has continued without many variations ever since.

The land system of New England. There were certain striking differences between the land systems of New England and those of the Southern colonies. In the early days in New England it was not customary to make grants of land directly to individual settlers, though a few individual grants were made, usually for conspicuous service. The usual method was to make a grant to a group of individuals who wished to found a settlement or town. From this group, or from the town which they constituted, the individual member received his grant or allotment, which was subject to certain restrictions imposed by the town. Weeden, in his "Social and Economic History of New England," says that "it was the admirable economic land tenure which shaped the early towns; without this, even their religious and political systems might not have established their distinctive system of living." The earlier towns were practically settled as church communities; that is to say, the formation of a town amounted practically to the organization of a church congregation and then settling as a congregation upon a tract of land and calling it a town. When a town was settled, all members who were admitted to citizenship were given grants of land.

"They elected, as it were, certain families to church membership," says Weeden, "and upon these fell the responsibilities of citizenship."

The granting of land in considerable tracts to towns, which in turn granted smaller tracts to individual settlers, remained the characteristic form of settlement in New England. It was not always, however, a church enterprise. Sometimes, especially during the latter part of the colonial period, a private individual or private company would undertake the settlement of a town as a business enterprise, expecting to make a profit from the sale of land. But in either case the settlement was made in the compact form (compact as compared with the form common in the Virginia and Southern colonies) of the town, and the town became, by reason of this method of settlement, the characteristic form of local government in New England.

Commons. Though the greater part of the land of a New England town was held in severalty by the individual settlers, there were common lands reserved for the pasture and woodland, and there was much communal work done in the way of fencing and ditching. Town herdsmen were sometimes appointed to herd the cattle of the citizens upon the common lands. Rights to pasture cattle upon the commons were usually restricted to the original settlers upon the land. In later years, when new families came to these towns, a distinction grew up between "commoners" and "noncommoners." This distinction sometimes led to difficulties. It was another phase of the world-old problem of the old-timers *vs.* the newcomers, the old families *vs.* the new families, the natives who are in possession *vs.* the immigrants who demand a share, or, in short, of the established *vs.* the unestablished.

Land system of the middle colonies. In the middle colonies there was considerable diversity in the forms of land tenure. Under English domination the land system of New York resembled that of New England rather than that of Virginia and the South. But under the Dutch a different system, known as the patroon system, had been developed along the valley of the Hudson. Under this system large tracts of land, ranging from 50,000 to 100,000 acres in extent, were granted to private individuals known as patroons, who formed a semifeudal nobility. These patroons were supposed to exert themselves to secure immigrants to settle on their estates, and then to rule as hereditary magistrates over them, receiving their support in the form of rents rather than taxes. They were supposed, in turn, to support schools, churches, and other public institutions out of the income received from rents.

In Pennsylvania and Maryland, and to a certain extent in New Jersey and Delaware, the proprietary system of government was based upon the land system. The land was granted by the British crown to large proprietors. These, in turn, made grants to actual settlers, bestirring themselves to attract colonists to their lands. In general, these grants were by sale in small farms to actual farmers who tilled the soil with their own labor, though some large grants were made, especially in Maryland. On these large grants something resembling the manorial system of rural economy developed.

The labor supply. Quite as important as the question of the relation of the people to the land is the question of the character of the labor supply. In a country where land is abundant and practically free, it is impossible that there should be any considerable body of hired laborers. If any laborer can become a landowner, he will not work for wages unless the wages are high enough to give him an income approximately as large as he could make as an independent landowning farmer. Where this is the case it will only occasionally, and under special circumstances, be profitable for a farmer to hire a laborer at such wages. Therefore the hired laborer is necessarily the exception rather than the rule. In such a situation as this, there are only two ways of getting the greater part of the farm work done. One is for the farmer to do it himself, the other is to make use of some kind of compulsory labor. In all the English colonies, south as well as north, it was customary in the earlier years for the farmers to till their own land. A little later considerable use was made, in both sections, of indentured servants.

Indentured servants. An indentured servant was one whose passage had been paid from the Old World to the New, and who had bound himself to work for a period of years in return for his passage money. At the expiration of the period he became free and could become a landowner like any other freeman.

Negro slaves. Use was also made of negro slaves, especially in the South after 1619. There were negro slaves in the Northern colonies also, but they were used mainly as house servants by the well-to-do townsmen. If any were used in agriculture, they were so few as to be a negligible factor in the agricultural development of the Northern colonies; but in the South they came to be used in large numbers in the culture of tobacco, which was the chief money crop of the region. Thus there developed a considerable difference in the type of farming in the two sections. In the Northern colonies the farms continued to be tilled mainly by the labor of the owners themselves, with some help from indentured white servants and a few hired laborers. In the South they tended to be cultivated less and less by the labor of the owners, but more and more by negro slaves. This tendency, however, was by no means rapid, and small farmers who tilled their own land were always numerous in the South. Still it is not an exaggeration to say that the dominant type of Southern agriculture came to be that carried on by means of slave labor. It was the difference in these two types of agriculture which prevailed in the North and the

South that gave such tremendous significance to Mason and Dixon's line, which happened to be the dividing line between two types of rural civilization. There was less difference between the cities of the two sections, though of course even the cities reflected some of the characteristics of the rural life with which they were surrounded.

Early experiments. While the early colonists learned their first lessons in successful agriculture from the Indians, and began growing corn or tobacco after the manner of their teachers, they were naturally unwilling to follow the Indian type of agriculture exclusively. Accordingly a great many experiments were tried. In Virginia especially these experiments were numerous. An attempt was made to develop the silk industry because mulberry trees were found growing wild, and to develop grape culture and wine making because wild grapes were found ; and attempts were also made to grow the fig, the olive, and other semitropical fruits. Jamestown is in about the same latitude as the northern coast of Africa, and this led the English people to think of Virginia as a semitropical country. Moreover, the early English explorers had usually visited the New World in the summer, and they had no opportunity to learn how severe the winters were, even as far south as Virginia. But after all their experimenting the Southern colonists fell back upon corn and tobacco as their leading field crops, though European grains, vegetables, and fruits were also introduced. Indigo and rice also became important crops in South Carolina and Georgia. In the middle colonies wheat became the staple crop, though corn was always grown, and European fruits and vegetables were cultivated in considerable quantities. There grew up a considerable export trade in wheat to the West Indies. In New England there were no great staple crops produced for export. Farming was of a more general sort, and products were grown mainly for the local markets.

Live stock. One of the most interesting phases of our colonial agricultural history is the live-stock industry. All the domestic animals and fowls now grown in the United States, except the turkey, were first brought from Europe. Everywhere the hog flourished, running half wild in the woods, living upon mast and roots, and multiplying rapidly in spite of the depredations of wolves, bears, and marauding Indians. Early in our colonial era Virginia hams and bacon acquired high reputation. Goats flourished also, being better able than sheep to protect themselves against wolves. Later, however, as the country became more settled, sheep displaced goats as a form of live stock. Sheep were grown in all the colonies where conditions were sufficiently settled to furnish protection from wolves. Cattle were naturally better fitted than sheep to defend themselves against the savage denizens of the woods, and have been bred in considerable numbers on the frontier ever since the earliest settlement. In Virginia and the Carolinas a flourishing cattle business, resembling modern cattle ranching, grew up. Annual round-ups were held at stated places (Cowpens), brands were registered, and most of the features of the modern business were developed. In New England the cattle business was mainly under the regulation of the towns, and each town was required to have its own brand, in order that cattle of different towns might be distinguished if they strayed beyond their proper feeding grounds.

There was little attention to horse breeding in the early part of the colonial era. Horses were brought by the first colonists, but were used almost wholly for riding and as pack animals. The heavy work about the farms was done by oxen, and there were no roads suitable for carriages. In Virginia horses multiplied in the woods and became wild and were sometimes chased for sport. During the latter part of the colonial period, that is, from about 1700 on, the more well-to-do Virginia planters began to give more and more attention to the improvement of the saddle horse. English thoroughbred stock, which had recently been developed in the mother country, was imported and crossed upon the so-called "native stock." This native stock, partly perhaps through its wild life in the woods, had acquired a hardiness and toughness which, in spite of its diminution in size, seem to have fitted it well to serve as a foundation for the improved breed of American saddle horses.

In Rhode Island, just before the close of the colonial era, there was a much-prized breed of saddle horses known as the Narragansett pacers. This once famous breed was supposed to be descended from a stallion imported from Spain. Individuals of this breed were in great demand, not only in the neighboring colonies but also in the West Indies. So many were sold and scattered that soon after the War of Independence these horses, never numerous, disappeared as a recognized breed.

With the exception of the turkey, all our farm animals and poultry were imported from the Old World. The first to reach the New World were brought by Columbus to the West Indies on his second voyage in 1493. Horses, cattle, hogs, goats, sheep, asses, chickens, ducks, and geese are known to have been brought at that time. During the colonial period there was considerable trade between our own colonies and the West Indies, and it is not improbable that specimens of all these Spanish varieties may have found their way to our shore. This is known to have been the case with horses, cattle, hogs, and sheep. Dutch cattle were brought to New York and Danish cattle to New Hampshire. In general, however, our farm animals came from the British Isles.

Rural life during the colonial era. The rural life of this early period has often been described and has become a part of our national tradition. In the South the rural life centered in the plantation. "A great plantation with its galleried manor house, its rows of negro quarters, and groups of barns and shops, was, in large measure, a self-sustained community. The planter needed little that could be obtained elsewhere in his own colony or in the South, and conducted his commercial operations directly with England, the West Indies, and the Northern colonies. . . . There were a few negroes on every plantation who were trained in the mechanic arts, and a small number of white craftsmen found work in traveling around the country doing such jobs as were beyond the capacity of the slaves." [1]

In the Northern colonies the farms were small and were operated mainly by the labor of the farmer and his family. This called for a great deal of coöperation among farmers and developed a wholesome social life. Accordingly, there were numerous quilting, spinning, husking, and paring bees, house and barn raisings, logrollings, and similar rural festivities.

The farming was everywhere of the pioneering kind. Less attention was given to the finer branches than to the rough work of clearing the forests, reducing the soil to cultivation, determining what crops could be raised to best advantage, and, in a general way, creating farms out of the rough materials which the new continent afforded. It would not be very inaccurate to say that the first object of the pioneer farmers was to produce farms, and the second to produce crops. However, every important crop now grown in the United States, except alfalfa, sorghum, and a few new varieties of the standard grains, was introduced and acclimated during the colonial period. Thus the pioneer farming of that period laid broad and deep the foundations of the agricultural development which was to follow. The problem of farm management was not how to save land, since land was abundant, but how to save labor, since labor was scarce ; and the colonial farmers solved their peculiar problems successfully.

[1] Thwaites, The Colonies, p. 102. Longmans Green & Co.

THE ERA OF NATIONAL DEVELOPMENT

1. *From 1776 to 1833. The Conquest of the Great Forest*

The shifting of the frontier. The War of Independence marks an era in our agricultural as well as in our political history. Shortly after this event a series of epoch-making changes began in agriculture. In the first place, the frontier moved rapidly westward into the great interior valley. The life of the pioneers on our frontier, wherever that frontier may happen to have been, has always retained certain of the essential features which it possessed in the colonial era.

The public-land policy. The next great epoch-making event was the establishment of the public-land policy of the federal government. At the close of the Revolution the land was all regarded as the property of the various states. By a series of acts the greater part of the unoccupied or unsold lands were ceded to the central government, which then began to devise plans for their sale to private individuals. No other policy than that of turning the public domain as rapidly as possible into private property for individual farmers ever seems to have been seriously considered. At first the policy was to sell the lands for the benefit of the national Treasury and the extinction of the national debt. By a series of changes the financial motive was abandoned altogether, and a policy was adopted which aimed to put the land in the hands of actual settlers without any direct profit to the national Treasury whatever.[1]

Transition from a financial to a social policy. This change in the land policy came about gradually, however, and covered more than three quarters of a century. Between 1783 and 1800 the public land was sold only in large tracts, 640 acres being the smallest. During the next twenty years (1801–1820)

[1] A very full account of this policy will be found in an article by A. B. Hart in the *Quarterly Journal of Economics*, Vol. I.

the smallest tract that the government would sell was 160 acres, and the lowest price was $2.00 per acre. During the next twenty years (1821–1840) the minimum price was $1.25 per acre, and 40 acres was the smallest tract that could be sold. In 1841 was passed the first general preëmption act, withdrawing the lands from sale to the general public and reserving them for sale to actual settlers. These were allowed to purchase limited areas, upon which they had actually settled, at the fixed minimum price of $1.25 per acre. The final stage in the transition was reached with the passage of the Homestead Act in 1862, and its modification in 1864. Under this law the actual settler who lived on and cultivated the land was given a title to a tract not exceeding 160 acres, without money and without price. Since the passage of this act there have been numerous supplementary acts like the Timber Culture Act, — giving a limited area of land to any one who would plant a limited portion of it in trees and cultivate them for a period of years, — the Desert Land Act, and others, all looking to the popularization of the land.

The first general ordinance for the sale of the national domain was passed in 1785. The most important feature of this act was that providing for a system of rectangular surveying, which is still in use. The system may be described as follows.

The rectangular system of surveying. Through a point selected as the initial point of the system a line is run north and south and another east and west. The first is known thereafter as a principal meridian and the latter as a base line, and from these two lines the townships are numbered. Each row of townships running north and south, whose east and west boundaries are parallel to the principal meridian, is called a range. The ranges are numbered east and west from the principal meridian. Within the range the townships are numbered north and south from the base line. The systems of numbering town-ships may be shown by the following diagram :

DIAGRAM I

The township marked A is 3 north and in range 3 west, and would be designated as Tp. 3 N., R. 3 W., while that marked B is 3 south in range 4 east, and would be designated as Tp. 3 S., R. 4 E.

Within the township the sections are numbered after the following order (Diagram II), always beginning at the northeast corner.

Within the section the quarter sections are designated by their directions from the center, being the northwest, northeast, southwest, and southeast quarters.

Thus if one wished to describe the quarter section lying in the extreme northwest of the township marked A in Diagram I, it would be done after this manner : N. W. Qr. of Sec. 6 of Tp. 3 N., R. 3 W. of the — P. M. Within the quarter section each forty-acre tract is again

R. 3 W.

6	5	4	3	2	1
7	8	9	10	11	12
18	17	16	15	14	13
19	20	21	22	23	24
30	29	28	27	26	25
31	32	33	34	35	36

Tp. 3 N.

DIAGRAM II

designated by its direction from the center of the quarter section. Thus if one wished to designate the forty acres lying in the southeast corner of the quarter section just described, it would be done after this manner : S. E. Qr. of the N. W. Qr. of Sec. 6, etc.

This system of surveys and of enumeration is probably of Roman origin, in some of its features at least, and is a model of simplicity and brevity. It was elaborated and adapted to American needs either by Thomas Jefferson or Albert Gallatin, it is uncertain which. The task of surveying such a vast expanse of territory, of recording the surveys, of keeping a record of sales, of entries and final proofs, and of issuing patents, was a work of great magnitude. It was at first performed under the supervision of the Secretary of the Treasury. In order to organize the work of surveying, the office of Surveyor General was created in 1796 and General Putnam was appointed Surveyor General of the Northwest Territory. In 1810 district land offices were established in the Northwest Territory, and the Surveyor General transmitted plans of the survey to these land offices instead of to the Secretary of the Treasury, as he had done before. In 1812 the General Land Office was established under a commissioner who took immediate charge of the public-land system, though still under the general supervision of the Treasury Department. This condition lasted until the creation of the Department of the Interior in 1849, since which time the General Land Office has remained under this department.

Allodial tenure. The famous Ordinance of 1787 related rather to the government of the territory ceded to the federal government by the several states than to the disposal of the public lands. It provided, however, for a popular form of land tenure, and this is at least of as great importance as the better-known provisions against slavery and for a republican form of government, concerning which so much has been written. The form of land tenure was to be allodial rather than feudal, the land was to be held in fee simple, was to be freely transferable by bargain and sale, and the estates of persons dying intestate were to be divided among their heirs in equal parts. By allodial tenure is meant the absolute ownership of the land, free from all obligations to an overlord, king, or any one else. By feudal tenure is meant the holding of land originally granted by a king or an overlord, on condition of the rendering of some service or the payment of some rental, which service or rental, however, is fixed in the original grant. Such tenure is permanent, provided the stipulated service is rendered or payment made. This form of tenure differs from the ordinary lease in that the latter holds only for a limited term and a new contract is made at the beginning of every new term. Land held in fee simple is held without condition or limitation, is perpetual, and belongs to the owner, his heirs, and assigns forever. This provision for a popular system of land tenure has determined the form of land ownership throughout the entire country, and even the older states, in which certain relics of feudal tenure still survived, have since remodeled their land laws after the pattern set by this ordinance.

The rise of the cotton industry. The next epochal change in the agricultural history of this period was the rise of cotton to the first place among Southern products. During the colonial era, and down to 1803, tobacco held first place, but at this date cotton began to outstrip it and soon left it far behind. This rise of cotton to a position of predominance came about as a result of several factors working together. During the latter half of the eighteenth century there had been a remarkable series of inventions, mainly in England, for the manufacture of cloth. These had greatly increased the demand for cotton on the markets of the world. In 1786 the long-staple or sea-island cotton was introduced and proved to be well adapted to the low lands of South Carolina and Georgia. But more important than all other factors was the invention of the saw gin in 1793. This was the first successful device for separating the seed from the short-staple or upland cotton. This is the kind of cotton from which the great bulk of the cotton fabrics of the world are manufactured, and the saw gin made its production profitable in this country where labor was scarce and land abundant.

Effect on slavery. One of the unpleasant results of this rise of the cotton industry, however, was to give slavery a new lease of life. It was already growing unpopular, even in the South; but the profit of growing cotton with slave labor was so great as to overcome, in the minds of a great many people, whatever moral objections they had to slavery as an institution. The prohibition, in 1808, of further importation of slaves kept the supply of this kind of property down to that furnished by its natural increase. The rapid increase in the demand for slaves on the cotton plantations, together with this limitation of supply, combined to make them a very valuable form of property.

It has been a common belief that slavery was a means of developing the agriculture of the South, even though it was morally wrong. This belief seems to rest upon some such argument as this: There were not many white farm laborers or small white farmers in the far South to do the work of cotton growing. Therefore if it had not been for the negro slaves, there would have been no one to do the work. This argument, however, overlooks the probability that it was negro slavery which kept white farm laborers and small white farmers out of the South. An immense tide of European immigration began to pour into the country early in the nineteenth century, but it sought the free states almost exclusively. There is no reason, except that furnished by slavery, why a part of these immigrants should not have sought the fertile lands and favorable climate of the South. But the presence of negro slavery was a sufficient reason. Free white laborers have generally avoided, as they would the plague, every community where they have had to compete with slave labor and share some of the social degradation that attaches to slavery. The best cotton growing is now carried on by white farmers who till their own farms, and there never was a time, even during the period of slavery, when there were not a few small neighborhoods of this type as oases in the general desert of wasteful and inefficient slave cultivation.

The almost complete exclusion of white labor from cotton growing was by far the most important effect of slavery upon American agriculture. Three other effects are commonly attributed to it. First, it is held responsible for the process of "land killing," by which is meant the practice of growing a few crops from a piece of land until its original virgin fertility was partially exhausted and then abandoning it for a new and unexhausted tract. It is doubtful, however, whether this practice was due more to slavery than to the presence of indefinite supplies of new land. If there is a field near by already fertilized by the accumulation of ages of vegetable mold, it is not always profitable to incur the expense of fertilizing an old field. It may be cheaper to move to the new field. This may be shortsighted from the point of view of the nation, but it is mere "business sense" from the point of view of the individual farmer. The blame, therefore, attaches to the nation as a whole, which permitted such a system, and not to the individual.

Second, slavery tended to concentrate cotton growing in large plantations worked by gangs of slaves under supervision. Slave labor, having no interest in its work, must of necessity be rigidly supervised. One overseer or superintendent can supervise the work of a gang as well as that of one or two. It would therefore be poor economy, as a rule, to try to grow cotton with the labor of one or two slaves in competition with plantations worked by larger numbers. Third, the tools and implements used in Southern agriculture remained crude and heavy long after improvements had been introduced in the North.

Tobacco, live stock, and general farming continued in the northern belt of slave states, that is, in Maryland, Virginia, North Carolina, Kentucky, Tennessee, and Missouri; but through the institution of slavery these states found their interests to be with the cotton states to the south of them rather than with the free states of the North. The cotton states furnished a market for slaves and also for the horses, mules, cattle, hogs, hay, and grain produced by these border states.

The mule. It was during the period we are now studying that the breeding of mules began to be a distinct business. George Washington himself was a pioneer in this enterprise, having received two valuable jacks as presents from Lafayette and the king of Spain. The extent of his influence in this direction is shown by the fact that there are now more than 2,000,000 mules in the country, and that they are still raised mainly in the border states of Virginia, Kentucky, Tennessee, Missouri, Kansas, and Texas.

Westward migration. The opening up of the Northwest Territory under the ordinances of 1785 and 1787 stimulated a rapid migration westward to this new territory. Inasmuch as the government at this period sold land to speculators as well as to settlers, this westward migration was made up of very diverse elements, though then, as well as later, the home seeker predominated. The land sought during this early period all lay in the continuous stretch of forest which extended westward from the coast to the present state of Indiana. Therefore the pioneering of this period differed, in some respects, from that which we have known later in the prairie states, though resembling that of the colonial period on the Atlantic seaboard. After locating his land and building a shelter, the first task of the settler was to clear his land of timber. The work of destroying the forest was prosecuted with such vigor and ingenuity as have probably never been equaled in the history of the world.

Farm implements. There were few changes in agricultural implements until after 1833. The plow and harrow were almost the only tools not driven by human muscle. The wooden plow with an iron share was still in use, though sometimes the wooden moldboard was protected by strips of iron. In 1798 Thomas Jefferson wrote a treatise on the proper form of a moldboard of a plow. A year earlier Charles Newbold of New Jersey had invented a cast-iron plow having the share, moldboard, and land side all in one piece. It did not come into general use at once because some one invented the absurd doctrine, which farmers seem to have believed, that the cast-iron plow poisoned the land so that crops would not grow. Jethro Wood of New York, a correspondent of Jefferson, took out patents for cast-iron plows in 1814 and 1819. He had designed a moldboard resembling somewhat those now in use.

Agricultural societies. Though there were few significant inventions of agricultural implements during the period from 1776 to 1833, there was the beginning of an interest in agricultural improvement which promised well for the future. Agricultural societies were founded in South Carolina in 1784, in Pennsylvania in 1785, in New York in 1791, in Massachusetts in 1792. In 1810 an exhibition of agricultural products was held in Georgetown, D. C., and another in Pittsfield, Massachusetts. In 1816 a somewhat larger exhibition was held in Brighton, Massachusetts. These were the forerunners of the agricultural fairs which have since had such a large development.

Improvements in live stock; the horse. During this period there were new importations of improved live stock, particularly Shorthorn and Hereford cattle, Kentucky, Massachusetts, and New York taking the lead. The famous sire of American trotting horses, Messenger, was imported from England to

Philadelphia in 1788, and the great Justin Morgan, the sire of the Morgan breed, was foaled in 1789. These were the beginnings of special types which might, without serious misrepresentation, be called American breeds. With these possible exceptions the United States has produced no distinctive breeds of the larger farm animals. Several varieties of pigs and poultry have been produced, and what might be called a special breed of the Merino sheep.

Sheep. One of the most interesting chapters in the history of American husbandry relates to the general introduction of the Merino sheep. The first animals of this breed were imported in 1773, but the industry was not yet in a flourishing condition. With the restrictions upon trade growing out of the Napoleonic disturbances in Europe, there grew up a necessity for a domestic supply of wool. At the same time the Peninsular War created such conditions in Spain that the herds of Merinos, which up to that time had been guarded as a quasi-national monopoly, were broken up and offered for sale. Enterprising American farmers began buying them, and by 1809 there were said to be 5000 in the country. The price of Merino wool soared, and the prices of sheep soared still higher. There grew up a speculative craze in Merinos,[1] and some fabulous prices were paid.

Hogs and the pork-packing industry. Hogs have always been an important agricultural product in the United States. The earliest settlers in all the colonies had found hogs very adaptable, multiplying rapidly and flourishing on the food found in the forest. The forests of the Ohio valley were especially rich in oak and beech mast, and hogs spread and flourished even more remarkably than they had east of the mountains. Every frontier settlement was thus provided with an abundant source of animal

[1] See C. W. Wright, " Wool Growing and the Tariff," *Harvard Economic Studies* (Boston, 1910), Vol. V.

food at a very low cost. Corn, the chief grain crop of the interior, was admirably fitted for the fattening of hogs. Therefore it was no accident that the production of pork became one of the early agricultural industries of the Middle West. During the period we are now studying, Ohio, Indiana, Kentucky, and Tennessee were the principal hog-growing states, and Cincinnati, the center of this region, soon became famous as the center of a large pork-packing industry, a position which she held until surpassed by Chicago many years later.

In 1805 fat cattle began to be driven across the Alleghenies to the eastern seaport cities, but a good part of the produce of the Ohio valley found its way southward, first to New Orleans and later to supply the cotton states. In 1825 the Erie Canal, connecting the Great Lakes with the Atlantic, was opened. This marked the beginning of a new outlet for the products of the great interior, especially the northern belt of that interior. Wheat became the leading export from the Northwest, but corn, beef, and pork remained the leading products of the Ohio River region.

2. *The Period of Transformation* [1]

Magnitude of the change. Beginning with 1833, there occurred on American soil during the next thirty years one of the most remarkable agricultural transformations ever known in the history of the world. In 1833 practically all the work of the farm except plowing and harrowing was done by hand. Though there had been minor improvements in hand tools, and considerable improvement in live stock and crops, particularly in Europe, yet it is safe to say that so far as the general character of the work actually performed by the farmer was concerned, there had been practically no change for 4000 years. Small grain was still sown broadcast, and reaped either with a cradle or the

[1] See also Bailey's Cyclopedia of American Agriculture (New York, 1909), Vol. IV, pp. 58 ff. The Macmillan Company.

still more primitive sickle. The cradle, however, was a relatively new invention, being a modification of the scythe, which had been used for centuries in mowing grass. The addition of the frame and "fingers" to the old-fashioned scythe, together with a few changes in the handle to restore the balance, made it into a so-called cradle and adapted it to the reaping of grain. But the sickle or reaping hook had been in use for thousands of years. Our younger readers may understand how recently this primitive tool went out of use from the fact that there are men now living (1911) who have reaped wheat with it in the United States. It is still in use in oriental countries and in some parts of Europe.

Grain was still threshed with a flail in 1833, or trodden out by horses and oxen, as it had been in ancient Egypt or Babylonia. Hay was mown with a scythe and raked and pitched by hand. Corn was planted and covered by hand and cultivated with a hoe. *By 1866 every one of these operations was done by machinery driven by horse power*, except in the more backward sections of the country. The increased use of farm machinery also helped the horse to displace the ox as a draft animal, the former being much better suited than the latter to the drawing of these improved implements.

Slaves in the South performed the same function as machinery in the North. This transformation of agricultural work was confined mainly to the North, where free labor prevailed. Though cotton production increased very rapidly during this period, being six times as great in 1860 as it was in 1830, this condition of affairs was the result mainly of an increase in the cultivated area and not of any striking improvement in the machinery and methods of cultivation. By spreading rapidly westward through the Gulf States the cotton industry grew by leaps and bounds. However, only a small fraction of the land in the cotton states was actually in cotton. It was estimated that at the outbreak of the Civil War the entire acreage in cotton was less than the geographical area of South Carolina.[1]

Causes of the transformation. The transformation which took place in the agriculture of the North was due to several causes, any one of which might be called epoch making. The first was the railroad. At the beginning of this period there were none. By 1860 there were 30,000 miles in operation and they had penetrated every state east of the Missouri River.

While the markets of the world were brought nearer to the Western farms by the building of the railroads, the markets themselves were growing larger. The building of the factory towns of New England called for larger supplies of food. In 1846 the English Corn Laws were repealed, though the repeal did not go into effect until 1849, when American foodstuffs began to be admitted to that country free of duty. The great Irish potato famine began in 1846. The continent of Europe was disturbed by the revolutions of 1848 and by the Crimean War of 1854. Finally, beginning with 1849 and lasting through the fifties, the gold fields of California and Australia were pouring a flood of new gold into the money markets of the world to stimulate prices, much as they have again been stimulated since 1897.

Another set of causes were at work in the form of a more liberal land policy. As we have already seen, the Preëmption Act of 1841 favored actual settlers rather than land speculators. The famines and political disturbances of Europe sent a tidal wave of immigrants hither, and many of them found their way to the Western lands and took advantage of the Preëmption Act.

The prairies. Another factor of great importance was the development of prairie farming. At the beginning of this period the vanguard of the westward-moving army of settlers was just emerging from the great primeval forest, which covered the

[1] For a fuller account see Hammond, "The Cotton Industry," *Publications of the American Association* (New Series), 1899, Vol. I.

entire eastern third of the continent, and was beginning to settle in the great natural meadows of the upper Mississippi Valley. In this new region the settler was saved the enormous task of clearing his land of timber. The abundance of this fertile land and the ease with which it could be reduced to cultivation created such an agricultural opportunity both for the landless man and the capitalistic farmer as had never been found before and may never be found again.

Agricultural machinery. But the most important factor of all was the series of inventions of agricultural machinery by means of which horse power was substituted for human muscles as a motor force. In 1831 William Manning of New Jersey was granted a patent for a mowing machine. In 1833 and 1834 Obed Hussey of Baltimore and Cyrus McCormick were each granted patents for reaping machines. After 1840, when these machines had been improved and their practicability demonstrated, they began to come into general use. About the same time the threshing machine began to be widely used, and very soon displaced the old primitive methods. It was not, however, until about 1850 that the " thresher " and the " separator," that is, the machine for beating out the grain and the machine for separating it from the straw and chaff, were combined. These machines were usually run by horse power, though a steam thresher was beginning to be used before 1864. John Deere made his first steel plow from an old saw blade in 1837.

Scarcely less important than the mower, the reaper, and the thresher were the corn planter and the two-horse cultivator, which came into use during this period. By means of these the farmer's ability to raise corn was greatly increased. Every part of the work of growing corn, except that of husking the crop, was done by horse power before 1864, except in certain sections where corn is a minor crop. In view of the fact that corn is and always has been our principal crop, it is doubtful whether the grain-harvesting machinery effected a greater saving of labor than did these improvements in the implements for corn production, by means of which horse power was substituted for man power.

Live stock,— horses. The Thoroughbred stallion Denmark was brought into Kentucky in 1839 and became the foundation of the stock of American saddle horses. It would be difficult to estimate the value to the country of an event like this; it would doubtless mount up into millions of dollars. It was during this period that interest in the trotting horse began to take definite shape. Heretofore this horse had been prized mainly for racing purposes; now its practical importance as a road horse began to be appreciated. "Up to 1840 the buggy was practically unknown, the common mode of travel being on horseback." A still more important event in the horse-breeding industry of the country "was the importation into Ohio of the Percheron stallion Louis Napoleon, from which time dates a great improvement in the draft horse."[1] Though less spectacular than the trotting horse, the draft horse is of even greater economic utility, and therefore this event is also of incalculable importance.

Hogs. Hogs continued to multiply and to flourish, nourished by the corn crops of the Western prairies. Cincinnati remained the center of the pork-packing industry until 1861, when it was surpassed by Chicago, which city had become, by the end of this period, the greatest market for agricultural products in the world, being the center of the region of prairie farming.

Abandoned farms. It was during this period also, and as a result of the changes already described, that the agricultural decline in New England began. As early as 1840 the abandonment of the hill farms began to attract attention. General farming on these rocky hills in competition with the prairie

[1] Bogart, Industrial History of the United States, pp. 242, 243.

farms and machine cultivation of the West was no longer possible, and only those sections suitable for dairying, stock raising, and market gardening continued to prosper. The competition of the eastern farmer with the farmer of the Western prairies might have been foreseen to be a hopeless one. So long as the eastern farmer was competing with the pioneer farmer of the earlier type, who had to spend the first ten or fifteen years in the task of clearing his land of trees and stumps, the eastern farmer could easily hold his own. The settler of the prairie farm escaped all that arduous toil. He could begin plowing his land at once, being hindered only by the natural toughness of the prairie sod. He could raise a fair crop the first year. After two or three years of cultivation the sod rotted and the soil, rich with thousands of years of vegetable mold, became as mellow and as easily cultivated as that of the old and highly improved farms of the eastern states and of Europe. It is interesting to note, however, that the earliest settlers in the prairie states, having come from heavily timbered states, habitually avoided the prairie lands and sought rather the fringes of timber that bordered the rivers and creeks. But it was soon seen that the prairie soil was not only more easily reduced to cultivation, but was actually better soil than that which bore timber.

Sometimes it was not even necessary to plow the prairie land before the crop could be raised. Furrows were plowed across the sod and the corn was planted in the bottom of these and covered with a hoe. The soil was so very rich and there were so few pests that a fair crop could be grown the first year with practically no cultivation. Another method of growing the first crop, however, was to plow the land and plant the corn in the upturned sod by means of an ax or mattock. For the turning of this sod a heavy breaking plow of a special design was used. It was commonly drawn by three or four yoke of oxen. It was the smoothness of this prairie land as much as anything else which led to the rapid development of farm machinery during this period when the prairie states were being settled. When these states began to be cultivated by means of effective modern machinery, and when the railroads began to transport the products of these states to the eastern seaboard, it became impossible for the farmer on the hilly lands of the Appalachian slopes to hold his own in competition with them.

Sheep and cattle. During the period now under discussion there was practically no increase in the number of sheep. Cattle, on the other hand, increased very rapidly on the Western prairies, which furnished natural pastures of high excellence. This was a period of great activity in the importation of breeding animals for the improvement of the native stock. These importations came commonly from England. In 1834 the Ohio Company for Importing English Cattle was organized. This company sent agents to England for the selection of the best specimens of the leading breeds of cattle. Nineteen head were sent in the first shipment, and other shipments were made in subsequent years. After 1840 these importations increased very rapidly, and surprisingly high prices were paid, especially for Shorthorns, individual animals sometimes bringing upwards of $5000. One result of these importations was the rapid improvement in the cattle, especially in the Ohio valley. There has never been a time since 1850 when herds of Shorthorns could not be found equal to any in the mother country. In 1840 five bulls and seventeen cows and heifers of the Hereford breed were brought to Albany, New York, and other importations followed, though some had been made earlier, notably by Henry Clay in 1817. It was not until a later period, however, that the Herefords began to attain a wide popularity. It was during the period of the development of the cattle-ranching business that they began to be appreciated, their special fitness for range conditions giving them a high value.

Dairying. Up to 1850 the butter and cheese made in this country was made on farms, but in the next year the associated system of dairying, known for a long time as the American system, was inaugurated. This so-called American system was similar to the modern cheese factory, to which farmers over a considerable area brought their milk and had it made into cheese.[1] By 1861 twenty-one cheese factories had been built. This was the beginning of a revolution in dairying which was carried much further during the subsequent period by the development of coöperative and capitalistic creameries.

The census of 1840 was the first to compile statistics of agriculture. Consequently we have very little complete or accurate knowledge of the agricultural production of the United States prior to that date. The following table shows the agricultural expansion from 1840 to 1860, the principal products being given in millions:[1]

Product	1840	1850	1860
Improved farm land (acres)		113.0	163.1
Corn (bushels)	377.5	592.0	838.8
Wheat (bushels)	84.8	100.4	173.1
Oats (bushels)	123.0	146.5	172.6
Rye (bushels)	18.6	14.1	21.1
Buckwheat (bushels)	7.3	8.9	17.5
Barley (bushels)	4.1	5.1	15.8
Potatoes (bushels)	104.2	104.0	153.2
Hay (tons)	10.2	13.8	19.0
Butter (pounds)		313.3	459.6
Cheese (pounds)		105.5	103.6
Wool (pounds)	35.8	52.5	60.2
Cotton (bales of 400 pounds)	1.5	2.4	5.3
Tobacco (pounds)	219.1	199.7	434.2
Rice (pounds)	80.8	215.3	187.1

[1] Cf. Bogart, Economic History of the United States, pp. 243, 244.

During the preceding period, as already mentioned, there had been a beginning made in the formation of agricultural associations and the holding of agricultural exhibitions. This movement received a great acceleration during the period from 1833 to 1864. By 1860 nearly every state had its agricultural society, and almost every county as well. Nothing perhaps signifies more clearly the interest in agriculture during that period than the rapid development and spread of the county and state fairs. These annual gatherings, with their opportunities to see what was new in agricultural machinery, in live stock, and in farm products, became effective agencies for stimulating improvements and spreading knowledge. Until the rise of the agricultural colleges, and the experiment stations which accompanied them, no other agency did so much for agricultural improvement as did these agricultural societies and the exhibitions and fairs held under their auspices. The New York state fair held in Buffalo in 1848 opened a remarkable competition in reapers and mowers. This exhibition of these machines, in such large number and variety, is thought by some to mark the real turning point in the transition from hand to machine production.[1]

3. *The Period of Westward Expansion* [2]

What caused the expansion. Though the expansion of agriculture during the period immediately preceding the Civil War had been marvelously rapid, it was even more rapid during the period immediately following. The Civil War scarcely imposed even a temporary check upon the development of agriculture in the North, though it completely disorganized the cotton industry of the South and involved it in temporary ruin. During the preceding period agriculture had pretty generally passed into the commercial stage, where farmers were living upon the

[1] See E. Levasseur, Agriculture aux Etáts-Unis (Paris, 1894), p. 48.
[2] See also Bailey's Cyclopedia of American Agriculture, Vol. IV, p. 64.

profits of farming rather than on the products of the farm itself, and it was now ready to respond to the new opportunities which had been created by the railroads, the inventions of farm machinery, the opening of the prairie states, and the development of the county fairs. There followed, therefore, such an expansion of agricultural enterprise as the world had never seen before, so far as we have any record, and such as it may never see again. The chief factors in stimulating this remarkable expansion were the Homestead Laws of 1862 and 1864, the disbanding of the armies, the invention of the twine binder, the roller process of manufacturing flour, the building of the transcontinental railroads, the permeation of every nook and corner of the Mississippi Valley by the so-called "granger roads," and the development of the immense cattle ranches of the Far West. While this tremendous expansion was going on in the North and West the cotton industry was undergoing a complete transformation in the South and getting ready for the expansion which was to come later. This transformation of the cotton industry was made necessary by the abolition of slavery.

Progress in the North unchecked by the Civil War. The improved machinery that had already come into use for the harvesting and threshing of small grain and for the planting and cultivation of corn enabled the North to increase its production of these crops during the Civil War in spite of the drain on its labor force. It is estimated that in 1864 there were 250,000 reapers in use in the United States, and a still greater increase was to come later. Between 1859 and 1863 the wheat crop of Indiana increased from about 15,000,000 bushels to 20,000,000 bushels, though one in every ten of her male population was in the army in 1863. By the use of these improved machines a smaller labor force was necessary to keep up the same rate of agricultural production. Again, the labor force of the North was in part replenished by immigration from

Europe, which continued during the years of the war with only a slight reduction. During the decade from 1860 to 1870 there were 2,314,824 immigrants, most of whom settled in the group of states known as the north central states, that is, the states north of the Ohio, west of New York, and east of the Missouri. This is the group sometimes called the grain states, and its population increased more than 42 per cent during this decade.

Expansion of farm area. During the next decade, however, that is, from 1870 to 1880, over 297,000 square miles, a territory equal in extent to Great Britain and France combined, were added to the cultivated area of the United States.[1] This increase in the cultivated area was due partly to the increased effectiveness of labor when it was equipped with the improved machinery which had come into use, partly to the westward migration of our native population, and partly to the enormous immigration of that decade. This immigration amounted to nearly 3,000,000 persons, a number not far short of the population of the entire country at the beginning of the War of Independence. But the immigration was still greater during the succeeding decade, that is, from 1880 to 1890, reaching the astonishing number of 5,250,000. Many of these immigrants continued, up to 1890, to find their way to the Western farms. The following figures from the United States census will show the increase in the principal grain crops since the census of 1840:

	CORN (bushels)	WHEAT (bushels)	OATS (bushels)
1839	377,531,875	84,823,272	123,071,341
1849	592,071,104	100,485,944	146,584,179
1859	838,792,742	173,104,924	172,643,185
1869	760,944,549	287,745,626	282,107,157
1879	1,754,591,676	459,483,137	407,858,999
1889	2,122,327,547	468,373,968	809,250,666
1899	2,666,440,279	658,534,252	943,389,375

[1] Bogart, op. cit., p. 267.

One result of this enormous increase in our agricultural productivity was the increase in the exportation of breadstuffs. This did not begin on a large scale until after 1860, but after that date it increased by leaps and bounds until within twenty years, that is, by 1880, this country had become the world's greatest exporter of wheat. Only a small fraction of the corn crop has ever been exported in the form of corn, a greater part being fed to live stock; our exports of corn, therefore, have been mostly in the form of animals and animal products.

As already suggested, one of the agencies which brought about this expansion of agricultural enterprise was the Homestead Laws; the policy of giving land to settlers free of cost tended to encourage the rapid settlement of the public domain. Another impetus was given by the disbanding of the armies of the Civil War. The throwing of such an immense labor force upon the market would, under ordinary conditions, have resulted in a glut of the labor market and would, in all probability, have produced civil disturbances. But Congress modified the Homestead Laws so as to make it very easy for an ex-soldier of the Union army to acquire government land. It was enacted that any honorably discharged Union soldier could deduct the time he served in the army from the time which the ordinary settler was required to live upon and cultivate his land before he could acquire a title to it. Thus the disbanding of the armies coöperated with the rising tide of immigration and the free-land system to bring about this remarkably rapid expansion.

Another factor not to be passed over lightly was the large number of horses and mules set free for productive work by the disbanding of the armies. Many of these were sold to farmers, and added to the supply of power necessary to run the farm machines. This event is regarded by some as fixing the date, if it can be fixed, of the displacement of the ox by the horse in agriculture. Before this period both horses and oxen were used, but for much of the heaviest work, such as breaking the sod, the latter seem to have been preferred. Since this time oxen have continued to be used in small numbers and in backward sections, but this date may be fixed upon as the turning point in the transition from the ox to the horse as the typical draft animal. This is a matter of greater importance than will appear to the casual reader. In agriculture, as in manufacturing, the question of power is a question of fundamental importance. The transition from ox to horse power is a matter of almost as great importance as that from water to steam power in manufacturing.

Agricultural disorganization. Though this free-land system did enable the country to absorb the immense labor supply without glutting the labor market and producing civil disturbances, it produced, on the other hand, a glut in the market for agricultural produce and disturbed the agricultural equilibrium not only of this country but of western Europe as well. Among other things this resulted in the partial disorganization of the agriculture of the eastern states. The abandonment of farms, which had begun during the preceding period, now reached its maximum. So eager were settlers to acquire Western land that, in many cases, this motive rather than the preference for agriculture itself led men to take up land and to turn farmers. Instead of acquiring land for the purpose of growing crops, it frequently happened that crops were grown in order that the settler might acquire land, that is, in order that he might occupy his time during the period which the government required him to live upon his land. Frequently, if not in the majority of cases, the crops were grown at a loss, if the farmer had counted his own wages as a part of the cost of growing these crops. They were certainly grown at a loss if he had counted as a part of the cost the expense necessary to restore to the soil the fertility that was extracted. But the farmer counted the anticipated rise in the value of his land as a partial compensation for his work; that is, he continued to grow and sell crops at a loss, calculating that the future rise in the value of his land would eventually recoup him for any temporary loss which he might incur.

Agricultural discontent. The natural result was an oversupply of farm products. Side by side with this wonderful expansion of the cultivated area and the consequent increase in agricultural production, there grew up a vast amount of agricultural discontent. This in turn gave rise to a series of farmers' movements, beginning with the Grange movement of the early seventies. This is one of the most striking episodes in the economic history of recent times. Everywhere, at all times, the agricultural interests have been looked upon as conservative. The farmers have been called the bulwark of the state; they have been relied upon as the people who stand for the existing order of things, while the manufacturing and commercial interests have commonly been regarded as furnishing the more radical and unstable elements in the life of modern states. In this country, however, between 1870 and 1900, that order was completely reversed. For the first time in modern history the landowning interests have been the turbulent, dissatisfied, radical, or semirevolutionary elements of our population. The Grange movement of the early seventies was not in its origin a radical movement, nor were its objects political, but it speedily developed into a political movement aiming primarily at reforms in the banking and railroad policy of the country. Next came the greenback movement of the later seventies and the early eighties, which threatened for a time to overturn our monetary system completely. Finally there came the free-silver movement of the nineties, another movement of the same kind, which subsided only at the return of prosperity to the agricultural interests. It was the overexpansion of agriculture and its consequent unprofitableness during this period, more than anything else, which brought about this condition of instability and discontent.

Railroads. The period which we are now studying was also one of rapid railway development. The substitution of steel for iron rails and the greater carrying capacity of the railroads which resulted, the development of the great trunk-line systems, the building in connection with them of the granger roads, and the construction also of the great transcontinental lines, — all contributed their share toward creating a condition under which the farmers of the Far West could compete on almost equal terms with those of the east in the supply of eastern markets. The building of the transcontinental railways in particular, stimulated by land grants by the federal government, has contributed to this result. They were built in advance of the demand, and tended, in turn, to stimulate a rapid settlement of the Far West.

Along with these improvements in railroad transportation there was developed a remarkable system of handling grain and live stock. The refrigerator car was brought into use in 1869, and gave an impetus to the meat-packing industry, which could now run continuously throughout the year. This led, beginning with 1876, to the exportation of fresh meats to foreign countries. The system of grading and classifying grain enables large amounts of grain of any specified grade to be handled in bulk at a very small expense per bushel. The building of immense elevators where grain can be handled and stored, where cars can be loaded and unloaded in a few minutes, and where ships can be loaded at the rate of 10,000 bushels per hour, — these and a number of other improvements contributed their share in the general expansion of trade in farm products and the opening of a world market to the American farmer. But this tended to produce an agricultural disturbance in Europe similar to that which took place in our own country.

Machinery. Among the more important inventions of agricultural machinery during this period the twine binder stands preëminent. Except where the summers are dry, as in the semiarid plains of the West, and where, therefore, the harvesting may be prolonged over a considerable period of time, and where huge combination harvesters can be used, the harvesting of the crop is a crucial point in the economy of grain growing. The farmer must ask himself, not how much wheat he can grow, but how much he can harvest. The amount which he can profitably grow is limited by the amount which it is physically possible for him to harvest. Before the invention of the twine binder harvesting was a much greater problem than it has been since. The amount which could profitably be grown was even more strictly limited by the physical impossibility of harvesting it. The invention of the twine binder, therefore, by increasing the amount which a farmer could harvest, increased by that precise amount the quantity which he could profitably grow. In other words, it was the twine binder more than any other single machine or implement that enabled the country to increase its production of grain, especially wheat, during this period. The per capita production of the country as a whole increased from about 5.6 bushels in 1860 to 9.2 bushels in 1880. There were also numerous minor improvements, and the general substitution of steam for horse power in the running of the threshing machines during the period now under discussion. All these improvements brought about a considerable increase in the efficiency of the threshing machine. However, all these things put together have not contributed so much toward the revolutionizing of the grain-growing industry as did the twine binder.

The roller process. Though not an agricultural process, the roller process of manufacturing flour was also a great factor in the agricultural expansion of this period. Flour made from spring wheat by the old process was so inferior in quality that many of our best agriculturists did not believe that there was any future for the growing of spring wheat in this country. But by the new process better flour could be made from the spring wheat than had ever been made from winter wheat. Contemporaneously with this discovery came the opening of the great spring-wheat areas of the Northwest, in Minnesota and the Dakotas. The population of these three states more than doubled in the decade from 1870 to 1880. Prior to this period Rochester, New York, had been the great flour-manufacturing center of the country, but its position of leadership was surrendered to Minneapolis, the early metropolis of the spring-wheat country, almost as soon as the roller process came into use.

Corn growing. Among the improved articles of machinery used in growing corn was the "check rower." This device attached to a corn planter enabled one man to do work which had formerly required two. It automatically drops the seed in rows running across the field at right angles to the direction in which the planter is being driven, thus planting the rows in two directions and permitting of cross cultivation. In the somewhat drier regions west of the Missouri corn came to be planted by means of the "lister," — a double-moldboard plow, throwing a deep furrow and planting the corn in the bottom by means of an automatic seeder. Though this method of planting does not permit of cross cultivation, it has certain advantages, chief of which is that the deeper planting of the seed enables the crop to withstand drouth somewhat more successfully than does the shallower planting practiced farther east. A number of other minor improvements, such as the weeder, the riding cultivator, which is merely a perfection of the older horse cultivator, and the two-row cultivator drawn by three horses, have combined to lighten the work of the corn grower and to enable each man to tend a larger crop. The bulk of the corn crop continued to be harvested by hand, no satisfactory machine having been designed for the husking of corn. Fortunately, however, there is no such need of haste in the harvesting of the corn crop as in the harvesting of the wheat crop.

Cattle ranching. During the period now under discussion the cattle industry in the Far West underwent a most interesting and spectacular development. Cattle ranching has always been associated with our frontier life, particularly in Virginia and the Carolinas. After the acquisition of Texas the American cattlemen who had already penetrated that territory took over the ranching business and reorganized it. The descendants of the Spanish cattle brought over by Cortes and his followers had multiplied rapidly in the mild climate of Mexico, which then included Texas, where they had run wild for more than two hundred years. Their Mexican owners found no satisfactory market for anything except hides and tallow, which bore transportation well. Therefore their chief interest in these herds of cattle was shown by their periodic harvests of these two products. Under American dominion, however, American cattlemen made various attempts to open up a market for Texas beef. As early as 1857 a few Texas cattle were driven to the cornfields of Illinois, but they did not become popular. During the Civil War the outlet for Texas cattle was cut off and yet the cattle continued to multiply. Consequently the ranges were ready to swarm in the late sixties.

It had been discovered that the grasses of the northern plains were very nutritious and would support cattle even during the winter season. From several sources [1] the story is told that this discovery was made by accident by a teamster who was hauling supplies to a United States fort in Utah. Being overtaken by a snowstorm while on the Laramie plains in the winter of 1864–1865, his supply of feed was soon exhausted and he turned his oxen out to shift for themselves, or, as he thought, to perish.

[1] Cf. J. H. Patton, The Natural Resources of the United States, pp. 387–388. Also Joseph Nimmo, Report on Range Cattle, Washington, 1885.

They never strayed very far from the camp, however, and when spring came they were found to be in better condition than when they were turned loose in the early winter. The winds had here and there laid bare the cured buffalo grass and the oxen had fed upon it for nearly four months.

The cattle trail. The quality of the grass in the northern plains is somewhat better than that in the Texas ranges, and it was discovered that the Texas cattle gained in weight more rapidly in the north than on their native ground. It was estimated that a four-year-old steer would gain 200 pounds on the northern ranges over and above what he would gain in Texas. Moreover, the beef was thought to be of slightly better quality, if raised in the north. The abundance of these northern ranges, as compared with the crowded conditions in Texas, together with the other advantages just named, led to a great migration of Texas cattle northward. This migration followed, in general, the western edge of the settlements. The line of this drift northward came to be known as the Texas cattle trail. The ranges of western Kansas, Nebraska, Colorado, and Wyoming were first sought, the most northern ranges being avoided because of the danger from the Indians. After the Custer Massacre of 1876 the northern Indians came to be more closely guarded by the federal government, and the great plains of the Dakotas and Montana were thereby opened to the cattlemen. These far northern ranges were, in some respects, the best of all. Consequently the great cattle trail soon extended up to the very northern boundary of the country. From 1870 to the close of the period we are now considering, the great cattle trail was pretty well marked as the route over which vast numbers of cattle drifted north from the great breeding grounds of Texas. The migrating cattle were mainly young steers, besides some heifers taken north for the stocking of the northern ranges. Inasmuch as cattle seemed to multiply more rapidly in Texas, because apparently cows were more prolific in the milder climate of that state, and inasmuch as young cattle grew more rapidly after being moved north, a territorial division of labor grew up. The ranches of the south supplied the young and immature cattle, and those of the north matured them and prepared them for beef. The points at which the cattle trail crossed the transcontinental railways became great cattle markets and shipping points. These shipping points developed some of the most picturesque features which have become associated with our frontier. Each became a great rendezvous for cattle-men and cowboys of every kind and description. These points, which came to be called cow towns, furnished many exciting scenes and episodes which remain a part of the legend and tradition of the Western states and will doubtless eventually become fixed in our national traditions. From 1870 to 1872 Newton, Kansas, was the point where the trail crossed the Atchison, Topeka, and Santa Fe Railroad, and Abilene was the point at which it crossed the Kansas Pacific. These were there-fore the noted cow towns of that period. But as settlements moved westward, the cattle trail was forced to shift westward so as to avoid trespassing upon farm land. Accordingly Great Bend on the Atchison, and Ellsworth on the Kansas Pacific, became the great shipping points. Again, Dodge City on the Atchison, and Hayes City on the Kansas Pacific, were the great cow towns. In 1885 they were Dodge City, as above, and Ogalala, Nebraska, on the Union Pacific. It was estimated that as many as 400,000 head of cattle were driven to these two points for shipment during the year 1884 alone. After 1885 the importance of the great cattle trail began to decline. The westward advance of the line of settlements tended to cut off this line of march, but the chief factor of the decline was the competition of the railroads, which were built into the heart of the cattle country and which transported the cattle more quickly and almost as cheaply as they could be driven overland. The following table from the report of Joseph Nimmo shows the estimated number of cattle driven northward from Texas over the old cattle trail from 1866 to 1884 :

1866 260,000		1876 321,000
1867 35,000		1877 201,000
1868 75,000		1878 265,000
1869 350,000		1879 257,000
1870 300,000		1880 394,000
1871 600,000		1881 250,000
1872 350,000		1882 250,000
1873 465,000		1883 267,000
1874 166,000		1884 300,000
1875 151,000		

But cattle ranching did not begin to decline with the decline of the cattle trail. The corn belt has had a great deal to do with the development of the Western cattle-ranching business. This corn belt lies immediately contiguous to the ranching country. Consequently the movement of cattle in more recent years has been eastward from the Western ranges rather than northward from Texas. During the latter part of the period we are now considering, that is, in the early eighties, cattle began to be shipped in large numbers from the Western ranges into the corn-growing regions of eastern Kansas, Nebraska, Iowa, Missouri, and Illinois, to be fattened upon the corn crops. It was therefore in the heart of the corn country rather than in the range country that the packing houses were built for the slaughtering of animals and the curing of meat products. Kansas City, St. Joseph, Omaha, Chicago, and St. Louis became great packing cities. Owing to the practice of allowing hogs to fatten on the droppings of the corn-fed cattle, pork came to be, in a measure, a by-product of the beef-producing industry.

Dairying. As previously stated, the beginning of the modern factory system of manufacturing butter and cheese was made just prior to the Civil War. But this system did not become general until later. During the sixties and seventies cheese making under the factory system developed somewhat rapidly, but after 1880 butter making began to absorb more of the energies of the American dairymen and to displace cheese making. Under the old system, where butter was made on farms, the butter-making industry had centered in the eastern and central states, especially in Vermont, Massachusetts, and New York. But under the new system the center shifted westward and a great butter-producing region developed in the territory which includes northern Illinois, southern Wisconsin, eastern Iowa, and southeastern Minnesota. Elgin, Illinois, became the central market of this region. Two factors of primary importance in the development of the butter-making industry were the Babcock test for the determination of the proportion of butter fat in milk, and the centrifugal separator, by means of which the cream could be extracted without having to set the milk and wait for the cream to rise through the influence of gravitation. Without these two inventions it is doubtful if the factory system could ever have supplanted the domestic system of producing butter. Another factor of great importance, though it is commonly overlooked, is found in the butter-consuming habits of the American people. The Americans, like the French, are bread eaters, and, unlike the French, uniformly consume butter with the bread. This in itself calls for a large butter-producing industry and encourages the dairyman to specialize on butter. When this specialization has taken place it is but natural that American dairymen should supply the markets of other countries of the world. On the other hand, Americans are not large consumers of cheese nor have they developed a high specialization of taste as cheese consumers. There is, therefore, very little encouragement to the American dairyman to specialize in the making of that commodity, and he has found it impossible to compete in the European markets with the more highly skilled European producers. Add to this the fact that butter is a more homogeneous product than cheese, and that in Europe each country or even each locality has its own special taste in that article of consumption, and we have additional reasons why there is no great demand for the American cheese in Europe. Another important factor in the centralization of butter production in the Western grain states is the introduction of the silo. By means of the silo Indian corn can be utilized to furnish succulent food for dairy cows throughout the winter. In northern Europe, where corn does not flourish, this has to be supplied by root crops such as turnips, beets, etc. But corn silage is a much cheaper and an equally good ration for dairy cows, and enables the American farmer to produce butter fat at a lower cost, probably, than any of his European rivals. Corn silage is cheaper than root crops, first, because the yield of feed per acre is somewhat larger, but mainly because it requires less labor.

Reorganization of the cotton industry. The most violent agricultural change which took place during the period we are now considering was in the cotton-growing industry of the South. The Civil War had emancipated the slaves and involved in financial ruin most of the cotton planters. This necessitated a complete reorganization of the cotton industry. The stagnation which took place during and immediately following that great cataclysm produced abnormally high prices for cotton. Something like a cotton famine had been felt in England during the war, because of the blockading of the Southern ports, and this famine could not be immediately alleviated after the restoration of peace, because of the disorganization of industry which followed emancipation. Cotton sold for 43 cents per pound in 1865 and 30 cents in 1866. Under the stimulus of these high prices many of the Southern planters undertook cotton growing on a large scale with hired negro labor and on borrowed capital. This brought down the price of cotton and at the same time brought bankruptcy to the planters. This system of cotton production proved expensive, and gradually it was replaced by the one which still predominates throughout the greater part of the cotton section, at least in the eastern half of it, namely, the growing of cotton by negro tenant farmers on small tracts which they rent on shares from the large landowners. This new system proved to be workable, and gradually cotton production began to increase again until, by 1879, the crop exceeded that of 1860. Under this system the negro tenant was in a somewhat peculiar position. Though he was called a tenant, he was in a sense only a hired man, who was paid a share of the crop instead of fixed wages; that is to say, he had little more independence than a hired man. The owner of the land furnished the seed, the tools, the mules, and the feed, and sometimes advanced corn meal and bacon to the tenant. Gradually, however, there appeared a better class of tenants, who attained a little more independence and became the owners of their mules and implements, becoming, in fact, real tenants.

Agricultural credit. Following this change in the method of cotton production, there came certain other changes in the economic and financial situation. A most vicious system of agricultural credit was developed, mainly through the agency of the local merchants. These merchants would undertake to advance supplies to the farmer and receive their pay from the proceeds of the cotton crop. In order to secure themselves they would take a mortgage on the crop. This tended to put the farmer at the mercy of the lender. He was almost compelled to buy his supplies from the storekeeper who held the mortgage on his crop, and the storekeeper would frequently dictate the amount and character of the crop which the farmer was to grow. This tended to accentuate the evils of the one-crop system and to concentrate the energy of the farmer on cotton to the exclusion of everything else. Though it would have been to the farmer's advantage to grow the corn and the bacon necessary for his sustenance, the storekeeper tended to discourage this because it would make the farmer less dependent upon the store. Corn and bacon were the articles which were sold to the farmers in largest quantities. "The raising of corn would not only give a less marketable crop into the hands of the merchant, but it would eventually lose him his customers, for the raising of his own supplies would release the farmer from the necessity of doing business on a credit basis." [1]

4. *The Period of Reorganization* [2]

About the year 1888 began a series of changes which produced a profound reaction on the whole agricultural situation in the United States, though the results did not begin to be visible until almost a decade later. This date is chosen as the beginning of the new period because of the fundamental importance of these changes. In the preceding year Congress passed the famous Hatch Act or Experiment Station Act. In the year 1888 began the enlarged organization of the teaching of agriculture under the stimulus of this act. This was the beginning of a more comprehensive and systematic application of the principles of experimental science to agriculture than had ever been attempted before. There had been experiment stations before this time, not only in European countries but in some of the eastern states as well ; but under this act they were organized on a more extensive scale and their work coördinated more effectively than ever before. Prior to 1888 there had been 20 experiment stations in the country, but in that year alone 26 new ones were established. Again, the pioneering period in American

[1] Hammond, "The Cotton Industry," *Publications of the American Economic Association* (New Series), 1899, Vol. I, p. 151.

[2] See also Bailey's Cyclopedia of American Agriculture (New York, 1909), Vol. IV, pp. 68 ff. The Macmillan Company.

agriculture was drawing to a close by reason of the practical exhaustion of the supply of free public lands, — that is, the supply of public lands which could be immediately reduced to cultivation by the settler without much previous expenditure of capital and labor. Since that time the greater part of the public lands that have been actually settled have required irrigation. Irrigated land requires a different type of settlement from that which prevailed from the earliest settlement of the American continent down to this date. This practical exhaustion of the free public lands soon began to have its effect upon the markets for agricultural products not only in this country but in our foreign markets as well. The lands farther east had no longer to compete with the newly settled lands of the frontier, and the farmers of the east no longer had to sell their products at a price dictated by the frontier farmer, who was induced to grow crops not so much by the prices he received as by the hope of a rise in the value of his land. There soon began, therefore, a general rise in the value of farm lands in the older settled portions of the country, and our people were beginning to see that the increased demand of our growing population for agricultural products could not be met any longer by merely extending the area of our pioneer farms westward. It must be met, if met at all, by increasing the product per acre of the farms already under cultivation, but this will only come about as the result of uniformly higher prices for agricultural products. Hereafter there will be a higher premium upon intensive and scientific farming than there has ever been before. So long as there was free public land to be had for the asking, the opportunities for the scientific farmer were limited by the possibilities open to the pioneer farmer, who needed nothing but a team and a few implements and a very meager equipment in the way of knowledge to enable him to grow crops successfully. From this time forward the scientific farmer will be free from that kind of competition and may reasonably expect to see the fruits of his own superior knowledge and intelligence. This means more for the future of American agriculture than anything else which has happened. These circumstances give tremendous significance to the experiment stations, by means of which scientific knowledge is to be made accessible to those who have the intelligence to use it. Fifty years earlier the same development of experiment stations would scarcely have been possible because of the lack of opportunity for the use of scientific knowledge in competition with pioneering. These two facts taken together — that is, the development of the experiment stations and the increasing opportunities for the use of scientific knowledge — will bring about a reorganization of agriculture and will create what some have chosen to call the New Agriculture.

Transition from extensive to intensive farming. Where land is cheap and labor dear, wasteful and extensive farming is natural and it is useless to preach against it. While extensive agriculture is wasteful of land, it is not always wasteful of labor ; in fact, it is usually economical rather than wasteful. We always tend to waste that which is cheap and to economize that which is dear. The condition of this country in all the preceding periods which we have studied dictated the wasteful use of land and the economic use of labor. This economical application of labor has been shown by the unprecedented development of agricultural machinery. But as land becomes dearer relatively to labor, as it inevitably will, the tendency will be equally inevitable toward more intensive agriculture, that is, toward a system which produces more per acre. This will follow, through the normal working of economic laws, as surely as water will flow downhill.

Large portions of the public domain are still unoccupied and the greater part of it will probably always remain so, but a considerable area in the aggregate may still be reclaimed by irrigation. Irrigation systems were developed in previous periods of our agricultural history, but it is only within the period we are now studying that public attention has been directed toward the problem on a comprehensive scale. In fact, it is only within this period that the people of the country in general have come to realize the magnitude of the problem. There is certain to be built an irrigated empire in the West. To build this empire will require statesmen with vision and with courage. Still more recently has public attention been directed toward the problem of drainage. It is estimated that within the territory of the United States, and capable of being drained and reduced to cultivation, there are swampy areas sufficient to support a population of 10,000,000 people, allowing 40 acres per family of five.

Stock raising. The extension of the area of the cultivated farms up to and within the borders of the dry belt, and the development of irrigation schemes within that belt, are forcing a complete reorganization of the cattle business. The cattle-ranching business has already declined considerably, but this has in part been made up by the slight increase in sheep herding. Some of the arid pastures of the West are better suited to sheep than to cattle, and sheep are therefore, by a process of natural selection, displacing cattle in parts of the range country. It is therefore highly probable that the range cattle will diminish in numbers, and that the country will be forced to rely on foreign meat or else upon beef grown as well as fattened upon the farms. It is not probable, however, that cattle ranching is doomed to extinction, though it can obviously never attain to the importance it reached in the seventies and eighties. There is a possibility, in the Appalachian highlands, of a revival of cattle raising on a somewhat smaller scale than that which developed on the Western range country. In this region, extending from Maine to Georgia, there are lands too broken to compete with the smooth and fertile lands of the Mississippi basin in the growing of field crops, but these highlands furnish excellent pasturage and there is not the slightest scarcity of water.

The general decline of the range industry may possibly, though not necessarily, bring about a diminution in the number of cattle grown in this country. It will certainly bring about such a diminution unless the price of beef rises and remains permanently above the average of the last century. In order that the decline in the number of range cattle may be counterbalanced, there must be a corresponding increase in the number of farm-bred cattle. But such an increase cannot come about until the price of beef rises sufficiently to compensate for the higher cost of raising cattle on the farms as compared with the ranges. As our population increases and as the demand for beef increases correspondingly, this demand can stimulate a commensurate increase of supply only by offering permanently higher prices. Eventually, however, it is not improbable that our country, especially the great seaboard cities, will come to depend more and more on foreign beef imported from countries where land is still cheap enough and abundant enough to make pasturage an economical use of it. Beef production requires more land per unit of food value produced than almost any other branch of agriculture, though under range conditions it is rather economical of labor. As the demand for food increases through the rapid growth of our population, it will become more and more the tendency to devote the land, wherever it is physically possible, to the production of those crops which require less land per unit of food value, and to depend more and more upon newer countries, where land is abundant and labor scarce, for such products as beef. The fact that the area of cattle grazing has always followed the frontier suggests, at least, that it may follow that frontier beyond those imaginary lines known as national boundaries.

The migration of the wheat belt. A similar movement is showing itself with respect to wheat. Wheat, like beef, has been, in a sense, a frontier crop. This is for no other reason than that it is a suitable crop to grow at long distances from market where land is abundant. That is to say, wheat, like beef, stands transportation well, and, more important still, it is most economically produced where there is abundance of cheap land in proportion to the supply of labor. When labor has become relatively more abundant and land relatively more scarce, there has been a tendency throughout our history for wheat and beef growing to give way to other products requiring less land and more labor for their economical production. For this reason wheat, like beef, has followed our frontier, and we need not be surprised or alarmed when the center of wheat production passes to the new frontiers beyond our national boundaries. This will not be a decline in agriculture but an advance.

However, it is not likely that the total amount of either wheat or beef will actually or seriously decline in this country, though it is unlikely that it will keep pace with our growth of population. Wheat will be found to fit into systems of crop rotation with other heavier-yielding crops. In parts of England, for example, the author has been told by farmers that they could not afford to grow wheat except for the above reason, and for the further reason that they needed straw as bedding for their cattle. If this satisfactorily explains why wheat continued to be grown in an old and densely populated country like England, we may safely predict that it will continue to be grown, to a certain extent, for a great many years in this country. Similarly, beef will continue to be raised, partly as a necessary adjunct to the dairy industry, partly to utilize land and pasture which is not well suited to tillage, partly by reason of the extension of such productive forage crops as alfalfa, and partly in a system of rotation where it is desirable to allow arable land a periodic rest by laying it down to pasturage. The same principles will apply and the same predictions may be ventured with respect to wool and mutton as with respect to beef and wheat.

With the relative decline in importance of such products of extensive culture as wheat, beef, wool, mutton, etc., will doubtless come an increase in the relative importance of our two great crops which lend themselves somewhat better to intensive culture, namely, corn and cotton. Still greater relative increase, however, is likely to take place in the growth of fruits and vegetables, which require still more intensive culture.

Growth of tenancy. The characteristic system of land tenure among American farmers has been that of ownership. Outside of the older cotton states, the great majority of the men who have worked the farms have also owned them. This has been a natural result of two factors working together, namely, cheap land and dear labor. So long as there was government land to be had, the way was open from the position of farm hand to that of farm owner to any one who cared to take the trouble to go West and take a claim. Even in the older states, where there was no government land to be had, it was not difficult for a farm hand to become a farm owner. His wages being high as compared with the wages in the Old World, it was not difficult for him to save. Both the rent and the price of land being low, it was easy for any man who had saved up a few hundred dollars to become an independent farmer, first on rented land and afterwards on land of his own. Already, however, a change is becoming perceptible, and the number of tenant farmers is increasing in comparison with farm owners. This is a natural result of the rise in the price of land, which followed the exhaustion of the supply of public land and the increase in the population. As the price of land becomes higher and higher it will become more and more difficult for the man who starts with nothing but his hands to become a farmer.

This is a situation which contains possibilities of evil in the form of separating our rural population into two groups, the landowners and the landless. Such a separation of classes has never failed in the history of the world to breed jealousies and animosities. It is not improbable that immigration, if the tide should again turn toward the country instead of toward the city, will still further accentuate the evil by placing in the country districts a landless class, by reducing wages through the increase in the number of laborers, and by making it therefore still more difficult for the landless man to become a landowner.

Agricultural education. Contemporaneously with the increased activity of the experiment stations, there has developed an increased appreciation of the value of agricultural education. A certain humorist has said that agriculture has tended to become a sedentary occupation. This, of course, is an exaggeration, but it is not too much to say that it is becoming a learned profession. To be a scientific farmer requires an education comparable in breadth and thoroughness with that of the engineer or the physician, and probably much more thorough than that of the lawyer or the preacher. Moreover, the enlarged use of machinery has freed the farmer and his family from a great deal of the drudgery and severe muscular labor to which they were subject at a time so recent as to be well remembered by many farmers now living. The transference from the farm to the creamery and cheese factory of the labor of manufacturing products of the dairy has effected a revolution of the work within the farm household, and has so lightened farm work that there is little except the isolation of farm life to hinder the enjoyment of a culture and refinement equal to that of the business and professional classes of the cities. In very recent years this isolation is being remedied by a variety of factors, chief among which is the rural telephone. Rural free delivery of mails, the improvements of roads, and, in the case of the more prosperous farmers, the automobile, are also helping to improve the opportunities for social life in the country. " Iron sharpeneth iron ; so a man sharpeneth the countenance of his friend." Thus the wise man stated long ago the very important truth that the association of minds is a stimulus to mental activity. With the remedying of the isolation of farm life, and the creation of opportunities for social intercourse in the country approximating those of the cities, will come, we may reasonably hope, a new era of culture and refinement in the country. This will prevent the increasing wealth of the farming class from being wasted in the crude ostentation so common in our cities. If it is poor economy to feed good corn and hay to scrub stock, it is still poorer economy to feed good bread and meat to scrub men and women, that is, to men and women with no education and with no ideals beyond the satisfaction of their animal instincts.

CHAPTER III

THE FACTORS OF AGRICULTURAL PRODUCTION

I. Land as a Factor of Agricultural Production

Dependence of agriculture upon area. One of the most important facts regarding agriculture, a fact which distinguishes it from all other industries, is its dependence upon land. This does not mean soil and chemical fertility alone; it means also land surface, — space, — room for plants to grow and spread their roots to the soil and moisture and their leaves to the sun and air. In its demands upon land surface agriculture exceeds every other industry, that is, it requires more surface in proportion to the quantity of its product than any other industry. In fact it is the only industry in which mere surface is ever a scarce factor of production, or in which any nation ever feels that it has not area enough within its boundaries.

Soil may be made, or infertile soil may be made fertile, but land surface cannot be materially increased except in small fringes along the shores of bodies of water. A manufacturing or mercantile establishment needs space only for standing room for men and machines, and storage room for materials. Besides, it can economize land surface by building up into the air, thus multiplying the floor space by the number of stories. A farm needs space for these purposes also; but its chief need is for room for crops to grow, and for this purpose land surface cannot be economized by erecting tall buildings. Even a mine needs land surface only as a means of getting access to the mineral deposit beneath, and the value of the product of the mine depends mainly upon the depth and richness of the deposit rather than upon the superficial area. In agriculture, however, no matter how deep the soil or how rich the deposit of plant food in a given area may be, there is a limit to the number of plants which can grow on that area, and therefore the product of that area does not depend exclusively upon the depth and richness of the deposit; it depends quite as much upon the size of the area, — quite as much upon the room which it affords to the plants as upon the food which it provides for them.

A soil of immeasurable depth and richness will produce only a very limited crop of wheat per acre, say a hundred bushels, but a mineral deposit of immeasurable depth and riches would yield a quantity of mineral per acre limited only by the number of laborers and machines that could find room to work. Even if the greatest conceivable skill were applied to the cultivation of the soil, it would still take vast areas of land to produce wheat enough to supply any modern nation with bread. A similar statement would hold true of any of the other great farm crops. That is why the question of land is of such vital importance to every agricultural nation.

Law of diminishing returns. Even assuming it to be possible to make one acre produce a hundred bushels of wheat, it by no means follows that it would be economical to try to do so. In fact, it most certainly would not be economical, for the reason that it would require such a quantity of labor and care in the preparation of the soil, in the selection of the seed, and in the nurture of the plants, as to amount to a great waste of time and energy, — a waste so great as to overbalance the economy of land. It would require much less labor to produce a hundred bushels on two acres than on one, probably less on three acres than on one, and quite possibly less on four than on one. This being the case, each farmer will find it to his advantage to spread his cultivation over more acres rather than to try to make each acre produce all that is physically possible. Where each and every farmer finds it to his advantage to spread out in this way, it follows that the agricultural nation as a whole spreads out over a wider and wider area as it increases in population, so long as there is more land to be had. It is only under stress of necessity, of sheer scarcity of land, that it begins to economize land by more intensive cultivation, — that is, by putting more labor on each acre in the attempt to make it produce a larger crop. When this necessity arises it will be very difficult for any nation to prevent its growing population from migrating to other countries, provided there are other countries where land is still abundant.[1]

The striking difference between agriculture and the urban industries, with respect to their demands upon land, may be seen by considering that it will require from 20,000 to 100,000 acres to produce 1,000,000 bushels of wheat, whereas one acre will suffice for grinding it into flour, and a very few acres for baking it into bread. While land is, of course, essential to an urban industry, the demand for land surface is so trifling as to be treated as a negligible factor. Accessibility to markets and certain public opportunities, and not mere surface, is the essential thing in a city business, and it is this accessibility which gives such amazing value to certain urban sites.

An agricultural *vs.* a manufacturing and commercial policy. Upon this particular difference between agriculture and the urban industries is based the broadest of all differences in national policy, — that between a commercial or manufacturing policy on the one hand, and an agricultural policy on the other. Until all the land of the country is occupied by factories, stores, and

---

[1] The state of Iowa furnishes a striking example of this. Though it is the richest agricultural state in the Union in proportion to its area, and one of the richest agricultural areas in the world, yet it is losing population through emigration to other areas where land is more abundant.

dwellings, there is no geographic limit to the quantity which a country can manufacture. Given only raw materials, there is never any question, therefore, of the nation's ability to manufacture everything it needs, no matter how populous it may become. For every additional man to be supplied with manufactured products there is always the same man who may be put to work manufacturing them, provided he can get the raw materials. There is never in the nation at large any lack of room for him to work. For every man who is to be supplied with beef and bread there is also, it may be said, the same man who may be put to work growing cattle and wheat. But this takes room, — land, superficial area, — and if the country becomes sufficiently populous, there may not be room enough for this kind of work. Leaving raw materials out of account, almost any conceivable population could manufacture clothing enough for itself, but only a limited population can grow wool and cotton enough within its own territory. This is for no other reason than that manufactures require little land, and agriculture much land, in proportion to the labor employed and the product obtained.

Dependence of manufacturers upon markets. This possibility of producing indefinitely in the urban industries is what has made a commercial and manufacturing policy so alluring to statesmen in modern times. If raw materials can be obtained, and if outside markets can be secured for the finished products, there is no conceivable limit to the population which can be supported by manufacturing, or to the wealth of that population. A nation can manufacture not only enough for its own use, but indefinitely more, *provided* it can buy raw materials and sell its finished products. In other words, the only conceivable limits to the population and wealth of a manufacturing country are those fixed by the available supply of its raw materials and the outside markets for its manufactured products.

When, therefore, a country begins to feel the slightest scarcity of agricultural land, when it begins to realize that it is nearing the limits of its population and wealth from that source, it not unnaturally turns its attention to manufacturing, provided markets can be found. These are needed, both as places for buying raw materials and for selling finished products, if the nation is to continue to grow beyond the limits set by its power to produce raw materials within its own territory. Every such expansion of the trade area is like the acquisition of new agricultural land, in that it enables the population to expand without feeling the pressure of land scarcity. When the markets are thus expanded a manufacturing population can increase its numbers without any appreciable diminution in its per capita production, or without any increase in the labor necessary to produce each unit of product. The question of markets is therefore the question of transcendent importance for a growing manufacturing population, as the question of land is for a growing agricultural population.

A commercial and manufacturing policy pure and simple, however, while highly profitable for a time if pursued by a small portion of mankind, is very illusive in the long run, and brings inevitable disaster if pursued by many nations or a large portion of mankind. For one nation to depend for its living, not upon the products of its own soil, mines, and fisheries, but upon the sale of its manufactured products in foreign markets, may be safe ; but for all nations or any considerable number of them to try to live in this way would reduce them to the condition alleged to exist on a certain island, where the people are said to make their living by taking in one another's washing. The prosperity of the world as a whole will and must depend fundamentally upon its primary or extractive industries.

If we turn our attention from the broader question of national economy to some of the narrower questions of urban economy, we shall find that, within the narrow area of a city, the question of land sometimes seems to limit the amount which the city can produce, even in the way of manufacturing. If the population will spread to new areas in the suburbs, there need be no scarcity of land. But men within the city area, moved by city pride, sometimes feel a profound interest in the building up of industry and wealth within the city limits, and are not satisfied with the mere fact of the growth of wealth in the country as a whole. In such cases they find, of course, that the scarcity of land within those limits is a serious hindrance to further development. But from a national standpoint this is not a problem worth considering.

As agriculture advances from the self-sufficing to the commercial stage, — that is, from the stage where the farm produces most of the things consumed by the farmer and his family to a stage where most of the products of the farm are sold and most of the things to be consumed are bought with the proceeds, — the question of markets for agricultural produce is a matter of growing importance ; but it never rises to the importance that it always has for manufacturing populations, nor does it ever compare in this respect with the question of land for a growing agricultural population.[1]

Dependence of agriculture upon land.[1] No matter how extensive the markets for agricultural produce may be, and no matter how numerous agricultural workers may be, there is a limit to the quantity which can be produced within a given area. When the farms have become contiguous, and all the best land in the given territory has been put to some agricultural use, the only possibility of increasing the total product necessary to sustain the

---

[1] By courtesy of the Carnegie Institution the author is permitted to use, in the following pages, some of the material which was written for the Agricultural History of the United States, which is being prepared under the direction of that institution.

increasing population is by cultivating the best land more intensively or spreading the cultivation over the inferior land. In order
to avoid either necessity, both of which mean a smaller per capita
product or a larger expenditure of labor and capital per unit of
product, men have consistently and persistently sought new territories, just as manufacturing peoples have sought new markets.

For a manufacturing population a lack of markets is sometimes called overproduction, and this condition is for them
what famine or underproduction is for a purely agricultural
people. The actual work of manufacturing not being *directly*
affected by wet or dry weather, by backward seasons, untimely
frosts, and other climatic conditions, a manufacturing population
is never threatened by underproduction in its own special work.
It may, however, be damaged by underproduction of its raw
materials, as in the case of the English factories during the
cotton famine of the American Civil War; but that is a case of
a contracting market, for a market is a place where materials
are bought as well as sold. Again, a manufacturing population
may be affected by a crop failure or some other form of underproduction among its customers, as a result of which these customers are unable to buy the manufactured products; but this
also is a question of markets. In almost every imaginable case
where underproduction is found to affect a manufacturing population, it will be found to affect it through its markets rather
than through its own power of production; that is, it will be
found to be difficult either to buy raw material or to sell finished products. Such a thing as inability to produce enough of
its own peculiar products, or such a thing as underproduction
in its own industries, is never considered as a real danger.

Overproduction, or a lack of markets for its finished products, is, however, a real danger for every growing manufacturing
population. Continued overproduction forces upon such a population one of two alternatives, the conquest of new markets or

the reduction of its numbers. New markets may be conquered by wise diplomacy, by careful advertising, or by war. The first two methods failing, few nations have had the grace to refrain from war where they thought there was a chance of success in winning wider markets. All three methods failing, the manufacturing population must be reduced by starvation or emigration. In this situation we have the key to the understanding of the commercial policies of the manufacturing and commercial nations.

For a growing agricultural population, however, there is a real danger of underproduction. Unless the arts of agricultural production improve with the increase of population, a growing agricultural population in a given territory will eventually mean a smaller per capita production. Each worker will eventually have so little land at his disposal as to cut down his total product, even though he does get a somewhat larger product per acre. Failure to offset the disadvantage of scarce land by agricultural improvements means, for such a population, continued underproduction, which forces upon it the necessity of getting more land or of reducing its numbers. Getting more land requires either wise diplomacy, as was practiced when land was purchased or acquired by treaty from the American Indians, or it requires a war of conquest. Reducing the numbers of an agricultural population means migration to new lands or to the cities, where it is transformed into a manufacturing, mining, or commercial population, which in turn requires expanding markets. To sum up, a growing agricultural population on a given area of land must choose at least one of four things, and there is no other choice. In the first place, it may improve the arts of production by new discoveries in the science of agriculture. In the second place, it may acquire new land either peacefully or by war. In the third place, it may reduce its population by migration either to new lands or to manufacturing, mining, or commercial centers. In the fourth place, it may reduce the standard of living, the average per capita wealth of the agricultural people growing less as their numbers increase. In this situation we have a key to the understanding not only of the policies of agricultural nations, but also to the movements of agricultural populations.

Formerly the choice was uniformly for war and conquest, but this solution of the problem is contrary to all the sentiments and ideals of civilization. Therefore the tendency is more and more toward one of the other solutions. All civilized countries are spending money and energy for the improvement of the methods of agricultural production, or for the improvement of lands already within their boundaries; but none of them are able to make improvements rapidly enough to avoid the emigration of their rural populations either to foreign countries or to their own cities, where they are open to the new danger of overproduction or lack of markets.

Rural as distinguished from urban migrations. One of the most striking facts in economic history is the different character of rural and urban migrations. Leaving out of account, for the moment, the transformation of a rural into an urban, or an urban into a rural population, and considering only the migration of rural people who remain rural and of urban people who remain urban, it will be easy to see the distinction. Rural migrations are uniformly from a densely to a sparsely settled territory, whereas urban migrations are *almost* as uniformly from a sparsely to a densely settled territory, that is, from smaller to larger towns and cities. In both cases there are of course countercurrents, and this is especially noticeable within the area of a given city. Though congested districts seem uniformly to grow more congested, there is also a recessive movement toward the suburbs. As between different cities, however, the tendency seems fairly clear. The larger the city, other things being equal, the more rapidly it grows.

Rural migrations are toward abundant land. This difference in the character of the two forms of migration is due mainly to the difference in the factors upon which the prosperity of the two classes of population depends. As we have just seen, agriculture is mainly dependent upon land, and urban industries upon markets. Therefore rural people engaged in agriculture tend to move to those places where land is abundant, while urban people move to those places where markets are wide. Abundance of land and sparseness of population usually mean the same thing; but, for some reason which has never been satisfactorily explained, the larger the city the more trade it seems to attract. However, both these propositions need careful qualification.

The proposition that rural people tend to move from the more densely to the less densely populated areas needs to be qualified by assuming that the soil is equally fertile, the climate equally attractive, and the government equally free and just, in the different areas. If the soil is infertile, the climate unattractive, or the government despotic, in the sparsely populated area, the migration to that area will be discouraged, and may be turned in the opposite direction. But within the temperate zone, and within such areas as possess abundant rainfall or sufficient water for irrigation purposes, and where the land is controlled by liberal and progressive governments, there is not the slightest doubt that the general movement of rural people has been and still is from densely to sparsely populated regions, or from regions where land is relatively scarce to regions where it is relatively abundant.

Again, the grower of an agricultural specialty is almost as much in need of a market as is a manufacturer. In order to succeed in this form of agriculture he must locate where there is a market, which will usually be best where population is densest. Therefore he will, as a rule, leave the sparsely populated area and locate in or near a densely populated area. This is in harmony with the general principle that those whose success depends mainly on land tend to scatter, and those whose success depends mainly upon markets tend to concentrate. But it is only in the case of agricultural specialties that success depends mainly upon markets. The growing of agricultural specialties, however, forms a very small and insignificant part of the total agricultural production, otherwise they would not be specialties. The tendency of growers of these specialties to concentrate does not offset the larger tendency of the growers of the great staple crops to scatter.

Urban migrations are toward wider markets. The proposition that the migrations of urban populations are uniformly from less densely to more densely populated areas needs several qualifications. In the first place, as pointed out before, the tendency is really to move to those places where markets are expanding most rapidly. Wherever it happens that markets are expanding more rapidly in small than in large towns and cities, the movement will be toward the small places. But, speaking generally, the tendency is the other way. The larger the city, the more rapidly its trade area seems to grow. In common language, the large city seems to " draw " trade. " Trade attracts trade," is another way of putting it. When a certain city comes to be known as a place where a certain article can always be bought in considerable quantity and variety, buyers naturally tend to go to that city. When a new manufacturer, or would-be manufacturer, is looking for a place to locate his factory, he in turn tends to locate at that place where buyers are accustomed to go. This, again, draws more buyers, and these, again, attract more producers. Thus a trade or manufacturing center seems to grow by what it feeds upon.

Again, as such a center of trade and manufacturing increases in size, there grows up an intense competition for the central sites or locations. Such high prices or ground rents are paid for space in these centers that many enterprises are forced to locate at a distance from the center in order to avoid the tremendous expense of a central location. Thus a recessive tendency shows itself, — a countermovement away from the more densely populated areas toward the suburbs. But the fact that there is such severe competition for the central locations, when the advantages for physical production are no greater, but where the opportunities are better for selling the products or buying the raw materials, shows how thoroughly urban industries and urban peoples are dominated by the question of markets, and how they therefore tend to concentrate themselves in more and more densely populated centers. Even the dispersive tendency noted above is usually not strong enough to offset the tendency of large cities to grow more rapidly than small cities and towns.

Again, there are sometimes marked physical advantages, like mines, water power, building materials, etc., which explain the location of a city. These physical advantages may be of limited extent or quantity. When the city has grown to the limit set by the natural physical advantage, there is sometimes a tendency for the increasing or surplus population to move to a new location where new and unused physical advantages are to be found. Thus new and small towns sometimes actually grow at the expense of the older and larger ones. This is particularly the case when new mines are opened, but it sometimes follows the development of a new source of power, such as water power. These are almost the only cases where the movement of urban populations is not determined by a search for markets. Being determined by a search for natural resources, which might be included in a definition of land, this movement resembles the movement of rural populations, which is determined by the search for land. But cities of this type are exceptions to the general rule and do not themselves represent the general tendency of city growth. The most conspicuous examples are the lumber and mining camps.

Shifting from rural to urban industries. Seldom, if ever, in the history of the civilized world have there been general and long-continued movements of population from urban to rural districts. Occasional and temporary movements there have been, but such cases usually result from a deliberate policy of colonization, by means of which a city gets rid of its surplus population by sending a body of colonists to occupy a territory acquired by purchase, treaty, or conquest; from the opening up of new lands or agricultural resources, by means of which people are attracted from the city to the country; or from a commercial cataclysm, by means of which a city's trade is destroyed, its subsistence cut off, and its inhabitants forced to disperse.

Relation of colonization to national greatness. One of the most interesting of all fields of study is the relation of the expansion of a people, through emigration and colonization, to national greatness. As a matter of fact every great nation has been a colonizing nation. The colonization, however, is probably more the effect than the cause of national greatness. A great nation must be made up of vigorous and efficient people. Such people make successful colonists for the simple reason that, when they emigrate and come into competition with outlying races, they can beat these outlying races in the arts of production. Having greater physical vigor and energy, a higher degree of mentality, and a more complete knowledge of and control over the forces of nature, and especially having a moral development of a more productive kind, which enables them to work together more efficiently, with less waste of energy due to distrust and suspicion of one another, with a keener sense of strict justice and less disposition to sacrifice the interests of society for the weak and inefficient, such a nation easily spreads over outlying lands and conquers them, not necessarily or mainly by the arts of destruction, but rather by their superior mastery of the arts of production. A weak race, on the other hand, is not uniformly successful when its members come in contact with outlying peoples. As a consequence its numbers incline to pile up in the home country, where they are protected by their own political and legal institutions against the equal competition of outside peoples. But as a result of this piling up of the population serious social and political problems arise. The surplus population, instead of moving out and colonizing those sections of the earth where lands and opportunities for achievement are abundant, congregate in the centers of population and clamor for a share of the wealth which has been accumulated. When that becomes the characteristic attitude of the mass of the people, national decay has set in. Artificial colonization or the preaching of a gospel of enterprise will do little good when the national pioneering spirit has decayed and the quality of the race has deteriorated.

II. Ways of economizing Land

Importance of the question. For a country which is too far advanced in civilization to be willing to acquire new lands by military conquest, and so situated as not to be able to acquire them in any other way, the question of questions is that of economizing the land which it already has. Foreign markets are limited, and their possession is always more or less uncertain ; therefore it is hazardous for any country to neglect its material resources and attempt to maintain an increasing population by manufacturing and commerce alone. As shown in the preceding chapter, these methods of maintaining a growing population depend upon foreign markets, and the stress of international competition for the control of markets is always severe. In this competition those nations will have the advantage which have economized their natural resources and developed their primary industries to the greatest degree.

This is not to be construed into an argument against foreign trade or in favor of national isolation. There are two situations under which a nation may thrive, for a time at least, by foreign trade. The first situation is that where the nation buys its raw material from abroad, manufactures it into finished products, and sells these again in foreign markets, maintaining itself on the profits of the transaction. This, as was shown in preceding pages, is an exceedingly attractive method wherever it is possible, or wherever foreign markets are sufficiently wide, because there is no physical limit to the wealth of such a country, or to the population which it can support. A nation whose population is increasing, and which tries to maintain this increase in numbers by manufacturing and commerce alone, without developing its own natural resources, will find itself approaching this condition. But this is a dangerous situation. Saying nothing of the possibility of wars and other disturbances which may cut off the supply of raw material or close markets to the finished products, there still remain such things as tariff barriers, embargoes, and other hostile acts of legislation which may have the same results. Again, this is a situation which obviously could not possibly be maintained by any considerable number of nations, because there would be no foreign markets of sufficient size left. Even a single nation could flourish under this situation only so long as there were undeveloped nations not yet in a position to manufacture for themselves, unless it happened to possess very exceptional advantages, such as water power or coal fields, far superior to those of any of its rivals.

The second situation under which a nation may thrive by foreign trade is one wherein it exchanges the products of its own land, either raw or in a finished state, for whose production its land is especially fitted, for the products of other lands, either raw or finished, for whose production its own land is not so well fitted. Under this situation the wealth and population which the country can maintain are, it is true, limited by the amount which it can produce from its land; but this is a much safer situation than the one described above. How much such a country will have, either for consumption or for exchange, will depend upon how well it has economized its natural resources.

In most countries, especially in the United States, the soil itself is by far the greatest physical resource. The products of the soil exceed in value many times over those of the mines and the fisheries, and many more people are supported by agriculture than by all these other extractive industries. Again, whereas the working of the mines tends necessarily to exhaust them, no such condition exists in the case of agriculture. Properly treated, the soil may continue producing its wealth and maintaining its population over indefinite periods of time. Therefore we see why it is that the question of economizing the land is of such transcendent importance to every growing country. Let us consider, then, the methods by which the land of a country can be economized and made to support a growing population.

CAUSES OF WASTE LAND

1. Bad physical conditions
   - a. Too stony
   - b. Too wet
   - c. Too dry

2. Bad chemical conditions
   - a. Too much acid
   - b. Too much alkali

3. Bad social conditions
   - a. Bad taxation
   - b. Too much speculation

Causes of waste land. If all the land of a country were once brought under cultivation, there would then be no way of economizing it except by making each acre produce more. But this is a condition which has probably never been reached in any country, certainly not in the United States. Therefore we have first to consider the question of bringing waste lands into use. Let us assume that the country is all " settled," — that is, that the population has increased and spread until all the land which is sufficiently productive to attract cultivators has actually been appropriated. In this case the existence of waste land will be due to one or more of three causes : (1) bad physical conditions : (2) bad chemical conditions ; (3) bad political conditions.

Bad physical conditions. There are many physical conditions which could be described as bad, any of which would tend to make land unattractive to cultivators, and therefore to cause it to go to waste. There are, however, three characteristic conditions which cause considerable quantities of land of three different types to go to waste. These lands may be described as (a) too stony, (b) too wet, (c) too dry.

Stony land. In the North Atlantic states of the United States the first of these conditions is the most conspicuous of the causes of waste land ; that is, most of the waste land is too stony, though there are some swamps there also. Along the Southern seaboard and the Gulf coast the second of these conditions is the most conspicuous ; that is, most of the waste land is too wet, though there are occasional patches of stony ground. But over a vast area in the Far West, comprising fully a third of the entire area of the United States, the land is too dry, and much of it goes to waste on that account. There is enough of this land to support an empire were it not for the absence of the one missing factor, — water. The early settlers in the eastern half of this country found another condition which gave them a great deal of trouble, namely, the presence of forests which had to be cleared ; but this is not a condition which creates a problem for the rural economist to-day. In fact it is now much more of a problem to preserve our forests than to find ways of clearing the land of them.

Of the land which is now going to waste because of its rocky condition, much of it is so exceedingly rocky as to make it forever useless as plowland or even for pasture. It would cost so much to clear it of stones that one could never hope to secure sufficient returns to repay the cost. Such land, however, need not go to waste. It is our natural forest land. With the growth of population the demand for timber continues to increase, and with the clearing of the virgin forests the supply continues to diminish. The time is not far distant when the products of the forest will be in such demand as to make even the rockiest of New England hills valuable, provided they have been allowed to grow up to trees.

This does not mean that these rocky hills are better for trees than the more level and tillable lands of the valleys and plains. But these other lands can be used for the growing of field and garden crops, whereas the rocky hills cannot. It is a wise economy, therefore, to devote these hills to the one purpose for which they are suited, reserving the tillable lands for other purposes. Besides the timber, these rocky and semimountainous lands are of some value as deer parks and game preserves. The supply of venison and other game which such lands will furnish, while of small value in comparison with the products of rich pastures devoted to the growing of domestic animals, is not a matter to be despised, especially when we consider that it produces itself without cost in the way of labor or care.

One difficulty in the way of the full utilization of land of this description for purposes of forestry is the slowness with which returns come in. It takes at least thirty years, more frequently fifty years, for a tree to grow to a usable size. So long a period of waiting is unattractive to the average individual, partly because of the limited span of human life and partly because of the shortness of human foresight. Another difficulty lies in the fact that the work of reforesting the rocky lands, to be effective, must be carried out on a considerable scale. This seems to call naturally for state and government enterprise. Since governments do not need to count on a natural death, they need not be deterred by the long period of waiting involved in forestry. A half century, or even a century, is not too long for a government to wait for returns, provided they are desirable.

On this point we need not be deterred by any absurd notions as to the propriety of a government undertaking work of this kind. There are people who believe that private enterprise is, *per se*, better than public, and others who believe that public enterprise is, *per se*, superior to private. Both views are equally irrational and equally based upon blind prejudice. The simple truth of the matter is that some enterprises are carried out very much more effectively under private initiative and management than under public, and there are others which are carried out very much more effectively under public initiative and management, while there are still others which thrive about equally well under either, it being impossible to show conclusively which is the better. The reforesting of rocky and semimountainous lands seems to succeed better under public than private management, though there are many excellently managed private forests. At any rate, wherever private management does not show a disposition to enter upon the work of reforesting these waste lands, it is obviously better that the state should do it than that it should not be done at all and the land be thus allowed to lie idle.

To be sure, even while these lands are apparently lying idle the forest is frequently reasserting itself and taking possession of them. Sometimes this results in the growth of valuable timber, and sometimes in the growth of inferior kinds of trees, — the " weeds " of the forest growth. A little intelligent direction at the proper time would save the land from these "weeds" and give it over to valuable timber.

Considerable portions of the rocky land of this country can be profitably utilized for pasturage. This is particularly true where these lands are contiguous to or near other lands suitable for the growing of winter forage. In this respect the rocky and semimountainous lands of the West and South are well situated, but those of New England are at some disadvantage. Good tillable land in New England can be utilized to such advantage for the growing of vegetables and the production of milk that it is usually relatively unprofitable to utilize it for the growing of winter forage. Even where the land is smooth enough to make the growing of hay an economic possibility it is usually found so profitable to sell the hay to the city buyers that the farmer finds it relatively unprofitable to feed it to animals. Much excellent pasture land among the New England hills is thus allowed to go to waste or to grow up to brush and timber, simply because no economical method has been found for bringing the animals through the long winter. However, in almost every part of the world where the cattle industry has had a considerable development it has been found profitable to drive or transport the cattle considerable distances from summer to winter pasture, or from pasture to feed lot. In the mountainous part of Europe, for example, cattle are driven in considerable numbers up to the hills and mountains for summer pasture, and back to the valleys to be wintered on the products of the fertile farms. With the growing scarcity of meat it will be found more and more profitable to utilize the rocky pastures of the Atlantic states in a similar way.

Even pasturage, however, is a less economical use of land than tillage, wherever tillage is possible, in the sense that a larger food supply per acre is secured by tillage than by pasturage. It is only where the land is unsuitable for tillage, or where the population is so sparse that a large product per acre is a matter of little importance, that it becomes economical to utilize land as permanent pasture. Pasturage in rotation with tillage, however, is quite another thing. As population increases, and with it the necessity for economizing land, the importance of enlarging the tillable area will increase correspondingly. Therefore the problem of clearing the land of stones and preparing it for the plow, wherever that is economically possible, will become a growing problem.

Much of the work of clearing the land of stones, which has been done hitherto, has been by the individual efforts of farmers and by the simplest possible methods. The stones have been lifted by hand, loaded onto a "stone boat," a sled, or a cart, hauled away, and disposed of in the quickest manner possible. This was a laborious method, suited to conditions where there were small accumulations of capital, and where it was necessary to clear only a small area of the less stony land. With the growth of population, the increase of capital, and the improvement of mechanical inventions, more effective methods may be adopted. In the first place, there are uses for the stones which are to be removed, in addition to that of building the time-honored stone fence. Building and road materials are increasing in demand, and, in some cases at least, it will be found economical to utilize for other purposes the stones removed from the land in the process of clearing it. Again, if the stones can be broken up and reduced to a size too small to interfere with cultivation, they do not need to be removed at all, but may better be left where they are. Left in the soil, subject to the forces of decomposition, and worn away by the friction involved in continuous cultivation, they form a store of plant food which will be let loose gradually as it is needed for the sustenance of crops. Portable crushing machines, driven by powerful engines, which will crush the stones and leave them on the land, may be the means of increasing the tillable area in the more densely populated sections where land is becoming valuable.

Milligan College Library
Milligan College, Tennessee

Here again seems to be a field for public enterprise. Though much of the clearing has been done by private enterprise, and much more will doubtless be done in the future, the public can materially increase the tillable area, especially in those states where political conditions are such as to forbid the employment of convicts in profitable labor. The argument used against convict labor is that it competes with free labor and tends to reduce the opportunity for its employment. Whether this argument be sound or not, — as a matter of fact it is not,— it could not possibly apply as against the employment of convicts in the clearing of land which would otherwise not be cleared at all. This employment of convicts would not compete with free labor, for the reason that no free labor is employed in work of that kind. Again, the clearing of such land and preparing it for cultivation would create new opportunities for the profitable employment of labor ; that is, there would then be a little more land to be cultivated, and this would require a little more labor. Moreover, it would increase the food supply of the laboring class in general.

Again, only the land most easily cleared of stones will ordinarily be cleared by private enterprise, because of the length of time which is necessary to wait for returns. Unless the private individual can get back the amount of outlay in twenty or thirty years, he is reluctant to undertake it. Yet a piece of land once thoroughly cleared of stones, and properly treated thereafter, will continue producing crops for centuries. An organization which is long-lived and capable of looking into the future more than thirty or fifty years might profitably undertake a work which would seem unattractive to a short-lived individual. Aside from the employment of convict labor, therefore, there are reasons why the public — that is, the state — might wisely undertake the clearing of a certain amount of land which is too unpromising to attract private enterprise, especially when land begins to become scarce as a result of increasing population.

Wet land. More attractive, however, is the problem of dealing with that class of waste land which is described as too wet. There are several factors in this problem which make it peculiarly interesting to constructive minds. In the first place, such lands are always low-lying, where they have received for ages the washings from the higher lands surrounding them. Consequently the soil is remarkably fertile after it is once drained and reduced to cultivation. In the second place, the abundance of water secures the cultivator against drought. When rainfall is insufficient for the higher lands, these low lands can be sure of sufficient moisture by the simple process of stopping the drains, or checking the rate at which surplus water is being drawn off. In the third place, the conquest of these lands is an engineering problem pure and simple, and the success of the enterprise does not depend upon the uncertainties of the weather, the amount of rainfall, and similar problems which frequently affect the success of irrigation enterprises. Finally, the conquest of such lands does more than to increase the area of productive land. It removes menaces to health, because these low-lying, swampy areas are sources of disease and furnish breeding places for mosquitoes, which are the bearers of disease germs. It removes hindrances to travel and transportation, because, next to mountains, these great swamps are the most serious obstacles in the way of the road builders.

Along the Atlantic seaboard from Maine to Florida, but most especially from Virginia to Florida, — besides portions of the Gulf coast, considerable areas around the Great Lakes, and other scattered sections, — there are vast swampy areas which are capable of reclamation if the work is undertaken on a comprehensive scale and carried out in a scientific manner. It is estimated that along the Atlantic coast alone there are 80,000,000 acres of these swamps, now of little or no use. They produce some timber, it is true, but they are menaces to health and obstacles to transportation, and it is difficult to tell whether they produce enough timber to compensate for these disadvantages, — that is to say, whether they are not worse than useless. Drained and reduced to cultivation, they would support a population at least twice as large as that of the United States at the time of the adoption of the Constitution. Allowing 40 acres to a family, 80,000,000 acres would support 2,000,000 families. Allowing 5 persons to a family, this would make a population of 10,000-000. Seeing that such lands would be very productive, and that most of them would be very accessible to the great centers of population, 40 acres to the family does not seem too small an allotment.

An undertaking of this magnitude can scarcely be carried out advantageously by private enterprise. To be done efficiently it must be done on a large and comprehensive scale, with no regard for private or even state boundaries; that is to say, the draining of a great swamp must be undertaken as a systematic whole or as a single great enterprise, rather than piecemeal as a multitude of individual enterprises, with endless duplications, conflicting interests, and other forms of wasted energy. This points clearly to the federal government, in coöperation with the state governments, as the proper authority for the carrying out of so vast an undertaking. The possibilities which such an undertaking promises, the great increase in national wealth which would result, and the vast population which could be supported on that wealth, ought to appeal to any constructive statesman with a vision of empire. The cost of such an undertaking would, of course, be enormous. It would be difficult to estimate how great, but it is said to be no greater than that of ten first-class battleships; and we should then have the land to show for our expenditure.

The example of Holland. The experience of Holland may serve as an example of this kind of enterprise. As is well known, much of the land of that country was formerly either under water or subject to severe inundations, and has had to be reclaimed by the building of dikes, the digging of numerous canals and ditches, and the construction of powerful pumping establishments. One of the most interesting examples is that of the draining of Haarlem Lake. This was a body of water covering approximately 42,000 acres, at an average depth of a little over 13 feet. In 1839 the necessary legislation was completed and the work of reclamation begun. Inasmuch as considerable traffic had been carried on over this body of water, it was thought necessary to provide for it in some other way. Accordingly a canal 38 miles long, 9 feet deep, and from 115 to 130 feet wide was built entirely around the lake. Besides providing for the traffic, this canal also aided in the drainage, the water being pumped from the lake into it. The canal was high enough above sea level to permit the water to be carried off by gravitation, though the bottom of the lake was not. Inasmuch as the bottom of the lake was itself below the level of the sea, it was necessary to build great pumping plants to lift as much as 1,000,000,000 tons of water out of it. Three engines were specially constructed, each one capable of discharging 1,000,000 tons in $25\frac{1}{2}$ hours. Pumping commenced in 1848 and the lake was dry in 1852.

The sale of land began at once, and ultimately it was all sold at a total price of $3,760,000, leaving a loss of about $1,250,-000 between the cost of drainage and the original selling price of the land. But the loss is not so great as it seems. In the first place the land has since increased in value. Though this increase goes to private owners rather than to the state, yet these owners are themselves at least a part of the state; and, besides, their taxpaying power has increased and the state benefits in that way. Again, the presence of this lake had formerly proved a menace on more than one occasion to both the cities of

Amsterdam and Leyden, their streets having been flooded by its waters in times of storm. Taking all these things into consideration, it has proved a profitable and wealth-producing enterprise.

The draining of the Haarlem Lake, it must be remembered, was more of an undertaking at that day than it would be now. Again, it was a greater undertaking to drain a body of water of such depth, without sufficient fall to make a natural outlet, than it would be to drain a swamp of similar size not covered with such a depth of water, and lying high enough to require very little pumping to carry the water away.

Dry land. The subject of the reclamation of dry lands has received more public attention in this country than that of reclaiming either stony or wet lands. This is probably because there is a much greater area of land going to waste because it is too dry than for both the other reasons combined. The two leading methods of dealing with this problem are irrigation and dry farming.

Irrigation. Historically, the first of these methods to receive public attention in this country was irrigation. Irrigation enterprises have been carried on in some form since the earliest settlement in the Far West. In fact, in various places there are found remains which show that this art was practiced long before the white man ever set foot upon this continent. The early Spanish missionaries who made their way from Mexico into what is now the southwestern portion of the United States, also constructed irrigation works on a small scale around their missions. But the first development of irrigation on a comprehensive scale was by English-speaking settlers, namely the Mormons, immediately after the founding of their colony on the Great Salt Lake in 1849.

Having settled in a land which was, to all appearances, a desert, and being forced to extract a living from their unpromising surroundings, they set to work with a vigor and an intelligence which has seldom been equaled. They saw that the one thing which the soil of the valley lacked was water, and that water was to be had in the mountain streams; therefore the obvious thing to do was to divert that water to the soil instead of allowing it to run to waste. Accordingly, canals and ditches were dug, the water was utilized, and the barren land was made into a fruitful garden. The Mormon community is to-day one of the most prosperous in the United States, and that prosperity is based primarily on the irrigation ditch. Meanwhile there were numerous scattered irrigation systems developed on a small scale by individual settlers on the banks of streams. Naturally this method was applicable only where the water was easily diverted and little outlay was needed.

The second attempt at irrigation on a comprehensive scale was at Greeley, Colorado. Here the coöperative principle was applied as it had been in Utah, though it was not, as it had been there, based upon a common religious belief and obedience to a common authority. That this community was unusually intelligent and progressive is shown not only by its irrigation works, but by its magnificent school, its lyceum, and other buildings designed to foster its intellectual and social life. The most scientific methods of irrigation and cultivation were adopted, and the community prospered and became the example for other colonies both in Colorado and California.

Later a new method of irrigation was adopted in California. "The spirit of speculation in which California was born soon fastened itself upon irrigation, as it had done in the case of mining, and ran a mad race through southern California. Irrigation in this state became corporate and speculative. Where Utah and Colorado had depended only upon their hands and teams for the building of irrigation works, California issued stocks and bonds, and so mortgaged its future. Men began to dream of a new race of millionaires, created by making merchandise of the melting snows, by selling 'rights' to the 'renting' of water, and by collecting toll from a new class of society to be known as 'water tenants.' [1]

As individual settlers were able to construct their own irrigation works only where very little outlay was necessary, so was the coöperative principle adaptable only where it was possible for a group of settlers, by their own labor, to construct the works. In order that the available water supply might be developed to its full capacity and applied in the most economic manner, it became necessary, in some cases at least, to plan the works on a comprehensive scale, requiring an expenditure of capital beyond the reach of coöperative colonies. Therefore the corporation method came into play. It was capable of undertaking projects larger than the coöperative, and vastly larger than the individual plan could carry out. Accordingly, when the opportunities for diverting water cheaply had been utilized by private individuals and by coöperative organizations, and before the federal or the state governments had awakened to the necessities of the case, all the larger and costlier irrigation works were built by corporations. Some magnificent works were built during this period, involving a vast outlay of capital and engineering feats of a very high order.

While some of these undertakings turned out to be financial successes, many of them proved ruinous failures. After the works were constructed and the water was made available for irrigation, it was found in several cases impossible to pay even the running expenses from the receipts, to say nothing of paying back the original expenditure. Accordingly, many of these companies failed, and in some cases the entire property was sold for one tenth of what its construction had cost. In many

[1] From "Rise and Future of Irrigation in the United States," by Elwood Mead, expert in charge of irrigation investigations, United States Department of Agriculture, in Yearbook of Department of Agriculture (1899), p. 594.

cases, however, the projects have been successful from the point of view of the communities, the loss falling upon the investors alone.

The failure of these irrigation companies was sometimes due to mismanagement, but generally resulted from other causes. Mr. Elwood Mead enumerates the following as the most important:

1. The necessarily long delay in securing settlers for the land to be irrigated, and in obtaining paying customers for the water to be furnished.

2. The large outlay and several years of unprofitable labor required, as a rule, to put wild land in condition for cultivation. Settlers of limited means cannot meet this outlay and in addition pay water rentals. Nearly all the settlers on arid public land are men of limited means; hence canal companies have, at the outset, to furnish water at small cost, or to supply a small number of consumers.

3. The unsuitability of the public-land laws to irrigation development.

4. The acquirement of the lands to be reclaimed, in many instances, before canals are completed, by nonresident or speculative holders, who would do nothing for their improvement.

5. Expenses of litigation. Experience has shown that, in the estimates of the cost of a large canal, provision should be made for a large and long-continued outlay for litigation. It begins with the adjudication of the stream and is protracted through the controversies over water rights.

These reasons, and the failure of private enterprise to grapple successfully with the larger problems involved, pointed unmistakably to the federal and state governments as the only agencies capable of handling the irrigation question successfully. Accordingly, the history of American irrigation has passed into the third stage, — that of public, or state and federal, control. As an illustration of what may be accomplished, there has recently been completed an irrigation system which brings into cultivation over 1,000,000 acres of remarkably fertile land, which was formerly worthless on account of lack of water. This land will furnish support for 10,000 families, or 50,000 people. The original cost to the government was less than that of a single battleship, and eventually the cost will be nothing at all, because it will be paid back by the owners of the land, who receive the benefit.

The possibilities of irrigation in western America may be imagined when we consider that the entire cultivated area of Egypt, all of which is irrigated by the Nile, does not exceed 6,000,000 acres. But this area now supports a population of 5,000,000 or more. It has been densely populated for a longer period than the historian can reckon, and was the seat of the most ancient civilization of which we have any record. No one can tell accurately how much land in the United States is capable of reclamation by irrigation, but some of our leading experts on that subject assert that the Missouri River and its tributaries can be made to irrigate three times the land now cultivated along the Nile. The dense population of Egypt is made possible partly by the low standard of living of the inhabitants, and partly by the remarkable fertility of the land, combining as it does rich alluvial soil made fertile by the annual deposits of Nile mud, with abundant moisture and intense semitropical heat. Of course it is neither probable nor desirable that the region to be watered by the Missouri River should ever be populated by men with such a low standard of living. Therefore it is not probable or desirable that it should sustain such a dense agricultural population, unless the land can be made vastly more fertile than that of Egypt. It is better to have a sparse population well supported than a dense population meagerly supported. According to the census of 1900 there were a little more than 7,250,000 acres already under irrigation, and the acreage has increased considerably since. It has been conservatively estimated that there will eventually be brought under irrigation in the western half of the United States an area equal to the whole of New England and New York combined. The greater part of this land is practically valueless without water, but when brought under an effective irrigation system it becomes as valuable and productive as any land in the country, and much more productive than the greater part of that which is now cultivated. In addition to the advantage of being able to control the moisture, irrigation has the further advantage of replenishing the soil with the sediment brought down from the decomposing rocks of the higher altitudes. Therefore irrigated land is not only highly productive but it tends to retain its productivity for long periods of time.

Dry farming. But after all the available water of the mountain streams has been diverted and utilized, only a small fraction of the acreage of this vast arid region will be under irrigation. Large as the irrigated area will be in the aggregate, it will form only a series of oases in the midst of vast wildernesses of desert or semidesert lands, incapable, without water, of being brought to a high state of cultivation. Of this land, however, some of it — it is impossible to say how much — can be brought under tillage by what has come to be known as dry farming. Except in certain high mountain altitudes, the rainfall gradually diminishes as one moves westward from the Mississippi River, until one nears the Pacific coast. It is difficult to say just where the region of adequate rainfall ends or where that of inadequate rainfall begins, even when judged from the standpoint of older methods of cultivation. But by a scientific study of the problems of moisture retention, and by the introduction of new drought-resisting crops, it has been found that this line can be moved much farther westward ; that is, that crops can be grown and a living made on lands which were formerly thought to be too dry for profitable cultivation.

Perhaps the most important factor in the successful cultivation of lands formerly thought to be too dry is that of maintaining a " dust mulch." It is found that one great source of loss of moisture is evaporation. The moisture which sinks into the ground when it rains tends to rise to the surface by capillary attraction, just as the oil rises in a lamp wick. If it rises quite to the surface, it is evaporated and carried off by the wind, just as the oil in the lamp is burned off. By keeping the surface soil constantly stirred and loosened up, the moisture is prevented from rising quite to the surface. The loosened surface soil being less compact, and the capillary ducts being broken, the water does not rise through this layer so readily. The moisture therefore tends to remain in the subsoil, being protected from the air by this layer of loose dirt as by a blanket. By practicing this simple method of preventing the waste of moisture by evaporation, it has been found possible to grow crops on land which was formerly thought to be too dry for that purpose. One danger, however, is that the wind will not only carry away the moisture but will blow the dust mulch itself entirely off the land.

A still further extension of the tillable area is made possible by the system of alternating crops and fallows, combined with that of maintaining a dust mulch. A growing crop itself extracts a great deal of moisture from the soil, where it is absorbed by the roots, carried up into the plant, and given off by evaporation from the leaves or blades. Where the land does not receive moisture enough to grow a crop every year, even with the system of constant cultivation and maintenance of the dust mulch, it is frequently possible to grow a crop every second year, allowing the land to lie fallow, but constantly stirring it, however, on the alternate year. Under this system a part of two years' supply of water is accumulated and utilized in the growing of a single crop. However, the farmer gets a crop from only half his land each year. But where there is little bad weather to interrupt his work, where the land is level and easily worked, where he can use ample horse power, gang plows, and efficient machinery, he can handle land enough to give him almost as large a crop each year as the eastern farmer can get where he grows a crop every year, but is so frequently interrupted by bad weather and other hindrances as not to be able to handle so much land. To be sure, this system of farming is not likely to support so dense a population as can be supported in regions of ample rainfall, but it is vastly better than allowing the land to go to waste. In case of necessity this method could be still further extended and a crop raised from each parcel of land only once in three years. It is quite possible for a farmer to make a good living in this way, where the land lies well, is fertile, and is easily worked.

There are many other elements in the general method of dry farming which require somewhat specialized knowledge, so that the man who expects to follow this method must make a special study of the problem in its many details. Deep plowing, which tends to increase the capacity of the soil to absorb the rainfall instead of allowing it to run off in the surface streams; increasing the proportion of humus or vegetable matter in the soil, to increase its capacity to hold moisture; subsoil packing; and other special methods have to be studied and applied. But it has been demonstrated that the farmer who will apply these various methods scientifically can make money from some of the lands which have hitherto been regarded as practically worthless. Doubtless more will yet be learned about dry-farming methods than we have hitherto dreamed of, and new crops will be introduced which are capable of resisting drought, and thus the tillable area of our great West will be materially increased.

But after all is done that we can at present hope for, there will doubtless remain considerable tracts of land which can only be regarded as waste. It will be pastured, much of it, it is true, but even as pastures a great deal of it is so poor as to be practically worthless.

Bad chemical conditions. The problem of reclaiming lands which are now going to waste because of bad chemical conditions is one which requires a degree of expert technical knowledge, which is, unfortunately, very rare as yet. Unlike the reclamation of dry or wet lands, which sometimes requires irrigation or drainage works on too large a scale for individual enterprise to undertake, the reclamation of these lands does not call for state or national enterprise except perhaps in the experimental stage. When it is once learned by scientific study and experiment how to treat such soils, private individuals and companies are quite as competent to handle the business questions involved as is the state or the nation. Consequently this is a problem for the soil expert rather than for the economist.

Alkali land. The most conspicuous type of land now going to waste because of bad chemical conditions, both in this country and over the rest of the world, is that which is commonly known as alkali land. These lands are usually found in regions of slight rainfall, where there is very little surplus water to be carried away in streams, but where the greater part of it is carried away by evaporation. Where there is an abundant rainfall and, as a consequence, a multitude of streams, the alkali salts are leached out of the soil and carried to the ocean, where they contribute to the saltness of the water. But where the rainfall is slight and most of the water is carried away by evaporation, these salts remain in the soil. Even here, however, the high, the sloping, and the well-drained land is usually found free from alkali, because even the slight rainfall leaches it out of the soil and carries it away, sometimes, however, only to the lower lands. But lands which are low or flat or badly drained are frequently so strongly impregnated with these salts as to interfere with plant growth or to destroy it altogether.

In the arid regions of every part of the globe these alkali lands are of frequent occurrence, forming a part of the landscape, which is repellent because of its dreary barrenness and disagreeable because of the fine powdery dust which is blown about by the winds, parching to the lips and stinging to the eyes and nostrils of the traveler. It is impossible to make any estimate of the amount of land which goes to waste on this account, partly because it is not known just how much there is of it, and partly because much of it would be unusable anyway on account of insufficient moisture. But inasmuch as it is usually the lower and less arid land of an arid region which is alkaline, it frequently happens that such lands are highly productive if these bad chemical conditions can be overcome. Therefore it is a problem of importance, and nowhere is it greater than in the western part of the United States.

Without attempting a detailed discussion of the methods of reclamation, the following are named as having been found effective,[1] though they require technical knowledge and skill to make them successful :

1. Underdrainage. By this means the water is allowed to leach the salts out of the soil and carry them away. This is said by Hilgard to be the final and universal remedy.

2. Leaching down. That is, without underdrainage, the alkali on the surface can sometimes be carried down several feet by flooding the land.

3. Removing a few inches of the surface soil bodily from the land. Since the salts are carried to the surface in solution with the water and there left when the water evaporates, it generally happens that the surface is more strongly impregnated than the

[1] Cf. E. W. Hilgard, Soils (New York, 1906), chaps. xxii, xxiii.

subsoil. Thus it is sometimes possible to remove from one third to one half the total alkali from the soil in a single year.

4. Very deep plowing. This has the effect of removing the crust of strongly impregnated surface soil to a greater depth, where it is mixed with the mass of the soil and is thus less injurious to plant growth.

5. Neutralizing the more injurious salts, that is, "black alkali." A liberal application of land plaster or gypsum is found, *in certain cases*, to be sufficient.

6. Counteracting evaporation. This is everywhere necessary, no matter what other methods are adopted. The "dust mulch" as applied to dry farming, artificial mulching, shading, or any method which will reduce the rate of evaporation will in light cases be found sufficient, and will in all cases be found helpful.

7. Introducing crops which will endure alkali. Alfalfa and Australian salt bushes are found adaptable in some cases, and experiments are still being carried on to find other crops which will grow in alkali soil.

Salt marshes. The salt marshes along the seacoasts and at the mouths of rivers form another type of land which is now going to waste, partly because of bad chemical conditions, but mainly, perhaps, because of bad physical conditions. The reclamation of such lands, however, is simply a matter of diking and draining, — diking to keep out the salt water, and draining to carry off the fresh water. The fresh water, if it can be carried off, will soon carry the salt with it and leave the soil in condition to grow crops. This is, therefore, merely a part of the drainage problem and should be treated as such.

Bad political conditions. No observer can have failed to notice considerable tracts of valuable land, especially in the neighborhood of our large cities, which are lying idle. This land is going to waste in the sense that it is producing nothing for the sustentation of the people, as truly as the alkali plains are going to waste. This is not because of the physical or chemical conditions, but because of bad political conditions. The land is generally held for purposes of speculation. The owners are making money out of it, or hoping to make money out of it, not by using it but by keeping it out of use; that is, they expect it to rise in price year by year. The money which they make in this way they make because the rest of the people are working and increasing the wealth of the community, or because the needs of the rest of the community are increasing. In either case the owner calculates that the community will soon be in greater need of his land and that he can then exact a higher price for it. It is a bad political condition where any one is allowed to make money not by using, but by keeping out of use, a natural resource of this kind, — not by increasing the productive power of the community, but by preventing the full use of that power.

In most of our American states men were formerly encouraged in this kind of waste, and are still encouraged in some of them, by bad tax laws. The man who held his land out of use was in the habit of asking that his taxes be reduced on that account, and it was customary for the assessor to grant his request. Since it was necessary to raise a certain amount of revenue, the taxes on other property had to be increased to make up for this loss. Thus it happened that a man was rewarded for allowing a natural resource to go to waste, and his neighbor was penalized for putting a natural resource to the use for which it was given him by the public. Gradually, however, the public mind is awakening to this situation, and the waster of land is not receiving so many favors as he once did, especially in those states where there is most enlightenment on public questions. It is still true, however, in every state, that the man who improves his land has to pay a higher tax than the man who does not, provided their lands have the same natural value. This goes under the head of taxing all forms of property, including improvements on land as well as the land itself, equally. If improved and unimproved land were all taxed alike, or according to its natural or unimproved value, it would seldom be found profitable to hold any piece of valuable land idle and unimproved. The taxes would eat up the anticipated rise in price, and the owner would find that the only way to make anything out of his land would be to use it as it ought to be used. This would also relieve somewhat the tax on improvements or the fruits of labor, thrift, and enterprise, and thus encourage men to make such improvements or to exercise the virtues of labor, thrift, and enterprise. Such an improvement in political conditions would eliminate a great deal of waste in the form of idle land. The seriousness of this waste is not to be measured in acres alone. Land which goes to waste in this way is usually the most valuable in the country, one acre of it frequently being worth a hundred of that which goes to waste in the region of dry farming.

Much has been said and written about the waste of land in parks, pleasure grounds, game preserves, etc., especially in European countries. Where there is a real waste, that is, where the land is so valuable for other purposes as to make its use for these purposes uneconomical, the evil could be cured in most cases by the simple device of taxing it according to its value for those other purposes. But it will be found that the evil has been greatly exaggerated. It is certainly true in many cases, and probably in most cases, that land devoted to these uses would have little value as agricultural land. It is usually the most broken, stony, or sterile land which is so used. In such cases the obvious thing to do with the land, if it cannot be profitably cleared for the plow, is to allow it to grow up to forest. If it can be made to yield a small profit in the production of game and to give pleasure as a park or hunting ground, in addition to its production of timber, so much the better. But where good agricultural land is put to these uses when it might be made more productive under tillage, and when it is needed as a source of food, it is an undoubted sign of bad political conditions. They who are permitted thus to pervert good land to these inferior uses ought at least to pay for the privilege. They ought, to say the least, to pay a tax on such land equal to that which it would yield, with its improvements, if it were brought under the plow. If this remedy were applied, it would, of course, not affect that land which is not suited to agriculture, but it would tend at least to force into agriculture such lands as were suited.

III. Ways of economizing Land (continued)

Getting a larger product per acre. It is not always easy, however, to tell the difference between bringing waste land under cultivation and increasing the productivity of land already in use. Land formerly used only for grazing, but now brought under the plow either by dry farming or irrigation, may sometimes be regarded as reclaimed land and sometimes as land brought to a higher state of productiveness. The arid lands of the Far West are sometimes used for pasturage even when the herbage is so scant as to require a great many acres to supply food for one diligent sheep. When such lands are brought under irrigation and made to produce immense crops of corn and alfalfa, it is quite proper to speak of them as reclaimed lands. But when land farther east, where rainfall and herbage are a little more abundant, and where the pasturage is therefore tolerably good, is brought under the plow by the methods of dry farming and made to produce a crop of wheat every second year, it is doubtful if this can properly be called reclaimed land, even though its productivity be somewhat increased. The problem of bringing waste land into use, therefore, shades off into the problem of getting a larger product from each acre, which is another way of economizing land.

At this point in our discussion a word of caution is necessary. It is sometimes assumed that a large product per acre is a desirable thing in itself. Such is not the case. What is really to be desired is a large product per man. It is only where the product per man is large that there is a high standard of living and a high state of well-being for the average man. Where the land is abundant a large product per man is most easily secured by extensive farming, — that is, by farming a large acreage per man, which usually means a small product per acre. When, however, all the land of a country is once occupied, if the population continues to increase, the continuance of a large product per man can only be secured by increasing the product per acre ; that is to say, while a large product per acre is not *in itself* a desirable achievement, it is sometimes desirable *as a means* of getting a large product per man, and is not desirable in any other sense whatever. It is quite possible to have a large product per acre with a very small product per man, but such a condition of affairs is always accompanied by squalor and misery, and we find this to be the actual situation in those countries which can point to the largest product per acre. And these are the countries which are so frequently held up by thoughtless people for our admiration !

Though it is sincerely to be hoped that a kind Providence will preserve us from the fate which has overtaken such countries, or rather that our people will themselves see to it that no such results occur here, nevertheless it seems inevitable that our population should increase considerably in the next few years, especially if the present rate of immigration should continue. Therefore it is of the highest importance that we should learn how to increase the productivity of our land per acre without reducing the productivity per farmer.

There are two general methods of increasing the productivity of each acre of land in use. One is the substitution of more productive for less productive crops. The other is the more intensive cultivation of each crop.

Substituting heavy-yielding for light-yielding crops. As already indicated, much of the so-called work of reclamation might be considered under the first of these heads. The substitution of cultivated for wild grasses, the substitution of tillage for pasturage, the substitution of crops requiring much cultivation but little land for crops requiring little cultivation but much land,— these are among the progressive stages in the economizing of land. One striking feature in this progressive economy is the movement of the wheat belt of the United States westward. While wheat is an important crop in the world's commerce, it is a poor one from the point of view of intensive farming. It requires comparatively little work to get a moderately good yield, but it does not respond so vigorously as do certain other crops to the efforts of the farmer to increase the yield. It requires more work to cultivate an acre of maize or Indian corn, on the other hand, but it is possible to produce a much heavier yield wherever the climate and soil are adapted to its cultivation ; that is to say, this crop responds to intensive cultivation much more vigorously than does wheat. In addition to this, wheat stands transportation remarkably well. It combines high value with small bulk and can be shipped long distances and sold for cash. Therefore it has happened for many years that the world's wheat supply has come largely from regions of sparse population distant from markets, where land was abundant though labor was scarce. It has been a frontier crop so far as this country is concerned, and the center of wheat production has been moving westward for a great many years. As the country has become more thickly settled and land consequently less abundant relatively to the supply of labor, it has been found more economical to substitute corn and other crops for wheat, or to grow wheat in rotation with some of these other crops instead of growing it exclusively. In either case the growing scarcity of land and the increasing supply of labor have brought about a certain amount of substitution of heavy-yielding for light-yielding crops.

This substitution of heavy-yielding for light-yielding crops presents some exceedingly complicated economic problems. As suggested above, one factor in the movement of the wheat belt westward was that of transportation, though the existence of cheap land and opportunities for extensive cultivation were the most important ones. The factor of transportation is also important in the cultivation of the still heavier-yielding but less transportable market-garden crops in the neighborhood of large cities. The general rule is that the products which are more bulky or perishable or otherwise difficult of transportation must be produced near the place of consumption, and those which are less bulky or perishable or are otherwise easier of transportation may be grown farther from places of consumption. This, however, is a means of economizing the labor of transportation rather than of economizing land. Moreover, this form of territorial division of labor is economical only when there are densely settled and sparsely settled regions of about equal fertility. As the whole country becomes more densely populated it will be found economical to give the land over more and more to these bulky and perishable as well as to the heavy-yielding crops, and to depend upon newer and more sparsely settled countries for our supplies of wheat and similar light-yielding as well as easily transportable crops, provided we have something to send to these new countries in exchange. It happens that wheat and beef are products well adapted to frontier conditions. Accordingly, we need not be surprised to find in the United States that, as the country settles, these two products will dwindle and other more profitable crops take their place. It is really a sign of advancement and not of deterioration.

Another illustration of the substitution of more productive for less productive crops is the general invasion of the cattle ranges of the Far West by settlers who are bringing the land under the plow. As the corn belt has pushed the wheat belt farther west, so the wheat belt has pushed the cattle belt farther west. So long as there was unoccupied range country into which the ranchmen could migrate, the ranches merely moved on ahead of the wheat belt. But when all the range country was once occupied, further migration of the wheat belt westward meant the extinction or partial extinction of the range-cattle industry. This is the tendency which has been showing itself in recent years. Even within the range country a similar process has been going on in the crowding out of the cattle by the sheep, the latter being better adapted to picking a living on those lean pastures.

With these migrations of the different "belts" of agricultural production there has probably been no material change in the relative acreage devoted to the different products for the supply of the markets of the whole commercial world. It is not possible to measure the different acreages accurately, but until the commercial world changes its habits of consumption it will continue to demand the different products in about the same proportion. If we could imagine the whole available land of the globe as occupied and brought under cultivation, and that such terms as "old countries" and "new countries" had lost their meaning, it would not then be possible to imagine these different belts of production as pushing one another farther and farther toward the new and cheaper lands. If, then, the consumers of the world were to continue with their present habits of consumption unchanged, further substitution of heavier-yielding crops for the lighter-yielding crops would scarcely be possible. This would be made possible only by a change in consumption of less meat and more milk and eggs, the substitution of corn for wheat as a breadstuff, or the substitution of potatoes for bread, etc. Such changes are likely to occur as the world becomes more thickly populated; in fact they must occur if the population increases very rapidly over a considerable period of time. It would, however, be economical for some countries to change their habits in this direction without regard to the question of population.

That milk is a more economical food than meat is shown by the fact that the milk furnished by one good dairy cow in the course of a year has a food value equal to from 3000 to 4000 pounds of beef. It will take five or six beef cattle to lay on that much first-class beef in a year, and they will together consume as much feed as three or four of these dairy cows. Therefore it would be a great economy of land if people would consent to consume more milk and less beef. This, however, is counterbalanced at the present time by the fact that the milk for the great centers of consumption must be produced near at hand, where land is scarce, whereas beef may be produced in new countries at great distances from the centers of consumption, where land is so cheap and abundant that it does not need to be severely economized as yet. Moreover, where beef can be produced under range conditions, it costs less labor per unit of food value than milk does. But a time may come when such a change in diet would be highly economical, either by reason of the settling of the last of these new countries, or, as is more likely, by the discovery of cheaper and more satisfactory ways of preserving milk so that it also may be transported greater distances. But either of these changes will bring about such a change in the relative price of milk and beef as to bring about a change in the relative consumption of these two articles, there being always a tendency to substitute a cheaper for a dearer article where the two serve the same purpose.

The following table shows, approximately, the food-producing powers of an acre of land under different crops :

	FOOD VALUE PER POUND (calories) [1]	POUNDS PER ACRE (good yield)	CALORIES PER ACRE	RATIO TO WHEAT AS BASIS (fractions omitted)
Entire wheat flour	1660	1800	2,988,000	100%
Native beef (as purchased)	1130	200	226,000	7%
Mutton (as purchased) . .	1275	250	318,750	11%
Whole milk	325	4000	1,300,000	43%
Corn meal (unbolted) . . .	1550	3600	5,580,000	186%
Oatmeal	1860	1800	3,348,000	112%
Rice	1630	2400	3,912,000	131%
Rye meal or flour	1630	1800	2,934,000	98%
Beans	1590	2400	3,816,000	129%
Potatoes	325	24,000	7,800,000	260%
Sweet potatoes	480	30,000	14,400,000	482%

Two things must be said, however, in qualification and explanation of this table. In the first place, food values are not to be measured in calories alone. Digestibility and appetizing qualities are of great value, to say nothing of the bone- and muscle-building power of certain ingredients. Therefore it does not follow that a sweet-potato diet is to be commended merely because an acre of this crop yields a large number of calories, though it does show that, when the product is so appetizing and digestible as the sweet potato, a considerable economy of land could be effected by a larger consumption of that vegetable.

In the second place, the yields per acre are only estimated on the basis of general observation. These estimates are not based upon statistics of average yields, nor upon maximum yields actually secured. They are merely what, in the author's opinion, an average acre of land, properly situated for the crop in question,

[1] The figures in this column are taken from *Bulletin 28*, of the United States Department of Agriculture, Office of Experiment Stations, by W. O. Atwater, Ph. D., and Charles D. Woods, B. S. (Government Printing Office, 1896).

might reasonably be expected to yield under thorough cultivation. Another author might reasonably ascribe different yields and get different results, though the present writer believes that his own estimates are reasonable, and he is certain that the yields which he has ascribed to the different crops are attainable.

In addition to the food-producing power of the different crops in our country, as shown by the table on page 161, that of an acre of tropical land in bananas, dates, and other tropical fruits is very great. When this is considered in connection with the fact that these fruits are grown in countries where land is still abundant and cheap, it is apparent that the food question is easily solved for a long time to come for those countries which are willing to accept the banana, the date, etc., as articles of diet, and which are able to produce something to give in exchange for these. Given these conditions, the food problem is merely one of transportation.

Effect on standard of living. The objection to such a change in habits of consumption as will require more of the heavy-yielding and less of the light-yielding crops is that it may be carried to the point of lowering the standard of living. Such is likely to be the case where a cheap diet is substituted for an expensive one without any increase in variety. The substitution of the potato for bread is one thing; the addition of the potato as a part of a diet which had previously consisted mainly of bread is quite another thing. The former lowers the standard of living, while the latter, by introducing greater variety, tends to improve it, and at the same time to reduce its cost.

It is, however, unfortunate for a people to become dependent upon a single heavy-yielding crop, especially if that crop be, like the potato and certain edible roots consumed in such large quantities in Japan, of rather low nutritive value per pound. The yield per acre being so enormously large, the food value per acre may be somewhat large also in spite of the low food value in proportion to weight. But it is the general opinion that it is difficult for a race to maintain a high degree of energy and efficiency without some more concentrated food-stuff. Just how far any country ought to go in the direction of introducing into its diet cheaper foods, or foods which are more economical of land, is therefore a difficult question. But there can scarcely be any question as to the economy of giving up vicious and wasteful habits of consumption ; that is, the consumption of such things as opium, alcohol, and tobacco, whose production requires so much valuable land and whose consumption adds nothing to comfort and well-being.

Vegetable *vs.* **meat diet.** It is sometimes argued that a vegetable diet is more economical than a meat diet. Where meat can be grown on wild land under what are called range conditions, such as prevailed on the Western plains a generation ago, and such as still prevail in other parts of the New World, it is very economical of labor and therefore a cheap food. It does undoubtedly require a great deal of land, and, as these new areas are settled and become thickly populated, the meat supply will have to come from farms. Here it is an expensive product if it is produced in large quantities. The nutriment in the grain required to fatten a beef animal under present conditions is usually much larger than that of the beef produced, to say nothing of the other things consumed by the animal. Again, the land required to pasture a beef animal for a year would, if put into grain or vegetables, yield a great deal more food than that of the beef which the animal will add to his carcass. These remarks apply, however, only to the production of meat as a staple crop. When produced in small quantities, and as a by-product of agriculture, meat is one of the most economical articles of diet which a country can produce. In the first place, in the growing of grain and vegetables there is a great deal of waste material unsuited to human consumption, but which animals can consume, digest, and turn into meat. The animal is, from this point of view, a machine for converting inedible waste products into excellent food. To be sure, the main purpose of such a machine may be to turn these waste products into milk, or, when fed to fowl, into eggs; but even the production of milk and eggs requires the maturing of the bodies of the animals and the fowls, and it is economical to utilize these bodies as food rather than to allow them to go to waste. This applies also to the production of mutton as a by-product of wool production. Where the prejudice against horseflesh does not exist, it applies equally well to that form of food wherever horses are needed as draft animals.

Another interesting bit of bucolic intelligence, emanating, however, from urban minds, is the argument that if calves were not killed as veal but allowed to grow to mature beefhood, there would be a great deal more food. This doctrine has actually been soberly promulgated on the floor of our national Congress, and has been further expanded by certain sapient editors of metropolitan newspapers. It is like saying that if builders would never stop work on any building until it was twenty stories high, we should have a great deal more houseroom. It is obviously true that if every calf born were to grow to weigh a ton before he was slaughtered, he would yield more food than if he were slaughtered when he weighed only 200 pounds. If he could draw his sustenance from interstellar space while he was growing to such a desirable size, it would doubtless be economical to let him grow as big as he could; but since he has to get his sustenance from the land, and since the older he grows the more food it takes to add a pound to his weight, it is obviously uneconomical to keep him any longer than necessary to bring him to a condition to satisfy consumers. As a matter of fact, a given amount of land and labor will produce more food in the form of veal than in the form of beef.

According to a writer in *Country Life in America* for July, 1905:

It is a demonstrated fact that as the fattening period is prolonged the cost of each pound of gain increases. In one experiment 730 lb. of grain were required for 100 lb. of gain during the first two months (of the fattening period), while 1000 lb. of grain were required for the same amount of gain at the end of six months. It has been shown that in some cattle it costs four times as much to produce a pound of meat at the end as at the beginning of the feeding period.

Again, according to the same authority:

It is true that the cost of gain increases with the age of the animal (aside from the period of forced fattening). From statistics covering feeding experiments with more than 50,000 cattle of different ages, it appears that the average daily gain in cattle at $\frac{1}{2}$ year of age is 2.3 lb.; at $1\frac{1}{4}$ years, 2.09 lb.; at $2\frac{1}{2}$ years, 1.58 lb.; at $3\frac{1}{2}$ years, 1.44 lb.; at $4\frac{1}{2}$ years 1.2 lb.

From these figures it ought to be sufficiently obvious that the way to increase the supply of meat is not to allow animals to grow to maturity, but to slaughter them as early as is consistent with the tastes and desires of the consumers. Our pastures and cornfields will yield more meat by supporting a larger number of animals and slaughtering them at an early age, than by supporting a smaller number for a longer period. Veal in particular, since it is a by-product of dairying, is a cheap form of meat.

It is not in the matter of food alone that land may be economized by a change of habits. The substitution of cotton for woolen clothing effects also an enormous saving of land. As much clothing can be made from the product of one acre of cotton as from the product of ten acres devoted to wool growing. Granting that the woolen clothing will last twice as long, there is still a great saving of land. To be sure, cotton clothing does not always serve the same purposes as woolen; nevertheless, within certain limits or for certain purposes, the two are substitutes for each other. Within these limits the preference for one or the other is merely a matter of cheapness on the one hand or of fashion on the other. It is not improbable that fashions will eventually, though rather slowly, change in the direction of cheapness. However, it is altogether probable that the substitution of cotton for wool as stuff for clothing will result in more clothing and in greater variety, rather than in the use of less land. This, however, would be economical of land in the sense of permitting a higher standard of living in the matter of clothing without requiring any more land. On the other hand, wool is easily transportable, and may therefore be grown in new countries at great distance from centers of consumption, — that is, where land is abundant and does not yet need to be severely economized. Cotton, on the other hand, requires considerable labor for its cultivation, and can only be grown where there is population enough to furnish a supply of labor, — that is, it is less suited to frontier production. Again, wherever mutton is relished and commands a good price, a certain amount of wool can be grown as a by-product and the cost of production of wool thereby reduced. It is a question, however, whether wool is a by-product of mutton, or mutton a by-product of wool. Where the former is the case, there is not yet such pressure in favor of cotton clothing as will come sometime unless some other fiber, such as ramie, should displace cotton.

Intensive cultivation. How to make each acre produce more of the crops which are now grown is a question of more immediate importance. This is what is commonly meant by intensive farming, though that term is sometimes applied also to the substitution of heavy-yielding for light-yielding crops. Intensive farming in the strict sense may mean any or all of the following methods :

1. The simple application of more labor in the preparation of the soil and the handling of the crop.

2. The use of more capital in connection with a given area of land and a given quantity of labor, thus enabling the same labor to prepare the soil more thoroughly and care for the crops more efficiently.

3. The application of more scientific methods to the improvement and maintenance of the fertility of the soil.

Doubtless the very best kind of intensive farming would include all three methods, but they are not always found in combination where that which is called intensive farming is found. In old and thickly populated countries, where land is dear and labor cheap, the first of these is the characteristic method of increasing the productivity of the land. Patient, painstaking, never-ending toil, combined with the utmost frugality of consumption and the most careful saving of every scrap of manure, have enabled these countries to cultivate every square foot of fertile land with the greatest care and to support their enormous populations upon the products of their own soil. Machinery is little used and would probably, in most of these cases, be uneconomical, because machinery requires power, and power, especially animal power, would require a share of the products of the land for its support. Unless the land could be made to produce enough more to maintain the additional number of draft animals, their maintenance would reduce the food supply available for the support of the people. In those countries where labor is so abundant and land so scarce, the great problem is not how to save labor but how to save land. It is difficult to see how the use of machinery would help the people of those countries to a solution of their particular class of problems, because machinery as we know it is primarily a means of saving labor rather than land.

Harder work. This particular method of saving land — that is, that form of intensive cultivation which merely applies more labor to the land — has little in it to attract the rural economist in the United States. It requires either that the farmers work harder, or that there be more of them in proportion to the land. As to the first alternative, it is distinctly to be rejected because there is not the least doubt that our farmers, on the average, work too hard now, rather than not hard enough. Instead of advocating that they work harder in order to cultivate their farms more intensively, we should rather advocate that they work less hard, even if that should result in poorer cultivation, if that were the only alternative. One serious need of rural life in America is a little more leisure to read, to meet in social ways, to discuss measures for rural improvement, and to organize for the promotion of rural interests. This is not saying that there are no drones in the country. There are doubtless men living on farms, and ostensibly farming, who idle away their time ; but most of them do not deserve the name of " farmer " any more than the vendor of shoestrings deserves the name of " merchant." The general rule is that real farmers work too hard, at least with their bodies. There is little danger, however, of farmers or any other class working too hard with their heads.

Smaller farms. As to the possibility of securing more intensity of cultivation by increasing the number of workers on farms, this has fewer objections, but at most does not hold out very alluring prospects. It means either smaller farms on the average, or a larger number of hired laborers on farms. It is not improbable that smaller farms would, in some sections at least, prove advantageous. In some sections farmers have been moved by a speculative spirit to get more land than they were prepared to farm efficiently. Hoping for a rise in the price of land, or for a future increase of capital which would enable them to stock the land properly, or planning to have land enough to divide among their children, they have bought large farms when they would have made more money, year by year, by buying less land and stocking it and equipping it better. But it is very easy to exaggerate this evil. In some sections of the country it is almost certainly true that the farms are too small on the average. This is particularly true in those parts of New England which are not favorably situated for market gardening. In many parts the farms average from 70 to 100 acres, one fourth to one half of which is timber. Farms of this size were well adapted to the growing of field crops under older methods; but the introduction of superior tools and machinery has enabled one man, with plenty of horse power, to do more work than he could formerly and to cultivate larger fields. Moreover, these larger implements require larger fields for their economical employment than the average New England farm affords. In the growing of field crops, therefore, New England agriculture requires larger rather than smaller farms on the average. For market gardening, and probably for dairying, they are quite large enough.

Even in the Middle West there is danger, if the farms should grow appreciably smaller, that the product per man would be reduced, and that could only be described as disastrous. If the farms are made too small, the most efficient tools cannot be used, or, if they are used, they will be used so little as to make their ownership unprofitable. If the farmer cannot use the most efficient tools and machinery, and is forced by the smallness of his farm to use more primitive and less productive methods, his product is decreased and he is impoverished, even though he does succeed in getting a large crop per acre from his small farm.

It is not possible to say in advance how large any man's farm ought to be. One can say, however, in general terms, that it ought to be large enough to occupy the reasonable working time of the farmer and his family when they use the best and most efficient tools and machinery known to the farming world, with ample horse power, or some other form of power, to drive that machinery. According to this rule it would be safe to say that in the growing of such field crops as corn, wheat, oats, and hay, a farm of much less than 160 acres would prove too small for the most economical use of labor, — that is, too small to give the maximum product per man. In rough and broken land, however, where modern machinery cannot be used, the farm might well be smaller, provided such crops are to be grown at all ; but it is doubtful if such land can be economically used for this purpose. Again, if this rough land is to be used mainly for pasturage, much larger farms would be necessary to give the maximum product per man. In the production of garden crops, or crops which require a considerable amount of handwork, much smaller farms might prove more economical.

More hired laborers. But it is possible to increase the amount of labor expended upon each acre of land without requiring each farmer to work harder or to reduce the size of his farm. It might be done by increasing the number of farm laborers or farm hands, who work for wages but do not own the land nor the tools with which they work, nor a share of the crops they help to produce. Where farm hands are scarce and hard to get, their wages are good and their position is a very comfortable and satisfactory one, in spite of the fact that they own none of the things with which they work. Though legally they may be dismissed, though theoretically they lack homes or permanent abiding places, yet practically and actually they are sought after and can choose their abiding places and their work. But when they become numerous the situation is changed. Instead of being sought after, they must hunt for jobs. Instead of being able to choose their abiding places and their work, they must take whatever they can get and be thankful. All this would be very pleasant for the owners of the farms, but not for the hired men. Since, man for man, the interest of one is as important as that of another, this is not a condition to be desired by the rural economist, who is supposed to have no class interest but to be interested in all alike. Moreover, a large increase in the number of hired laborers in any of the older states, though it would tend to increase the product per acre, would tend to reduce the product per man. Under the great law of agricultural production known as the law of diminishing returns, two men of equal ability will not produce twice as much as one man on a farm which was of a proper size to yield the maximum product to one man's work. Under the operation of this law, the more laborers you put upon such a farm the less will be the product per laborer (though the larger will be the yield per acre), unless the increase in the number of laborers is accompanied by an increase in the capital, an improvement in the quality of the tools and machinery, or an improvement in the methods of farming. This is not saying that a *small* increase in the number of hired men in some farming sections would not be desirable. Farm owners are sometimes incapacitated for farm work by sickness, accident, or age. In such cases they are sometimes under great disadvantage because of the scarcity of hired help; but it is not necessary to have a large and permanent class of agricultural laborers in order to remove this difficulty. On the whole, it is a better agricultural system where each farm owner normally expects to do his own work, than it is where he normally expects to hire all his work done.

More capital. An increase in the supply of capital to be used in conjunction with the labor of the farmers in the cultivation of their farms is another possibility. By this method a given supply of labor on a fixed quantity of land can cultivate that land more effectively, and thus increase not only the product per acre but the product per man as well. This capital is usually expressed in dollars, and may at first consist in money or general purchasing power in the hands of the farmer. But it eventually takes the form of, or is paid out for, buildings, tools, machinery, draft animals and other live stock, fences, drains, pumping and irrigation works, fertilizers, seed, feed, fuel, etc.

Where land is abundant and labor scarce, the usual effect of an increase in these forms of capital is merely to save labor or to enable a given supply of labor to cultivate more land; but there is no reason why they may not be used with equal effect to enable labor to cultivate the same quantity of land more intensively and to get larger crops from it when land becomes scarce and the necessity arises for economizing it. This may, however, require some readjustment in the form of capital. Instead of taking his increased capital in the form of more tools, which would enable him to cover more land, the farmer may possess himself of better tools, which will enable him to do a better quality of work, — plows which will turn deeper furrows, harrows which will pulverize more thoroughly and prepare better seed beds, other tools better suited to the work of exterminating weeds in order that all the moisture and fertility of the soil may be saved for the crops, better horses to draw these tools, superior breeds of live stock to convert what they consume into more valuable products than our common scrub stock are capable of doing. In these and a multitude of other ways the increased use of capital will enable the farmers to increase the product of their land while increasing, at the same time, the product of their labor.

More intelligence. This increased use of capital is, however, very closely associated with more scientific methods of cultivation, though not identical with them. It is not identical because, without any new discoveries or without any new knowledge, the farmer will necessarily work in a somewhat different way if he has an abundance of capital from that in which he would work if he lacked capital and could not get it. He might know perfectly well the virtues of deep plowing, cross-plowing, and sub-soiling, with multifarious harrowings and cross harrowings, and he might know also that it is better to drill one's grain than to sow it broadcast; yet if he lacks sufficient team force to do all this plowing and harrowing, and does not possess and cannot afford to buy a grain drill, it may pay him better to cultivate all his land somewhat less intensively than to concentrate all his force on a part of the land, allowing the rest to lie idle. Even the latter method of using land would be less economical than to employ an abundance of capital and cultivate it all thoroughly, provided he had or could get the capital. Without any superior knowledge of scientific farming, therefore, but merely by the possession of more capital, it is quite possible for the farmers generally to economize their land and make it produce more per acre as well as per man.

When a superior knowledge of agricultural science is added to the possession of more and more capital, the possibilities of economizing land are very greatly increased. A scientific rotation of crops suited to all the conditions of the individual farm, including not only its soil, its climate, its elevation and contour, but its markets and its sources of supply as well, is a problem calling for profound study, and can only be mastered by a man of scientific training or long experience. When several generations of scientific farmers have lived on the same farm and have handed down their knowledge and experience from one to another, many of the problems will doubtless be solved and much waste of land and labor eliminated.

Then there are the problems of tillage and fertilization, of improving the physical and the chemical condition of the soil ; the problems of animal and plant breeding, involving a knowledge of the laws of heredity ; the problems created by that multitude of pests which *seem* to come from a mysterious nowhere to vex the soul of the farmer, — these and a thousand other problems call for solution, and the failure to solve them means a waste not only of land but of labor as well. However, the detailed discussion of these scientific methods would take us into the fields of technical agriculture rather than rural economy.

IV. Labor as a Factor in Agricultural Production

That labor and land are the original or primary factors of
production, while capital is a secondary though important factor, is one of the commonplaces of political economy. Upon the
character of the labor even more than upon the character of
the land does the prosperity of agriculture depend. Again, upon
the economizing of labor and the conservation of our human
resources even more than upon the economizing of land and
the conservation of natural resources does the prosperity of the
nation depend. Communities and nations have remained poor
in the midst of rich surroundings, or fallen into decay and poverty in spite of the fertility of their soil and the abundance of
their natural resources, merely because the human factor was of
poor quality or was allowed to deteriorate or run to waste. Other
communities have grown rich and prosperous in spite of their
sterile soils and poor surroundings by reason of the fact that
their people were painstaking and intelligent, and were *all* at
work at some useful occupation. The labor power of a community is the human factor in production and includes mental
as well as bodily strength and efficiency. The genius of the inventor, the executive talent of the manager, and the learning
of the teacher are included, as well as the skill of the mechanic,
the resourcefulness and reliability of the good farm hand, or the
muscular strength of the day laborer. It is even more important, therefore, that a community should economize and conserve
its labor power than that it should economize and conserve its
land. To waste any of this labor power is a greater crime than
to waste land or mineral or forest resources, and will bring
national calamity even more certainly and swiftly, though of
course it is highly desirable that both the labor and the physical resources of a nation be conserved and developed to the
highest degree.

Economizing labor means a large product per man. In discussing the economy of labor the important distinction must be carefully borne in mind that the aim of rational industrial management and statesmanship is, or always should be, to secure as large a product per man as possible, and not necessarily as large a product per acre as possible. In fact a large product per acre is desirable *only* when it means a large product per man, and never otherwise. Again, the policy of agricultural statesmanship is, or always should be, to preserve those conditions which will secure a large product *for* each worker rather than merely to secure a large product *from* each acre of land. A large supply of very cheap labor is sometimes a means of getting a large product per acre, and this is just what certain misguided persons, ignorant of the first principles of economics, are constantly clamoring for. But a large supply of cheap labor means a large number of families supported on very low wages; and that means, in turn, widespread poverty, which is precisely what the study of political economy aims to prevent. Since our purpose is to find how to eliminate poverty and to secure a wide diffusion of prosperity, it is essential that we find how to make the product per man as large as possible. It follows, therefore, that while we may consistently desire a large supply of very cheap land, a large supply of cheap labor is the last thing in the world which we ought to strive for, or rather, it is the very thing which we ought to strive to prevent.

However, it is one thing to desire a large product per acre regardless of the number of people among whom it is to be distributed, and it is quite a different thing to desire that the existing population may be able to produce as large a product per acre as possible. If the existing or prospective farming population can increase the productivity of their land, their incomes will increase. It is better to have one family on every 160 acres, even though each acre is thus made to produce only $20 worth of produce, than to have one family on every 80 acres, even though the product per acre could thus be raised to $30. But, of course, if we actually have one family on every 80 acres, it is obviously much better that each acre should produce $30 than $20 worth. This is the point of view from which to approach the problem of increasing the product of the land. Such a result is to be secured not by a mere increase in the farming population, but by a more economical, a more intelligent, a more efficient application of the labor power already possessed by the country. In general terms, this is what is meant by economizing labor. Seeing that our population is likely to increase rapidly for a good many years to come, and that our supply of land is limited, it is obvious that the present average rate of production per head cannot be increased or even maintained at the present level, except by increasing the average productivity of the land. It therefore behooves us to study more effective ways of applying our labor to our land in order that the returns to labor may not be diminished but increased.

Why intensive cultivation is not always economical of labor. There are two great obstacles to be overcome in the accomplishment of this task. One is the tendency of the soil to decline in fertility as larger and larger supplies of food, etc. are extracted from it. To counteract this tendency requires the exercise of the greatest intelligence in cultivation, in rotation of crops, and in the application of manure and artificial fertilizers. The other great obstacle is the law of diminishing returns, sometimes called the great law of agricultural production. This law may be stated briefly as follows : In a given state of civilization, and a given state of knowledge of the art of husbandry, an increase in the labor and capital applied to the cultivation of a given piece of land will increase the product of the land, but not in the same proportion as the labor and capital are increased. That is to say, assuming a reasonably good state of cultivation to begin with, and assuming that the farmer has not learned new and better methods of applying his labor, or acquired superior seed or tools or other accessories, if he doubles the amount of labor applied to the cultivation of the same land he will not double the crop, though he will probably increase it somewhat. Another way of stating the same thing would be to say, under the same assumptions as before, that if he abandons half his land and puts upon the remaining half all the labor which he has formerly put upon the whole, he will not get so large a crop, though he may get more than half as large a crop ; that is, he will get a larger crop per acre though not twice as large a crop per acre. That such a law is universally recognized may be shown by the following considerations.

Why the farmer cultivates his second-best land.[1] Ask any farmer you may happen to meet about the quality of his land, and unless his is an exceptional farm, he will tell you that it is not all alike, — that one field is more productive than the rest and will yield a larger and more valuable crop in proportion to the labor and capital expended in its cultivation. But if you were to advise him for that reason to put all his labor and capital on the superior field, letting the rest of his farm go to waste, he would certainly not take your advice and he would think very poorly of your intelligence besides. Yet if one knew absolutely nothing about farming, and were possessed of the temerity which sometimes accompanies such ignorance, one might argue the matter with the farmer, reasoning somewhat as follows : If a certain amount of labor and capital on the more productive field will produce a more valuable crop than the same amount will produce if expended on a less productive field, it is a mistake to waste any labor and capital on the poorer land. If, for example, one hundred days' labor (with the appropriate tools) on the best field will produce a crop worth $500, while the same amount of labor on any other part of the farm will produce a crop worth

[1] Cf. the author's Distribution of Wealth (New York, 1905), chap. ii.

only $400, the farmer has only $900 for his two hundred days' labor. But if one hundred days' labor on the best field will produce a crop worth $500, two hundred days' labor on the same field ought to produce twice as big a crop, — worth $1000. Therefore the farmer loses $100 by putting half his labor on his inferior land.

If it were true that the second hundred days' labor on the best field would produce as much as the first hundred, or, to put it more accurately, if two hundred days' labor on that field would produce twice as much as one hundred, and three hundred days' labor three times as much, and so on indefinitely, the argument would be unanswerable and the farmer would be very foolish not to follow your advice. Moreover, the community at large would be acting very unwisely in not concentrating all its energies upon a relatively small area of its best land. But the farmer knows perfectly well, and so does the community at large, that such is not the case, — that the produce of a given piece of land cannot be doubled, trebled, quadrupled, and so on indefinitely, by merely doubling, trebling, and quadrupling the amount of labor and capital expended in its cultivation. In the case already assumed it is more probable that although one hundred days' labor would produce a crop worth $500, two hundred days on the same field would produce a crop worth only $800. In that case it would pay better by $100, under the conditions assumed, to put the second hundred days' labor on some other part of the farm. It is because the farmer, who is in the best position to judge, knows that such conditions are real that he does not concentrate all his energies on the small fraction of his farm which includes only his best land.

Why more land is better than less land. To say that the farmer knows better than to concentrate all his energies on his best land is the same as saying that he knows and acts upon one of the fundamental laws of economics, namely, the law of diminishing returns. This law of diminishing returns is simply a part of the general observation that the product of any given piece of land does not, even under the same conditions of soil and season, bear a constant ratio to the amount of labor and capital used in producing it. That is to say, the product does not vary in the same proportion as the labor and capital, increasing in proportion as they increase and decreasing in proportion as they decrease, but rather that the product increases and decreases less rapidly than these factors of production when the quantity of the factor, land, remains constant. This simply means that there are several factors in the production of any crop, including labor, capital, and land ; and that the amount of the crop is not determined by any one or any two of these factors, but by all of them combined. Labor and capital, being only a part of the factors, cannot alone determine the crop.

It is well known to practical men that a niggardly application of labor and capital to a piece of land in the cultivation of any crop is little better than wasted, because it will produce so little in proportion to itself ; whereas a more generous application will yield a crop not only larger, but larger in proportion to the amount of labor and capital employed. Up to this point the land is said to yield increasing returns to the labor and capital employed in its cultivation. But if the amount of these factors used in cultivating a given piece of land is still further increased, a point will eventually be reached where the product will no longer increase as fast as these factors are increased. Beyond this point the land is said to yield diminishing returns to the labor and capital employed. Though larger applications of labor and capital may continue to produce larger crops per acre, the crops will not be so large per unit of labor and capital.

In growing such a specific crop as corn, for example, a single day's labor of a man and team with the appropriate tools, if spread over a whole ten-acre field, would be thrown away because it would produce no crop at all. Five days on the same field might produce something of a crop, but it would be a poor one. Ten days would certainly produce more than twice as large a crop as five, and twenty days' labor might possibly produce more than twice as much as ten. But forty days' labor would hardly produce twice as much as twenty, eighty would certainly not produce four times as much, and two hundred days' labor would fall far short of producing ten times as much. If these assumptions are true of the particular field in question, it could be said to yield increasing returns up to the point where twenty days' labor were expended. Beyond that point it would be said to yield diminishing returns.

This may be further illustrated by means of Table A, which purports to show, in an assumed case, how much corn could be produced on a ten-acre field by using different amounts of labor and capital, the amounts being expressed in terms of days' labor of a man and team with the appropriate tools. The ratio between the product on the one hand and the labor and capital on the other is shown in the last column, which gives the amount of product, or the number of bushels produced, per day's labor.

TABLE A

Days' labor of man and team with tools	Total crop in bushels	Bushels per day's labor	
1	0	0	
5	50	10	
10	150	15	Increasing returns
15	270	18	
20	380	19	
25	450	18	
30	510	17	
35	560	16	Diminishing returns
40	600	15	
45	630	14	
50	650	13	

According to this table, as will be seen, increasing returns stop and diminishing returns begin at the point where twenty days' labor are expended in the cultivation of the field.

TABLE B

Days' labor of man and team with tools	Total crop in bushels	Bushels per day's labor	
1	0	0	
5	40	8	Increasing
10	130	13	returns
15	240	16	
20	300	15	
25	350	14	
30	390	13	Diminishing
35	420	12	returns
40	440	11	
45	450	10	
50	455	9.1	

In any real case it would be impossible to tell, without putting it to the test, at just what point diminishing returns begin, though a capable farmer can tell, on the basis of his experience, closely enough for practical purposes. Whenever you find a competent farmer deliberately devoting a part of his labor and capital to the growing of any crop on more than one grade of land, you may be sure that he thinks it pays better to do so than to concentrate all his energies on his best land. But this could not possibly be true unless he had such an amount of these factors as would, if applied exclusively to his best land, carry its cultivation beyond the point of diminishing returns. If we may assume, for example, that Table A represents the amount of corn produced by varying amounts of labor and capital when applied to the farmer's best ten-acre field, and Table B the same for his second-best ten-acre field, we shall find by comparing the two tables that if he had only twenty days' labor to use, he would get more bushels by concentrating them all on the best field than by dividing them between the two fields.[1]

Increasing the population which has to be fed, clothed, housed, and otherwise provided for in a given territory makes it necessary, of course, to extract increasing crops from the soil unless the people resort to manufactures and commerce and draw their supplies of agricultural produce from outside areas. The effort to get larger and larger quantities from the same soil tends, as already stated, to exhaust its fertility. At the same time, to extract this increasing quantity from the land, even where the soil retains its fertility unimpaired, requires, under the law of diminishing returns, more than proportionally increasing expenditures of labor in cultivation, unless new and superior methods of cultivation are discovered and applied.

Experimental proofs. In addition to the general experience of farmers, as indicated above, we have upon this subject the specific testimony of Sir John Lawes, probably the greatest agriculturist of modern times. Before a parliamentary commission in 1897 he stated that the result of all his experiments tended to show that as you increase your crops by more intensive cultivation, "each bushel after a certain amount costs you more and more. . . The last bushel always costs you more than all the others." [2] Consequently, when prices were low, he further stated that it was necessary to reduce rather than increase the intensity of cultivation. From this it would necessarily follow that as population increases and greater and greater demands are made upon the soil, prices must inevitably rise to cover the increased cost of the additional products demanded. This is specific testimony, and is backed by the experiments carried on over a long period of years. It is backed also by the general

[1] Cf. the author's Distribution of Wealth (New York, 1905), chap. ii. The Macmillan Company.

[2] Parliamentary Reports, Commissioners (1897), XV, 106.

experience and the common sense of farmers everywhere, and it ought to go a long way toward disabusing the public mind of the absurd notions taught by certain long-distance farmers, who are telling us nowadays that more intensive cultivation, smaller farms, etc. are the solution of all our agricultural problems.

Some very clear and tangible illustrations of the operation of this law of diminishing returns are furnished also by certain experiments in wheat growing at Rothamstead, where the invaluable work of Sir John Lawes was carried on. Five plots of land of approximately equal fertility were treated alike, except that different quantities of nitrogen were applied, increasing the dose of this particular ingredient by 43 pounds, as follows : [1]

	Average yield in bushels for 8 years	Gain for 43 lb. nitrogen
Plot 5. Mixed minerals alone	19	
Plot 6. Mixed minerals and 43 lb. nitrogen . .	$27\frac{7}{8}$	$8\frac{7}{8}$
Plot 7. Mixed minerals and 86 lb. nitrogen . .	$35\frac{1}{2}$	$7\frac{5}{8}$
Plot 8. Mixed minerals and 129 lb. nitrogen .	$36\frac{7}{8}$	$1\frac{3}{8}$
Plot 16. Mixed minerals and 172 lb. nitrogen .	$37\frac{1}{2}$	$\frac{5}{8}$

According to this table diminishing returns are secured after the first dose of 43 pounds of nitrogen is applied, as shown in the last column. That is to say, the second increment of 43 pounds (Plot 7) adds a little less to the product than the first dose (Plot 6) added to that which preceded, and the third dose (Plot 8) still less, etc. The gain in Plot 16 over that in Plot 8 was so slight as to be obviously unprofitable, the $\frac{5}{8}$ of a bushel increase not being sufficient to pay for the 43 pounds increase in nitrogen. Therefore this plot was discontinued, but the other four were continued for forty-eight years, with average results as follows :

[1] These figures are taken from a most excellent article by Eugene Davenport, dean of the College of Agriculture in the University of Illinois, in Bailey's Cyclopedia of American Agriculture. The Macmillan Company.

	Yield in bushels	Gain for 43 lb. nitrogen
Plot 5	15	
Plot 6	24	9
Plot 7	33	9
Plot 8	$36\frac{3}{4}$	$3\frac{3}{4}$

Here the number of plots is rather small, though the results are valuable because they are the average for a long period of time. They show constant returns from the first two doses (Plots 6 and 7), but sharply diminishing returns from the third dose (Plot 8). Allowing that 43 pounds of nitrogen cost $6.50 and that wheat sells for $1 a bushel, the profits are as follows:

	Yield	Gain	Value of gain	Cost of gain	Profit
Plot 5	15				
Plot 6	24	9	$9.00	$6.50	$2.50
Plot 7	33	9	9.00	6.50	2.50
Plot 8	$36\frac{3}{4}$	$3\frac{3}{4}$	3.75	6.50	− 2.75

However, if the price of wheat were higher or the cost of nitrogen lower, the loss from the third dose of nitrogen (Plot 8) might be turned into a profit.

Waste labor. Though the student can easily see how very important it is that we should economize the labor power of the community, yet the principle is not universally understood. That waste labor power is the form of waste which is least understood and appreciated is shown by the fact that a great many people, perhaps a majority, not only do not deprecate it, but actually think it a good thing. A leisure class to consume the products of the workers is thought by many to be an economic necessity. However, nothing is more certain than that waste of any kind, particularly the waste of a factor of production, increases the burden upon those who work, and tends, in general, toward the impoverishment rather than toward the enrichment of the country as a whole.

Of waste labor there are four principal kinds, — the unemployed, the improperly employed, the imperfectly employed, and the voluntarily idle. In the elimination of these four forms of waste lie greater opportunities for the constructive economist than in any other direction.

The unemployed. Of these four the least important is the unemployed, and yet it is almost the only form which has received any attention. It is the least important because, first, it is normally and on the average the least efficient labor which remains unemployed; second, because the utilization of the labor power which is now going to waste at the upper end of the social scale will go a long way toward solving the problem of unemployment at the lower end of the scale.

The improperly employed. By improperly employed labor is meant that which is engaged in acquiring rather than producing wealth; that is, labor power which is used up in what are called uneconomic as opposed to economic ways of getting a living (see Chapter I). Enterprises whose sole purpose is to cause two dollars to emerge from the pockets of other men where one had emerged before, absorb a considerable fund of energy which ought to be concerned with making two blades of grass and similar things to grow where one had grown before. A really productive enterprise, carried on by purely productive methods, increases the wealth in the hands of other people in proportion as it is successful; and in proportion as a man grows rich in such an enterprise by such methods, he makes the country richer instead of poorer. The lawgiver who can turn our labor power, mental and physical, into such channels, will make the country so productive that nothing short of a foreign invasion or a geological cataclysm could prevent us from becoming rich, even if our material resources were all as meager as those of New England.

The imperfectly employed. By imperfectly employed labor is meant that which is employed productively, but less productively than it might be. Wherever there is a man doing unskilled work who might, had he received the proper training, be doing skilled work, or doing skilled manual work who might be doing the more highly skilled and more needed work of managing and directing, there is a case of imperfectly employed labor. It is as great a waste of productive energy as it would be to have good garden land used for pasturing Longhorn steers. Here again is a statesman's opportunity for enriching his nation by providing the means for economizing to the greatest degree the labor power of the people. Much of it is now going to waste in the sense that it has to be utilized in ways which are of little value merely because of its oversupply, while other kinds of work are suffering because of the scarcity of competent men. As a chain is only as strong as its weakest link, so an industry can expand only as far as its scarcest factor will permit. The scarcest factor is managing ability, and any policy, educational or moral, which will increase the supply of managing ability will enable industry to expand and to absorb greater numbers of the unemployed. Incidentally this would do more than anything else to equalize the distribution of wealth.

The voluntarily idle. The voluntarily idle are of two classes,— those who have retired on a well-earned competence, and those who live on wealth which they themselves have not earned. The first class does not trouble us much in America, though we are in some danger of being influenced by European critics, who, through an aberration of the mind, have persuaded themselves that this form of conspicuous waste is a mark of gentility or even of " culture." Until recently we have not been very much troubled with the second class, but our own prosperity is creating it and we need to look to the future. Those who live on inherited wealth and on wealth accruing from a rise in land values make up the greater part of this class. Here is another situation which challenges the constructive statesman. The loss of this kind of labor power is especially regrettable, because it is usually labor power of the very highest type which goes to waste in this form. The man who inherits a fortune from his father must, on the average, have had a father of unusual business capacity. Under the law of heredity the chances are in favor, rather than otherwise, of the son's having inherited some of that capacity. But there is a strong probability that this natural capacity will have been spoiled by the fact that he inherited a fortune and is therefore relieved of the necessity of working. This latent business capacity, if developed, would add to the productive resources of our country at the very point where they are scarcest and therefore most needed. It is the kind of power which, if set to work, would increase the supply of the scarcest factor in industrial development, would strengthen industry where it is now weakest, and would contribute most to our national prosperity.

Dissipated energy. The greatest source of waste labor power is vice and immorality. In a broad and comprehensive sense all vice and immorality are ways of dissipating human energy, and every form of dissipation of human energy is vice or immorality. Idleness, drunkenness, rowdyism, brawling, neighborhood quarreling, dishonesty, are extreme and well-recognized sources of waste energy. Less extreme but equally clear cases are general listlessness, irresponsibility, and lack of interest in one's work. Where labor is performed in this spirit it will not only be inefficient, but will require more supervision than would otherwise be necessary. The necessity of this extreme supervision causes a waste of labor power which might otherwise be employed directly in production, instead of indirectly in seeing that others do their work properly. Every characteristic of a people which reduces its productive power either by making its labor inefficient

or turning or causing it to be turned from the work of production or service into the work of supervision, regulation, or
compulsion, is a source of waste energy, and is therefore to be
called vice or immorality. Morality, from this point of view
and as thus understood, is the greatest economizer of labor. It
is no accident, therefore, that those countries with the highest
standards of rational morality are also the most prosperous and
powerful. It is because their system of practical morality enables
them to economize their productive energy more effectively than
other nations are able to do with their inferior systems.

While we are devising ways and means, therefore, for con-
serving our material resources, let us not overlook the enormous
waste of human energy which is now going on, lest we be guilty
of saving at the spigot and wasting at the bunghole. These considerations, however, apply to the economizing of labor power
in general, and not specifically to the economizing of labor in
agriculture. That will form the topic of the next section.

Shall we economize labor or land? It cannot be emphasized
too much that the object of economizing labor, as stated in
preceding pages, is to secure the maximum product per unit of
labor and not to secure the maximum product per unit of land.
For securing the maximum economy of labor, as thus defined, the chief requisites are: (1) an adequate supply of land;
(2) an adequate equipment in power, tools, and machinery;
(3) adequate technical knowledge of the science and art of agriculture; and (4) superior business management. The reasons
for an adequate supply of land are chiefly summed up in the
law of diminishing returns, as outlined above. This brings
us face to face with one of the greatest of all economic
problems, because the maximum economy of labor is secured
by means of a use of land so extensive as to seem almost
wasteful, whereas the maximum economy of land is secured
by an application of labor so lavish as to be wasteful of that

factor. This is a dilemma from which there is no possible escape. It furnishes a perennial problem in agricultural management and calls for perpetual recalculation and readjustment. To put so much labor into the cultivation of a given piece of land as to secure the maximum product per acre will give a relatively small product per unit of labor, whereas to use so much land in connection with each unit of labor as to give the maximum product per unit will yield a relatively small product per acre.

How the alternative presents itself. Let us assume that one man could, by putting all his labor (with the appropriate tools) into the cultivation of 10 acres of corn, secure a product of 1000 bushels, or 100 bushels per acre; whereas by putting the same amount of labor into the cultivation of 20 acres he could secure a product of 1500 bushels, or 75 bushels per acre; by spreading his labor over 30 acres he could get a product of only 1800 bushels, or 60 bushels per acre; by cultivating 40 acres he could get 2000 bushels, or 50 bushels per acre; and from 50 acres he could get no more than from 40 acres, namely 2000 bushels, or 40 bushels per acre. Under these assumptions the result of the different experiments could be represented in the diagram on page 190.

Thus it is obvious that the farmer gets the largest total product for his year's work, namely 2000 bushels, from the use of either 40 or 50 acres. But since he is able to produce no more on 50 than on 40 acres, it is evident that this is a wasteful use of land. The last 10 acres are entirely wasted and might as well have been allowed to lie idle. Again, the use of 40 acres gives him a slightly larger crop for his year's work than 30 acres, that is, 2000 bushels as against 1800. Yet this is, from one point of view, a somewhat wasteful use of land, since the use of the last 10 acres results in only 200 bushels. Furthermore, while 30 acres gives him 300 bushels more than he could get from 20 acres, yet this is not a very economical use of land, since in this case his last 10 acres give him only 300 bushels over and above what he could produce without them. Again, while 20 acres give him a larger crop than 10 acres (1500 bushels as against 1000), yet even this is not the most economical use of land, since his second 10 acres add only 500 bushels to the total crop, whereas the first 10 acres when

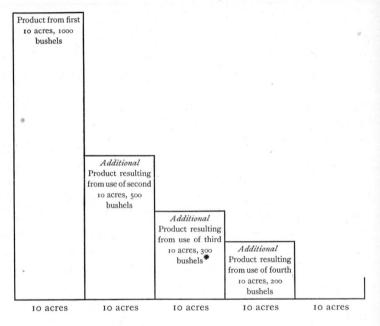

Product from first 10 acres, 1000 bushels

Additional Product resulting from use of second 10 acres, 500 bushels

Additional Product resulting from use of third 10 acres, 300 bushels

Additional Product resulting from use of fourth 10 acres, 200 bushels

10 acres   10 acres   10 acres   10 acres   10 acres

cultivated alone yielded 1000 bushels. So far as this illustration carries us, it is obviously a more economical use of land to have one man to every 10 acres. That this would be a somewhat wasteful use of labor will appear from the following consideration:

If one man cultivating 20 acres gets a product, according to the illustration, of 1500 bushels, and two men cultivating the same 20 acres, or 10 acres each, get a total product of 2000 bushels, it is obvious that the second man has added only 500 bushels to the product obtained by the first man. That is all that is added to the corn crop of that area by having two men instead of one. This is a relatively wasteful application of labor, at least as compared with the results of having 40 acres to each man, under which he gets, in the illustration, 2000 bushels.

To carry the analysis further, let us assume a community where all the land is equally fertile, and where all the farmers are equally skillful and industrious, and all supplied with equally good tools, and where, moreover, the conditions of the forego-ing illustration prevail with respect to the productivity of labor applied to land. Let us assume further that there is at first one man to every 40 acres. Each man would then be able to pro-duce 2000 bushels of corn. Later the number of men increases until there is one man to every 30 acres. Each man would then be able to produce, *on the average*, only 1800 bushels. But—and this is very significant—these additional men would be able to *add* only 1200 bushels apiece to what the smaller number could produce without them. One man to every 30 acres is equal to one and one-third men to every 40 acres, or one man putting in full time and another a third of his time. One man on 30 acres could, under the illustration, produce 1800 bushels of corn. At that rate one and one-third men on 40 acres could produce one and a third times as much as one man on 30 acres, or 2400 bushels. Since one man on 40 acres could produce 2000 bushels, and one and one-third men on the same land could produce 2400 bushels, the difference, 400 bushels, must be attributed to the third of a man, or one third of a man's labor. If one third of a man's time produces 400 bushels, his whole time would produce 1200 bushels. This quantity per man, therefore, is all that can be attributed to the additional force of men. That is all they add to the product over and above what was produced before they came.

If, now, there should be still further immigration, or increase of numbers from any source, so that there would be one man for every 20 acres, the following results would occur, under the terms of the illustration : One man on 20 acres produces 1500 bushels ; on 40 acres, therefore, two men would produce 3000 bushels, or 600 bushels more than $1\frac{1}{3}$ men. This 600 bushels, therefore, is to be attributed to the increase of two thirds of a man, or two thirds of a man's time. If two thirds of a man's time adds 600 bushels to the product of 40 acres over and above what was produced without it, the whole of a man's time would add 900 bushels. That quantity, therefore, is the amount to be attributed to each of the new installment of men who have come to that community. That is all that they add to the quantity which was produced before they came, or which could be produced without their aid.

If, finally, there should be a still further increase in the number of men so that there would be one man to every 10 acres, the following results would happen, under the terms of the illustration : Since one man on 10 acres produces 1000 bushels, two such men, each cultivating 10 acres, would produce a total of 2000 bushels. But one man to every 20 acres produces 1500. Two men on the same area produce only 500 bushels more than one man. Therefore 500 bushels per man is all that can be attributed to each of this new supply of men. That is all they add to the crop which was produced before they came, or to the crop which would have been produced without their aid. If this is not a waste of labor, it is certainly something very much like it. However, if there is actually that much labor power in the community, it must of course be employed, and there is nothing to be done except to make the most of the situation, but it necessarily means a low productivity per man. The diagram on the following page shows graphically the results of this analysis :

This illustration will serve, however, to show the folly of striving for a large product per acre, regardless of the product per man, as is so often advocated by shortsighted writers on agricultural topics. But the principal purpose is to show how important it is that each unit of labor be supplied with an adequate amount of land if we are to continue to secure a large product per man in agriculture, and how difficult it will be to do this if

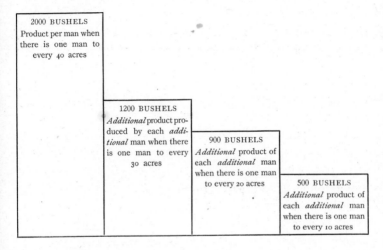

2000 BUSHELS
Product per man when there is one man to every 40 acres

1200 BUSHELS
Additional product produced by each *additional* man when there is one man to every 30 acres

900 BUSHELS
Additional product of each *additional* man when there is one man to every 20 acres

500 BUSHELS
Additional product of each *additional* man when there is one man to every 10 acres

our agricultural population should continue to increase without a proportional increase in the area of cultivated land.

This will also serve to point out the error of trying to base too many conclusions upon the comparative yield of crops *per acre* in different countries, without trying to find out the comparative yield per man. As frequently happens, the actual workers are, in this case, much wiser than some of the sophisticated writers about the work. The farmers of the Middle West are spreading out, — enlarging their farms, — and the surplus numbers are moving to places where an adequate supply of land is to be had, and they know what they are doing.

It is impossible to arrive at any satisfactory figures as to the average yield per man on the wheat farms of different countries; but there are numerous cases in the western part of the United States, of men who have averaged upwards of 2000 bushels of wheat per year over a period of years. Nothing like this result can be shown in any country which follows the methods of intensive cultivation. According to Dr. L. G. Powers, expert in charge of the agricultural statistics of the twelfth and thirteenth censuses, 9,000,000 agricultural workers in the United States produce almost half as much grain as 66,000,000 in Europe. They who look upon the yield per acre as the test of good agriculture are accustomed to compare us unfavorably with those countries. But we need not feel humiliated in the least when we understand that the product per man is the real test.

Again, it has been shown by the census figures that the average yield of corn per acre is greater in Massachusetts than in either Illinois or Iowa; but this does not signify that Massachusetts is a better corn state, or that corn growing is carried on more economically in Massachusetts than in those two great corn-producing states.

Adequate capital necessary. Since tools and machinery are almost universally regarded as labor-saving devices, it is scarcely necessary to say that an adequate supply of such devices is necessary to secure the maximum economy of labor. However, the term " labor-saving device " is not in every respect a suitable one. The term " product-increasing device " would sometimes be better. However, if it is clearly understood that tools save labor in the sense of enabling the worker to do more and better work than he could otherwise do, and to get a larger product with the same labor, there can be no possible objection to calling tools labor-saving devices.

To what an extent farm machinery has increased the effectiveness of labor in the growing of our leading crops is shown

by the following tables, taken from an excellent monograph by
H. W. Quaintance on " The Influence of Farm Machinery upon
Production and Labor." [1]

DAY'S WORK NECESSARY TO PRODUCE BY HAND METHODS

	Crop of	Methods of	Day's work
Barley	1896	1829–1830	14,771,515
Corn	1894	1855	117,487,098
Cotton	1895	1841	80,108,771
Hay	1895	1850	99,257,257
Oats	1893	1830	105,810,334
Potatoes.	1895	1866	14,715,501
Rice	1896	1870	396,687
Rye . . . . :	1895	1847–1848	6,854,942
Wheat	1896	1829–1830	130,621,927
Total	. . .	. . . . .	570,024,032

DAY'S WORK NECESSARY TO PRODUCE BY MACHINE METHODS

	Crop of	Methods of	Day's work	Day's work saved by machinery	Per cent saved
Barley .	1896	1895–1896	630,354	14,141,161	95.7
Corn . .	1894	1894	45,873,027	71,614,071	60.9
Cotton .	1895	1895	28,178,904	51,929,867	64.8
Hay . .	1895	1895	18,556,791	80,700,466	81.3
Oats . .	1893	1893	11,334,266	94,476,068	89.2
Potatoes	1895	1895	5,134,100	9,581,401	65.1
Rice . .	1896	1896	108,889	287,796	72.5
Rye . .	1895	1894–1895	2,739,147	4,115,795	60.0
Wheat .	1896	1895–1896	7,099,560	123,522,367	94.5
Total	. . .	. . . .	119,655,038	450,368,992	79.0

Though the use of adequate tools and equipment is of the
first importance in agriculture, especially in a country where
farm labor is so scarce and wages so high as they are in this
country, yet no writer on this subject can do his whole duty

[1] *Publications of the American Economic Association* (3d series), Vol. V,
No. 4, p. 39.

without throwing out a word of caution. Every careful observer of agricultural conditions and practices in America will have seen cases of overinvestment in expensive tools and machines. While these cases are not so numerous as those of the opposite description, — that is, of a niggardly use of labor-saving implements, — yet the consequences are about equally bad. To buy expensive implements without a very careful consideration of the saving to be effected on the one hand, and of the cost on the other, is unbusinesslike and spells ruin, as many a farmer has found by bitter experience. The undiscriminating buyer almost always underestimates the cost side of the account. The interest on the first investment is very easily calculated, but it is the smallest item in the cost. Repairs are not so easily calculated, and they mount up rapidly, — more rapidly than the inexperienced farmer, or the farmer who is not in the habit of keeping careful accounts, usually anticipates.

It is a notorious fact that farm machinery deteriorates very rapidly, and the cost of deterioration will surprise any farmer who has not kept accounts over a period of years. According to investigations carried on by the Minnesota Experiment Station over a period of five years, the average annual depreciation of farm machinery was 7.3 per cent. The estimates vary with different implements, from 4.89 per cent for farm wagons to 10.03 per cent for corn binders. Therefore the farmer needs to calculate very carefully before buying an expensive machine, to make sure that he has use enough for it to give him a safe margin of profit over any probable cost in the way of interest, maintenance, repairs, and deterioration. He must be able to see pretty definitely just where he is going to get his money back ; that is, where he will save enough in his wages bill, if he is an employer of labor, or where he will increase the product of his farm enough to recompense him for his outlay, with a safe margin of profit to cover possible miscalculations.

However, overcaution in this direction is as bad as too little caution. While too little caution will bring speedy bankruptcy, too much perpetuates backward or unprogressive methods of agriculture and toilsome and monotonous drudgery in the life of the farmer. Having made a careful calculation and having satisfied himself that the probable gain will exceed the probable loss, the farmer must not hesitate to invest, even if he has to borrow heavily in order to do so.

Inefficiency of peasant farming. Americans in particular are too much inclined to criticize the primitive and backward methods of the European peasant farmers. Comparing the large teams and powerful machines in use on some of the large farms in the western part of the United States with the simple hand methods of these peasant farmers, we are likely to make the mistake of thinking that the peasant is himself unintelligent and unprogressive. The truth may be that the individual peasant is eminently wise and practical in adapting his methods to the conditions under which he is forced to work. It is the system which is to blame, and not the individual farmer. The general discussion of the merits and demerits of peasant farming as a system will be deferred to a future chapter.[1] Here we may point out, however, that on a very small farm there will not ordinarily be work enough for these highly efficient but expensive machines. In many cases there is not work enough to make it profitable to keep two horses or even one horse. A horse would eat up more than he could *add* to the produce of so small a farm. In such cases it is often more economical to work a cow. The light work of such a farm will not interfere seriously with her function as a giver of milk, nor add very much to the cost of her feed. Accordingly she becomes what is sometimes called an "all-purpose" animal. On these peasant farms one frequently finds that the plowing, the harrowing, and

[1] See Chapter IV.

the drawing of loads from the field to the barn are all done by a pair of cows; sometimes, where the farms are a little larger, by the bull, or by the bull and one horse; while on the smaller farms it is frequently done by one cow. All the other work of such farms — the planting, cultivating, harvesting, threshing, etc. — is necessarily done by hand.

Again, there is little doubt that these primitive hand processes are frequently more economical for the individual farmer, under the circumstances which surround him, than more efficient machine methods would be. Let us consider, for example, the question whether he shall thresh his wheat with a flail or hire a steam thresher to do it for him. In the first place, he has a very small farm, and his whole wheat crop does not exceed five acres. In the second place, his whole living must be made from the produce of that farm. In the third place, he has no other use for his time. There is no chance for him to work elsewhere for wages when work is slack on his own farm. If he could work elsewhere for wages, it would undoubtedly be more economical for him to hire his threshing done by machinery; but, having no such opportunity, his time is on his hands, and if he does not utilize it in flailing out his wheat, his own labor will simply go to waste. Under these circumstances his threshing may be said to cost him nothing when he does it himself during the long winter, whereas if he hired it done, the cost would deduct an appreciable sum from his cash income from the farm.

However economical it may be for him *under the circumstances* to thresh his own wheat, there is no doubt that where such circumstances exist they are the occasion of a great deal of waste labor. The spectacle of dozens and scores of these small farmers laboriously flailing out their wheat crops is sufficient to prove that. If they could once get the mastery of their circumstances, and create conditions which would enable them to utilize their whole time in productive work instead of having it hanging on their hands during a portion of the year, they could thresh their wheat crops with vastly less labor and more profit to themselves. One possibility would be for the more capable farmer to buy out a few of his neighbors, unite their small farms into one of reasonable size, and then hire the former owners to work for him as farm hands. The customs and traditions of some countries, and even the difficulties in the way of land transfer, tend to prevent this; otherwise this result would eventually come about. In some countries, for example, the cost involved in making a transfer of land is equal to half the price of the farm. Under such conditions there is a serious hindrance to the buying and selling of land.

Coöperation among a number of small farmers, by means of which they can work together in the operation of a machine thresher, would accomplish something, though unless they could employ the time profitably which they were thus enabled to save, it would be doubtful economy, because the initial expense of such a machine is considerable. The only real solution of the problem, therefore, is for them to find productive work to do during the time which they save by the use of the machine. That is the only thing which will enable them to pay the cost of the machine. The same or similar considerations will apply also to the economy of using other machines, as compared with the hand processes, on these small peasant farms. Observation and study among these peasant farmers have convinced the writer that while the agricultural system which forces such methods upon them is undoubtedly a bad one, yet the individual farmer is usually eminently wise in adjusting himself to the system as he finds it. The consideration of the comparative merits of different systems of farming will be deferred to a later chapter.

Scientific knowledge. Closely associated with the use of efficient tools and implements is the possession by the farmer himself of thorough scientific knowledge of agriculture. To be a thoroughly equipped, scientific farmer probably requires a higher education, certainly a more complete scientific education, than any of the learned professions, with the possible exception of medicine. Such a farmer must obviously know something of botany, zoölogy, chemistry, physics, and surveying; and some special and difficult branches of these sciences he must know extremely well. Principles of plant and animal breeding ought to be thoroughly understood if that were possible, but it is not possible now because there is no one, either within or without the agricultural class, who thoroughly understands them. He must know something of such difficult subjects as soil chemistry, soil physics, the bacteriology of the soil, food values and the balancing of rations, and a number of other subjects, each one of which is engaging the attention of scientific specialists, though of course no single human being, farmer or otherwise, can really become a master in all these subjects.

There is an old saying, current among farmers, that what one does not have in one's head one must have in one's heels. This sums up very tersely the importance of management as a means of economizing labor. There is no doubt whatever that more labor is wasted on the farms of this country through bad management than through any other single course. This, however, will be the theme of a special chapter on management.

A progressive attitude. Perhaps the greatest obstacle to the effective economy of labor is found in the character of the farmers or the farm laborers themselves. More striking illustrations of this can be found in older countries, or in countries which are ruled by hidebound custom, than we are likely to find in this country. The sheer unwillingness of farm laborers in oriental countries, and in some of the Latin-American countries, to change their methods of work is sometimes a factor to be reckoned with, like the character of the soil or the climate, and about as difficult to change. Dean Davenport mentions that a valuable cart was allowed to rot on a certain South American estate for the reason that the native laborers refused to use it because it did not squeak like their old wooden carts.[1]

But while we can doubtless find more amusing instances of this kind of conservatism by looking beyond our own borders, we need not look so far as that to find illustrations of the same kind. Every farm manager has had his patience tried to the limit by the stupidity or pig-headedness of hired men who thought that certain things had to be done in certain ways, and neither persuasion nor authority could induce them to do otherwise. Even self-employed farmers are still found who plant their crops only when the moon is right, who employ a water witch to locate a well for them, etc. More particularly are they slow to adopt newer, quicker, and less laborious methods of performing old tasks. You may demonstrate to some farm hands over and over again that by a certain method of husking an ear of corn, or hitching up a team, or doing any of the common but important tasks of the farm, the number of motions can be reduced and the time of the operation cut in half, and yet they will refuse even to try the new method. Their attitude is not unlike that of a certain man who saw a camel for the first time. After gazing at the animal for a long time he turned away with an air of positive conviction and said, "There ain't no such beast." A progressive attitude of mind, a willingness to change, to learn a new method when it is once demonstrated to be better than the old one, is one of the first requisites to an efficient and economical employment of the labor power of a community. The mere process of changing, or of learning a new method, is so painful to certain temperaments that they will prefer common drudgery and poverty to lighter work and a better income if the latter are to be won at the expense of so much initial pain.

[1] See Bailey, Cyclopedia of American Agriculture, Vol. IV, p. 93.

Some students of social problems have concluded that this character of progressiveness on the part of the people at large is of even more value than technical scientific knowledge. Technical scientific knowledge can easily be borrowed from another nation if our people have but the disposition to use it ; but the disposition itself cannot be borrowed : it must be bred into the blood and bone of the people, as it is the result of generations of training. The Japanese, for example, have been able to borrow from the occidentals all that they knew about the art of warfare, together with armaments and equipments. What they did not borrow, and from the nature of the case could not borrow, was that splendid courage, discipline, and enthusiasm which enabled them to use these technical advantages with such effect. It is not too much to say that if our educational system succeeds in developing a progressive attitude of mind, a genuine desire to be always improving, our people will manage in some way to get the necessary technical knowledge of agriculture. If, in addition to the development of the progressive attitude, the schools can also supply the farmer with technical knowledge, they will have done doubly well.

V. Capital as a Factor in Agricultural Production

In preceding chapters we have seen that capital is a means of utilizing land more perfectly, or of economizing it, and also of economizing in the use of labor. We have now to examine the nature of capital, and to inquire into the conditions under which it comes into existence and the part it plays in agricultural production.

What are economic goods ? All useful things may be divided into two great classes, called economic goods, and noneconomic or free goods. The former are scarce ; that is, they do not exist in usable form in sufficient abundance to satisfy all our wants, and therefore they have to be economized. The latter are so

The Classification of Goods from the Economist's Point of View

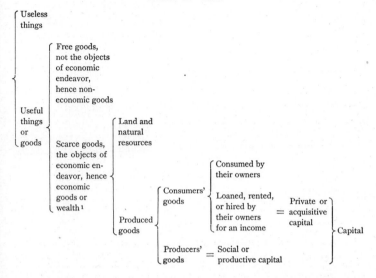

[1] Though, in an absolute sense, well-being depends upon free goods quite as much as upon scarce goods, yet in a relative and practical sense it does not. Where air, water, sunlight, etc., are abundant and free, our well-being is not improved by getting more of these things, and we cannot count ourselves as possessing more wealth when we increase our possession of them. But when they are scarce, our economic efforts are directed toward getting more of them, or substitutes for them. By such efforts our well-being is improved. Such things are therefore properly called wealth, because our well-being depends upon them in this relative, immediate, and practical sense. Here, as frequently happens elsewhere, the general common sense of mankind, which sanctions this use of the word "wealth," shows more wisdom than the hasty judgment of the partially trained thinker who rejects this usage and insists that wealth should include free goods as well.

abundant that everybody can have all he wants, and there is therefore no occasion for economizing with respect to them. It will readily occur to any one that the same thing may be an economic good in one time or place and a noneconomic good in another, depending upon its relative scarcity or abundance. Economic goods, or goods which are scarce, are the objects of all economic activity, — of economizing, saving, storing, and exchanging. They are the things we labor to produce ; they are the objects for which the whole economic system has been developed ; they alone have value or power in exchange, for the simple reason that no one exchanges for a thing unless it is scarce, that is, unless he has less of it than he wants. All other goods the economist ignores, as we all do so far as our efforts to get a living are concerned.

Producers' and consumers' goods. Some of these economic goods yield their utilities directly to their users or consumers, whereas others yield their utilities or satisfy wants only indirectly, through the medium of other goods. A loaf of bread is an illustration of the former, which are called consumers' goods ; and a plow of the latter, which are called producers' goods. In other words, consumers' goods are goods used for direct consumption or the direct satisfaction of wants ; whereas producers' goods are used for the production of other goods, or for the indirect satisfaction of wants through the medium of the other goods which they help to produce. Some goods may, however, be producers' goods at one time and consumers' goods at another, or partly one and partly the other at the same time. The farmer's driving team, for example, may be used as a help in his business and also for pleasure driving, or the musician's instrument may be used to make a living and also to please himself.

What is capital. All producers' goods except land are commonly called capital. They are used for the purpose of securing an income in the form of other goods. There are certain things commonly called consumers' goods which are also sometimes called capital. Capital thus includes not only all producers' goods, but also those consumers' goods which are used by their owners (as distinct from their users) to get an income, that is, consumers' goods whose owners loan, rent, or hire them to users. To their owners, at any rate, they are capital or sources of income, for capital is wealth which is used to get an income. An income is understood to mean a quantity of goods and not a flow of immaterial satisfactions such as are furnished by goods which are not capital.

However, a distinction is sometimes made between these two kinds of capital, the one being called productive or social capital, the other acquisitive or private capital. Producers' goods, or productive capital, are called social capital because they increase the productive power of the whole community, and the more of this kind of capital there is, the more will the whole community be able to produce. Consumers' goods which are loaned, rented, or hired by their owners to their users are called private as distinguished from social capital, because they do not add anything to the productive power of the community. They are a means merely of redistributing the wealth already produced; that is, they are a source of income to their individual owners, but not to society as a whole. It is the productive capital only which we need to consider in this chapter, since private or acquisitive capital, as defined above, is not a factor in agricultural production.

That land is different from capital and belongs in a separate class is generally conceded, though they also have much in common. From the standpoint of the accountant or of the private business man, the differences are not great, and land is frequently included under capital. In the accounts of a private business it may be so treated and no confusion will result; but from the standpoint of the economist, who looks at the problem from a social or political angle, land differs from capital in several important particulars. In the first place, land is a natural product, whereas capital — that is, tools, buildings, etc. — is a product of human labor. In the second place, the supply of land is practically fixed, whereas capital can be indefinitely increased or diminished. In the third place, since the supply is practically fixed, but the demand not, there is no conceivable limit to the price or the rent of land. If the population and the demand for land increase sufficiently, fabulous prices may be and are paid for land. But since the supply of any form of capital is not fixed, but can be indefinitely increased, there is a pretty definite limit to the price which any piece of capital can bring. If the demand increases and the price rises, the supply can increase to meet the demand and check a further rise in price.

From the standpoint of the agricultural economist it is particularly important to keep clearly in mind the distinction between land and capital. The agricultural land of the country is a free gift of nature, but the tools and equipment necessary to utilize that land to the best advantage come only by forethought, abstinence, and labor. Capital never comes into existence of itself. It is always the result of human effort. The initial act in the creation of capital is one of choosing to wait, that is, to wait longer than would otherwise be necessary before satisfying one's desire for consumers' goods. This waiting may be done in a multitude of ways. Having earned a dollar, one may either spend it for consumption or use it in a way which will not increase his present consumption but will increase his future income. In the latter case one becomes a capitalist to the extent of a dollar. If one buys a tool, or a pig, or any other object which will increase his future earnings, he has increased the future productive power of the whole community, because he is a part of the community; that is to say, by offering to pay a dollar for a tool he encourages the toolmakers and sets them to work making tools, to the extent of a dollar. If he offers to pay the dollar for a pig, he encourages the stock raisers and sets them to work growing young pigs, to the extent of a dollar. Whether he invests a dollar or a million dollars, the nature of the transaction is the same and the results are proportionally the same.

But one may invest his dollar indirectly, that is, one may deposit it in a bank, in which case one virtually lends it to the bank and the bank in turn lends it to some one who invests it, that is, who buys tools, live stock, or some other productive agent. Every conceivable case where capital originates, or the world's stock of capital increases, will be found to be a case which began in an act of waiting or saving — of deferring consumption to a future time in order that one may possess one's self of a source of future income. Forethought is therefore the basis of all capitalistic production.

Money and capital. In the illustrations just used money figured as the thing immediately saved and invested. Of course there was capital before there was money, and capital may sometimes originate to-day without the use of money. But since we are now living in an age when money is everywhere the medium of exchange, the form in which wages are paid, and the means of making investments, it happens that capital normally or generally takes the form of money first. That is, it is generally the case that the first stage in the process of making use of capital is to possess one's self of money or to get control of it through credit. Afterwards this money is exchanged for tools, live stock, and other equipment. Since this is the form in which one first gets his capital, it is not uncommon to speak of capital as though it consisted of money. But, as we have seen above, all producers' goods are capital. Again, since all one's producers' goods were bought with money, and since they all continue to have a selling price, it has become customary to speak even of these things in terms of money, as so many dollars' worth. This merely means that since all one's tools, implements, live stock, etc., possess value, it is convenient to speak of them all in terms of that one quality. This has led some people into the mistaken notion that capital is some kind of a spiritual or immaterial entity inhabiting the material bodies called tools, machines, etc. As a matter of fact, it is only the value of these things which men are thinking about when they speak or write thus. Ask any farmer or business man *how much* capital he has, and he will answer in terms of dollars. Ask him, however, *in what his capital consists*, and he will not answer in terms of dollars at all, but in terms of plows, horses, cattle, buildings, machinery, etc. His answers will show very clearly that he knows exactly what capital is, even though he sometimes uses words incorrectly. However, there is nothing incorrect in using the idea of value as a means of expressing quantity, — of telling how much wealth one possesses. There is no way of expressing the quantity of a number of unlike things except by reducing them all to a common denominator, as length, bulk, weight, etc. But it would be absurd for a farmer to try to tell you how much capital he has in any of these terms, — to say, for example, that he has so many pounds, or cubic feet, of tools, horses, and cattle. His only method is to give you the sum of their values and to state these values in terms of money.

Relation of abstinence to capital. As indicated above, forethought and abstinence are at the very foundation of the whole capitalistic process of production. Let every one consume his entire income and there will be no new capital — that is, no new tools — produced, and the existing stock will eventually wear out. Such a community would speedily decay. Let every one, on the average, save just enough of his income to replace the worn-out capital, and that will be a stationary community. Let every one, on the average, save more than enough to replace the worn-out capital, and you have a community growing in wealth and productive power. The same thing can be stated more briefly thus : Let consumption equal or exceed production, and you have industrial decay ; let production exceed consumption, and you have industrial progress.

In what sense capital is productive. Persons engaged in nursing special reforms or revolutions have written a great deal to prove that capital is unproductive. Such arguments invariably begin by confusing the meaning of capital. Let it once be clearly understood that capital is tools, and no person with a sound mind could say with a straight face that it is unproductive, for that would mean that tools are not useful. If tools are useful at all, they must be useful *for something*. That *something* is production. They enable us to produce more than we could without their help. That is the sense, and the only sense, in which they were ever said to be productive.

It is argued, however, that though tools are undoubtedly useful, capital in its first and original form is not productive. We have seen in preceding paragraphs that, nowadays at least, capital seems to take the form of money in its first stage, — that the individual who wishes to own or control capital ordinarily gets possession first of a sum of money, either directly or by means of credit. But while this is the usual process, it is by no means the only one, nor is it essential. It is essential, however, that the individual should get possession of more wealth than he consumes ; that is, he must possess himself of a sum of surplus wealth. Whether this surplus be in the form of money or not does not matter. Is this surplus wealth, considered merely as a surplus, productive ? Not unless it is actually used as a means of increasing future production. If it is so used, it is not inaccurate to speak of it as productive, though there need be no quarrel over the meaning of words. It is only necessary to agree that it is a good thing for the community to have this surplus wealth to be used in future production.

How capital is increased. That the future increase in the number, the power, and the effectiveness of the tools of the community requires a present surplus of production over consumption may be shown by the following considerations : (1) In order that the number of tools may be increased, a larger share of the productive energy of the present must be turned toward the making of tools than would otherwise be necessary. This larger productive energy does not come from nowhere ; it is simply subtracted from that which is engaged in producing consumers' goods, thereby reducing that share. The community must be able to live in the present on the consumers' goods produced by a part of its productive energy, the rest being directed toward the making of tools, which do not support life in the immediate present, but in a more or less prolonged future. In the community at large, therefore, a surplus of productive power over the needs of present consumption is absolutely essential to the increasing of the supply of tools. (2) In the present order of society the community as a whole does not usually decree that this share of its productive energy shall be turned aside from the production of consumers' goods and set to work producing tools. In a few cases this is done, such as in the maintenance of lighthouses, roads, canals, and public works of various kinds ; but it is ordinarily done by individual initiative. Some individual considers whether he would better spend all his income for consumers' goods or a part of it for producers' goods. If he does the former, he, to that extent, directs productive energy toward the production of consumers' goods. But where he decides to spend a part of his income for producers' goods, either directly or through savings institutions, he, to that extent, directs productive energy toward the making of producers' goods or tools.

In view of the necessity of having this surplus fund of productive energy before tools can be produced, it cannot be very inaccurate to say that capital, even in this initial form, is a factor of production. It certainly is a means whereby the future productive power of the community is increased, and its absence would be a means whereby this power would be diminished. Even money is an aid in production in the sense that it saves a great deal of time and energy in making the necessary exchanges. Any one will be convinced of this if he will consider the difficulties he would have in supplying himself with the necessaries of life by trading his services or his products for these things if there were no money of any kind in circulation. Money may, from this standpoint, be called a labor-saving tool, and included under capital.

Ways of economizing in the use of money. While it is a mistake to call capital money, it is not incorrect, as we saw in the last section, to call money a form of capital. Whether we agree to call it by that name or not, there can be no disagreement as to the advisability of economizing it or making a little of it go a long way. This, however, does not mean simply that the individual needs to spend his money wisely; it means rather that the whole community ought so to arrange things as to make it possible to carry on the necessary exchanges with the smallest possible amount of money. Whether some form of pure credit currency, unsupported by metallic money of any kind, will ever be possible or not, it is certain that no nation has ever yet been able to get along without at least a certain amount of money made of some material which has a high value for other purposes than money.

In recent times gold and silver have served this purpose. But such money is expensive. It requires that a certain amount of the productive energy of the world shall be used in getting these metals for this purpose. If it were possible to get along, that is, to carry on all our exchanges, with one half the present amount of metallic money, one half the productive energy which is now used in providing these metals could then be turned toward the production of other things which we cannot get along without.

Credit. One way of economizing in the use of metallic money is to substitute credit in some form or other. In a highly organized system of credit one dollar of metallic money is frequently enabled to do as much work as four or five could do in the absence of a credit system. One dollar lying in a bank, for example, may enable checks to be drawn and accounts to be canceled one against another, and thus really do as much work, with the assistance of the credit arrangements and practices, as several dollars could do without their help. Theoretically it would be an ideal system if all this mutual cancellation of accounts and debts could be done without the use of the dollar. This ideal has been compared to that of building all our roads through the air, thus saving much good land. But both ideals are probably incapable of complete realization, though progress can doubtless be made toward both. If we could eliminate friction, even perpetual motion might not be impossible ; but we cannot eliminate friction, so there is an end of the matter. Similarly, if we could eliminate certain tendencies of human nature, such as selfishness and an occasional lack of confidence in others, a pure credit currency might be possible ; but we have never yet been able to eliminate these peculiarities, which may be called social friction, and therefore it is useless for the lawmaker of the present time to attempt to create a pure credit currency.

However, it has proved practicable to organize the credit of a country in such a way as to effect considerable economies in the use of money ; that is, either to enable the business of the country to be carried on with a smaller *per capita* circulation of metallic money, or, as is more usually the case, to enable a much larger volume of business to be carried on without a proportionate increase in the metallic money.

Organization of exchange. Again, money is economized by having the markets of the country well organized, so that buyers and sellers can meet in considerable numbers and at frequent intervals. This enables the money to circulate more rapidly and makes it unnecessary to carry it about over long distances or to keep it idle during long intervals. Money lying idle in people's pockets, or locked up in safes, is obviously not doing any work. The more quickly it circulates, the more work each dollar will do, and the fewer dollars there will have to be to do the necessary work. " The nimble sixpence does the work of the slow shilling."

Thrift. But money is only one small part of the capital of the country. In considering the ways of economizing capital in general, including all kinds and descriptions, it is necessary to consider it in its various stages. As pointed out above, capital comes into existence through the decision of some one not to consume his whole income, but to invest a part of it in tools and equipment, either directly or indirectly. In the absence of such decisions there would never be another iota of capital added to the wealth of the country. The more numerous such decisions become, the more will our supply of capital increase. The first step, therefore, in the economizing of capital is to increase the number of such decisions. This is to transform potential capital into actual capital.

The two great hindrances to such decisions are uncertainty and lack of forethought. The inability to plan for the future, the preference for the ephemeral pleasure of present indulgence to the prospective advantages of future investments, is a characteristic of all undeveloped people. One of the most striking differences between the civilized man and the savage, or between the successful business man and the spendthrift, lies just here. The savage mind is unable to appreciate future advantages, and therefore they seem to him, at the moment of decision, to be trifling, whereas the needs of the present seem large. The encouragement of habits of thrift and forethought, especially in children, is one of the most effective ways of increasing capital.

Security. An almost equally great hindrance to saving and investment is uncertainty. "A bird in the hand is worth two in the bush." Better consume your income now while you have it. If you invest it, you may never see it again. Where the conditions are such as to justify that course of reasoning, there will, of course, be very little accumulation of capital.

This uncertainty is of many kinds. In turbulent times, disturbed by frequent wars, invasions, plundering expeditions, or general lawlessness, it is notorious that industry is backward and accumulations are meager. Men are not only uncertain as to the reward of forethought, but they are frequently afraid to increase their accumulations lest they attract the notice of plunderers. With the era of peace and order came a new incentive to accumulation. When men felt reasonably certain that they would get the benefit of their own frugality and forethought, they began to exercise these virtues.

But uncertainty results also from bad government. Under a whimsical and despotic government the citizen never knows what the taxgatherer may demand of him. In other words, he never knows when he may be plundered in the name of the law and under the form of taxation. This form of uncertainty is common even in the most democratic governments. A democracy where the people have a strong sense of justice and of law and order furnishes perhaps the safest possible conditions ; but a democracy ruled by the mob spirit, where the people are easily stirred by denunciations of the criminally rich, but with no very clear notion as to the distinction between the honestly rich and the criminally rich, and unable to see that there may be more criminally poor than criminally rich men, is probably the worst form of government known.

Again, a weak and inefficient government, unable to hold in check the rapacity of large combinations of wealth, may permit conditions which make it hazardous for the small investor. This is, of course, the day of large capitalistic undertakings,— the carrying out under one management of vast undertakings requiring more capital than any one can supply. This calls for the combination of many small fortunes, which is effected by the organization of joint-stock companies, or corporations, and by the selling of shares. These shares ought to be, and if the government were honest and efficient they would be, the natural savings bank of the people with small incomes. Any one who has succeeded in saving a hundred dollars, or even less, ought to be able to invest safely in the stocks or bonds of any of the great and well-established railroads, manufacturing plants, mines, etc. But owing to the machinations of the large stockholders it is, wherever the government — particularly the judicial branch — is too corrupt or inefficient to control them, extremely hazardous for such a person to invest in this way. This uncertainty is sometimes partially overcome by good laws relating to savings banks, supplemented by excellent banking practice or even by postal savings banks, so that the small capitalist may invest through these institutions. But under a really efficient government there would be comparatively little need for such institutions.

Taxation. Finally, even though the people be law-abiding and the government efficient, a mistaken theory as to the nature of taxes and their effects upon industry may, when put into practice, act as a hindrance to the effective accumulation of capital. A system of taxation which taxes every such positive accumulation of capital, instead of land and natural advantages, has this effect. If, for example, the law should be such that of two farmers living side by side, owning farms equally fertile and equally well located, the more thrifty and progressive is made to pay the higher taxes, the tendency will be to discourage thrift and progressiveness. One, for example, vegetates, never improves his farm or adds to its value by draining, fencing, erecting buildings, stocking it with superior equipment, etc.; while the other plans ahead, improves his farm, drains it, fences it, erects good buildings, stocks it with superior breeds of live stock, equips it with superior tools, until it becomes, as the result of his own labor and forethought, worth twice as much as the other. If he is then made to pay twice as much in taxes as the other man, who started with as good land as he did, the government is not doing very much to encourage labor and forethought, to say the least.

The law of proportions. But the problem of economizing capital has in view mainly the idea of making existing accumulations accomplish as much as possible. The first great law to be laid down with respect to this problem is the law of proportion. Stated abstractly, this law is simply that the different forms of capital must be combined in the best proportions. Stated concretely, it means, among other things, that there should not be too many horses for the size of the plow, or too large a plow for the number and strength of the horses; that the number and size of the harrows should bear the proper proportion to the number and size of the plows, horses, etc.; that the number and size of the reaping machines should bear the proper proportion to the number and size of the harrows, plows, horses, etc. This is a law with an infinite number of applications, all of them more or less interrelated and, in the aggregate, of the greatest possible importance.

In the simple matter of the plow team, for example, a part of the fatigue of plowing is due to the mere fact of walking, and only a part to the fact of pulling the plow. There would be some fatigue, or wearing out of horse flesh, if the team were walked up and down the field all day without pulling anything, though the pulling of the plow will add something to the fatigue. The size of the plow to be pulled by two horses must be such as to so adjust the two sources of fatigue that the total fatigue will be reduced to the minimum in proportion to the work done.

Two horses drawing a plow that turns a twelve-inch furrow will travel eight miles in plowing an acre (omitting the distance they travel in turning at the end of the field), but with a fourteen-inch plow they will travel seven and one-seventh miles. The fatigue from walking will be slightly reduced; that from pulling will be slightly increased. Which should actually prove the less fatiguing would depend partly upon the character of the soil, partly upon the character of the horses. If they were of the roadster type, good travelers but poor pullers, the smaller plow would doubtless prove less fatiguing; but if they were heavy draft horses, the larger plow would be better. The principle of proportionality has to be worked out by experiment in either case. This is one of the simplest possible cases.

Suppose, now, that you have a fourteen-inch plow and are considering whether to use two or three horses, though you expect to plow the same depth in either case. The probabilities are that if you are able to plow two acres a day with two horses, you will not be able to plow anything like three acres a day with three horses, without greatly increasing the fatigue of both horses and man. Instead of traveling $14\frac{2}{7}$ miles, it would be necessary to travel $21\frac{3}{7}$ miles, which in itself would prove rather fatiguing without any plow. The reduction of one third in the draft upon each horse would not compensate for the adding of one half to the distance he had to travel. Moreover, it would not reduce the draft by one third because of the greater speed. Any one knows that it takes more than twice as much

power to propel a boat eight miles in an hour as it does to propel
it four miles in the same time. The resistance of the water is
greater the greater the speed. Similarly with the plow; to pull
it through the soil and turn the furrow at an increased rate of
speed requires more than a proportionally increased tension
on the clevis. Again, beyond a certain point increased exertion
produces more than proportionally increased fatigue. It is more
than twice as fatiguing to a team to double its rate of speed
beyond a good comfortable gait.

While it is practically certain that three horses with a common
fourteen-inch plow could not plow three acres in a day as easily as
two could plow two acres, it is quite possible that if the size of the
plow were increased they could do it with the same ease. Here
again it is a question of finding the proper proportion among the
various parts of the combination. Theoretically the nature of this
proportion can be stated a little more exactly by means of the following illustration, though the practical application of the principle
always has to be worked out on the spot by experimentation.

Let us assume that two horses, without overwork but working
up to their reasonable capacity, can plow two acres a day, whereas
three horses, with the same plow and the same fatigue to man
and beast, can plow not three acres but two and one half. One
half acre is then the result of adding a third horse to the team.
Does it pay? Well, if the third horse would otherwise be standing idle, it doubtless would. But suppose it is a question of hiring
a third horse, or of keeping three horses on the farm instead of
two; it would then be a question as to whether the value of the
one half acre of plowing was sufficient to pay the cost of his keep,
plus risk and deterioration, interest on his cost price, etc. If the
total cost of the horse is $1.50 a day, while plowing is worth only
$2.00 an acre, it is obviously a bad proportion, and two horses
are more profitable than three. But if his daily cost were anything less than $1, then it would be a profitable combination.

In general we may state the law thus : If you take one part of the combination — the plow in the foregoing illustration — as the basis, or the fixed unit, and vary the other factors, — the horses, for example, — the law of proportion requires that the last unit added to the variable factor, the third horse in the foregoing illustration, must add to the product as much as it adds to the cost; and, moreover, that it will pay to add to that factor so long as the last unit added will add to the product anything above what it adds to the cost. This statement of the law sounds formidable, no doubt, but it is a law which must be followed if the largest success is to be attained. However, most successful farmers approximate pretty closely to the law, frequently without knowing that it is a law.

The advantage of knowing that it is a law is that it enables a farm manager, if he cares to do so, to substitute methods of exact experimentation for general good judgment in determining such questions as how many horses to use to each plow, what size of plow to use with each team, how large a team and plow to put in charge of each man, etc. The same law is involved in the question of how many acres to cultivate with each man and team, how large a ration and in what combination to feed to his animals, and a multitude of others which the farm manager must decide rightly or wrongly, offhand or by the methods of exact experimentation. This law, it may be remarked, is merely a more general statement of the law of diminishing returns from land, as explained in preceding pages. It may be further elucidated by means of the figures on the following page, which are assumed arbitrarily for purposes of illustration.

Let us assume that the basis, or the fixed unit, in the plowing combination is one man. He may plow with one, two, three, four, or as many as eight horses, using different plows suited to the number of horses in the team. Let us assume further that with one horse he can plow one acre. If that be true, it is altogether probable that he can, with no greater fatigue to himself or to either horse, plow two acres with two horses, using a larger plow. A little time would be lost in feeding, cleaning, harnessing, hitching, and unhitching two horses rather than one, but the loss of time would be so slight as to be almost negligible. With three horses to care for, feed, harness, etc., the loss of time begins, let us say, to be appreciable, and unless the man works longer hours he will not be able to plow three acres with three horses, even though he uses a larger plow.

We are, for the moment, leaving out of consideration the probability that a large plow pulls more than proportionally harder than a small one, owing to the greater height to which a large sod has to be lifted in order to turn it over. With the same amount of time a man will, let us say, plow not 3 acres but $2\frac{7}{8}$; and for the same reasons he will plow with 4 horses not 4 acres but $3\frac{5}{8}$, with 5 horses not 5 acres but $4\frac{1}{4}$, with 6 horses not 6 acres but $4\frac{3}{4}$, with 7 horses not 7 acres but $5\frac{1}{8}$, and with 8 horses not 8 acres but $5\frac{3}{8}$. Of course, by getting up earlier in the morning to do the preliminary feeding and harnessing, by allowing himself a shorter noon hour because of the feeding and watering of the larger team, and by working longer in the evening after the return from the field, he may succeed in maintaining a fixed proportion between the number of horses and the number of acres plowed; that is, he might succeed in plowing one acre per horse regardless of the size of the team. But working longer hours in this case would mean doing more work, which, economically speaking, is the same as increasing the number of men.

Under the assumptions which we have made, it will appear that the addition of the second horse *added* 1 acre to the amount plowed with one horse, the addition of the third horse *added* $\frac{7}{8}$ of an acre to the amount plowed with two horses, the addition of the fourth horse *added* $\frac{3}{4}$ of an acre to the amount

plowed with three horses, and so on, the *addition* made by each
horse as others are added being $\frac{5}{8}$ of an acre, $\frac{1}{2}$ of an acre, $\frac{3}{8}$ of
an acre, and $\frac{1}{4}$ of an acre.

Reducing these figures to the following diagram, let the work
done with one horse be represented by the rectangle 1, that
done with two horses by the sum of the rectangles 1 and 2,
that done with three horses by the sum of the rectangles 1, 2,
and 3, etc. The rectangle 3 then represents the *additional*

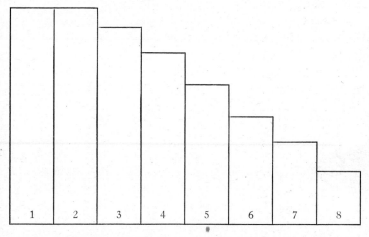

work done with the third horse over and above what could be
done with two, etc; that is, rectangle 3 is the effective work
done by the third horse, and measures his value in the team.
The value of the additional horses thus dwindles away until the
rectangle 8 represents the effective value of the eighth horse.
If the value of a quarter of an acre of plowing (rectangle 8) is,
under the circumstances of time and place, greater than the cost
per day of one horse, then it pays to use eight horses; otherwise
not. Find the rectangle in this diagram which represents sufficient plowing to have the value which approximates most closely
to the daily cost of one horse (including, of course, all the items

of cost, such as deterioration, insurance, interest, etc.), and you have solved the problem of how many horses can most profitably be combined with one man in the plowing combination.

As suggested above, the same law is involved when a given piece of land is taken as the base or fixed unit in a general farming combination, and the problem is as to the quantity of the various other factors to combine with it. This problem is to be determined by the same method, and the same or a similar diagram could be used to illustrate it. In fact it is a universal principle applying to all combinations of different factors for a common purpose. In the fattening of an animal, for example, it will eventually transpire, if the feeding is sufficiently prolonged, that the daily gains will dwindle. For every additional day there will be a smaller and smaller additional gain in weight or value. When the time arrives that the daily gains in value no longer exceed the cost of the daily ration, it is obviously time to sell and stop feeding. This problem also could be illustrated by a diagram similar to that given above. Allow the different rectangles to represent the daily or weekly gains in value, then find the rectangle which approximates most closely to the cost of the daily or weekly ration, and you have solved the problem of when to sell.

One phase of the great law of proportionality as applied to agriculture is the rule that every form of capital should be used to its full capacity. A gang plow, or even a twine binder, on a small farm where it could be only partially utilized, would be a violation of this law. Two horses kept where there is work enough for only one, the possession of many tools, some of which are seldom used, are frequent examples of the same kind of bad economy. To avoid wasting capital in this way, and at the same time to provide adequate equipment for the efficient working of the farm, requires the most careful judgment on the part of the farm manager.

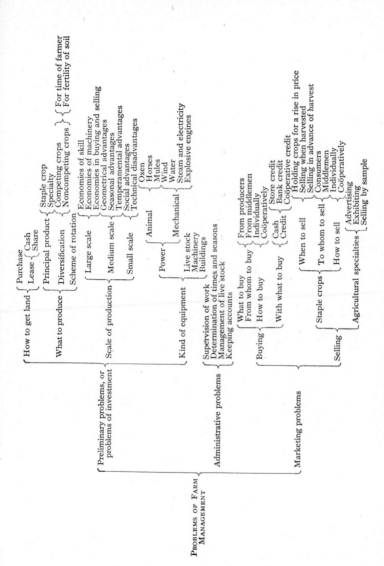

PROBLEMS OF FARM MANAGEMENT

Preliminary problems, or problems of investment
- How to get land
  - Purchase
  - Lease { Cash, Share }
- What to produce
  - Principal product { Staple crop, Specialty }
  - Diversification { Competing crops, Noncompeting crops } { For time of farmer, For fertility of soil }
  - Scheme of rotation
- Scale of production
  - Large scale { Economies of skill, Economies of machinery, Economies in buying and selling, Geometrical advantages, Seasonal advantages, Temperamental advantages, Social advantages, Technical disadvantages }
  - Medium scale
  - Small scale
- Kind of equipment
  - Power
    - Animal { Oxen, Horses, Mules, Wind, Water }
    - Mechanical { Steam and electricity, Explosive engines }
  - Live stock
  - Machinery
  - Buildings

Administrative problems
- Supervision of work
- Determination of times and seasons
- Management of live stock
- Keeping accounts

Marketing problems
- Buying
  - What to buy
  - From whom to buy { From producers, From middlemen }
  - How to buy { Individually, Coöperatively }
  - With what to buy { Cash, Credit { Store credit, Bank credit, Coöperative credit } }
- Selling
  - Staple crops
    - When to sell { Holding crops for a rise in price, Selling when harvested, Selling in advance of harvest }
    - To whom to sell { Consumers, Middlemen }
    - How to sell { Individually, Coöperatively }
  - Agricultural specialties { Advertising, Exhibiting, Selling by sample }

CHAPTER IV

MANAGEMENT AS A FACTOR IN AGRICULTURAL PRODUCTION [1]

The manager as the economizer. After all is said that can be said regarding the economizing of land, labor, and capital in agriculture, the actual working out of these problems in the concrete is the task of the farm manager. Wise legislation, efficient administration of the laws already enacted, and new scientific discoveries may create favorable conditions or opportunities for agriculture, but upon the farm manager rests the responsibility of making agriculture respond to these favorable conditions, or of making use of the opportunities thus created. However ingenious a new agricultural invention may be, unless the farm managers have the wisdom, the foresight, and the power of initiative to readjust their methods and reorganize their farms, it will not be used, and the inventor will gain neither fame nor profit from his work. However wise and efficient the government may be in its agricultural policy, if the farm managers are unprogressive, if they are under the power and domination of a superstitious form of religion or of unscrupulous demagogues, the work of the legislator will be in vain. His one chance to benefit agriculture under such circumstances is to begin at the bottom and provide such an educational system as may eventually enlighten the people sufficiently to enable them

[1] By the courtesy of the Carnegie Institution the author is permitted to use in this chapter some of the material included in a chapter on The Economic Characteristics of the Agricultural Industry, which he wrote for the " History of American Agriculture," which is being prepared under the direction of that institution.

to throw off these hindrances to progress. Even then these same unprogressive agencies may pervert the educational system or prevent the people from profiting by it.

The farm manager is preëminently the economizer. Upon him more than upon any one else falls the burden of seeing that the productive resources of the community are productively employed, and not wasted in useless or futile experiments. Though he may be, and usually is in the United States, not only manager but landowner, laborer, and capitalist combined, his work as manager is easily distinguishable from these other functions. Whether he be merely a manager, renting land of another, borrowing his capital from another, and hiring his labor; or whether he is manager, landowner, capitalist, and laborer, or any or all these combined, he must perform three important functions: first, that of deciding certain fundamental questions of investment; second, that of pushing the work along and seeing that it is properly performed; and third, that of buying and selling, that is, buying the necessary equipment — seed, fertilizers, live stock, etc. — and selling the produce of the farm. It is seldom that these three functions are separated or divided up among different men in the same agricultural enterprise, though it is sometimes done. That is, one man may perform the first function, that of deciding the fundamental question of the kinds of crops to grow, on how large a scale to grow them, what kind of equipment to use, etc. Another man, a foreman, may have the task of pushing the work along, superintending the men, and seeing that they do the work promptly and in a satisfactory manner. Finally, a third man may act as a buying and selling agent. But this subdivision of the functions of the manager is possible only where the agricultural operations are carried out on a scale which is very seldom reached in this country. We shall assume, therefore, that they are all to be performed by the same man, though, for purposes of discussion, they may be treated separately.

I. Fundamental Problems, or Problems of Investment

The fundamental questions to be decided by the farm manager concern, first, the manager's relation to the land, that is, his tenure; second, the type of agriculture to be undertaken, that is, what kind of products to produce; third, the scale upon which he shall undertake the production, that is, the size of the business unit which he shall undertake to manage; and fourth, the equipment to be used and the proportion in which the various kinds of equipment are to be combined. The third of these questions has to do in part with the law of proportion as stated in the last chapter.

The problem of the relation of the farmer to the land is of perennial interest not only to the farmer but to the economist as well. Is it better for the farmer to own his land, to rent, or to work on a salary? If he rents, is it better to pay cash rent or a share of the produce, or a combination of both?

Ownership or tenancy. It has generally been assumed as a matter of course by American farmers that it is better to own the land upon which they work. Aside from the merits of this theory, there are at least three purely accidental factors, having nothing to do with the efficiency of agriculture, which have contributed to the support of this practice. The first is the fact that the land policy of the federal government has, at least since 1841, put the ownership of the land in the first instance directly into the hands of its cultivators. The second is the fact that over the greater part of the country, and during the greater part of our history, land has tended to rise in value. This rise in value has been considered as a part of the profits of farming, and every shrewd farmer has put himself into a position to get this increment of wealth. He could secure this increment, of course, only by owning the land. The third factor in the problem has been the lack of an intelligent system of leasing land.

This has doubtless been due, in turn, to the fact that few of our best farmers have cared to lease land. However that may be, the fact remains that we have not worked out the problem of a system of tenancy which is attractive to a progressive and far-sighted farmer. Our system of short leases, under which the tenant has little control or initiative, is about as well calculated to stifle initiative and enterprise as anything could well be. On the other hand, it must be said that the interests of the landowner are so poorly safeguarded by our laws and customs as to make it hazardous for him to let his land on a long lease, or to allow any large measure of control to pass into the hands of the tenant. This defect, if it can be called a defect, in our legal system has contributed its share toward making the tenancy system in this country more unpopular than it would otherwise have been.

Aside from these factors just mentioned, which, as suggested, have nothing to do with efficient agriculture, there are certain undoubted advantages arising from the ownership of the soil by those who cultivate it. It obviates all vexatious questions relating to leases and the interpretation of the terms of the contract; it frees the cultivator from the irritation of continuous inspection by the landowner, who, in order to protect his land from exploitation, must insist upon proper manuring, weeding, rotation of crops, repairing, etc.; and it gives the cultivator a permanent interest in the farm and the community, and a sense of responsibility which a mere tenant can scarcely feel.

On the other hand, we have the large and stubborn fact, difficult to argue out of existence, that the best agriculture in the world is carried on under the tenancy system. The most efficient system of general farming is found in England, where the tenancy system prevails; and the most efficient growing of agricultural specialties is found on the very small gardens in the neighborhood of Paris, where the land is not generally owned by the gardener. In both these cases, however, there are special reasons why the cultivator does not desire especially to own the land. In England the ownership of land is a kind of passport to good society. At least it confers a certain amount of dignity upon the owner, and for this reason the competition for ownership is severe among the well-to-do classes. This competition forces the selling price of land up to a high figure as compared with its rental value. In this country, land which rents for $5 an acre net will sell for $100 or $150. In England it will sell for twice that amount. This allows the owner so small an interest on his investment as to prove unattractive to one who is not seeking social distinction. The farmer who is seeking only the profits of farming finds that he can make more from his capital in some other form than when invested in land. Even if he owned his land, he would be tempted to sell if he were offered say $300 an acre for it, with the privilege of renting for from $5 to $7 an acre. By putting the large sum of money which he might receive from the sale of the land into stock and equipment he could get a larger income than would be possible by retaining the ownership of the land. If he is not the owner, he would find it, for the same reason, less profitable to buy the land than to lease it.

In the neighborhood of Paris there are also special reasons why the gardener frequently does not own his tiny plot of land. Much of this land is being held as future building sites, and has a speculative value for that purpose far in excess of its present value as garden land. The man who wants it as garden land alone could not afford to pay such a price. However, the owner is willing to let it at a rental which will not yield normal interest upon its speculative price, rather than not get any income from it at all. However, some of this gardening is done on land near the military fortifications, where regulations prevent the erection of permanent buildings.

Arthur Young's famous dictum that " The magic of property turns sand into gold " was inspired by the spectacle of the small peasant proprietors of northern Europe laboring incessantly upon their tiny plots of land and bringing tracts of barren waste to a high degree of fertility. Like all such aphorisms, it states a certain large truth, but does not take the place of a scientific treatise. It was not the magic of property, or any other form of magic, but merely patient labor under the pressure of dire need, which forced these people to undertake the painful, heartbreaking toil of wresting a meager living from the sand dunes which Young describes. That they succeeded is greatly to the credit of those sturdy, courageous people who could not be daunted by the prospect of hard work and frugal fare. There have always been as good opportunities in England, and there are just as good opportunities in New England to-day, for property to work its magic, if there is any magic about it, as there ever were in Europe. And the English farm laborers and the immigrants into New England are as sturdy and courageous as were those continental peasants ; but the pressure of need has not been so severe in England or New England. The simple fact is, that the sturdy English laborer could make a better living by working for wages, or, if he were sufficiently capable, by leasing good land, than he could by reclaiming the kind of waste land which Young describes, and by the laborious methods of the people whom he praises. Similarly, the immigrants into New England can generally do better at something else than at the work of reclaiming waste land under the stimulus of private property. However, on Cape Cod and elsewhere there are a few notable cases of market and fruit farms created in unpromising situations by Portuguese and Italian immigrants. Even in these cases, however, the standard of living is low ; but they show what can be done by our growing population if the conditions ever become bad enough to force people to it. There is very little land, even in barren New England, which could not be made to support a dense agricultural population if the standard of living were reduced to a low enough level.

Our immediate problem, however, is whether the farm manager would better own or rent his land. No general answer can be made, since it depends upon circumstances of time and place. Of course, if there is a good prospect of land rising in value, the advantage of buying is obvious. Many an indifferent farmer in the United States has found himself carried along on the general current of prosperity merely because of the fact that he became the owner of land when it was cheap and held onto it while it rose in value. But this has nothing to do with his success as a farmer; his prosperity arises from his success as a land speculator. Of course, if the land should decline in value after he bought it, the disadvantages of ownership would be equally obvious.

Aside from the factor of land speculation, there are other considerations already hinted at. The terms upon which land can be leased is a most important factor in the problem. Where, under the customary terms of tenancy, the farmer has little control and a very short tenure, every capable farmer will try to become an owner as soon as possible, if for no other reason, merely because it gives him fixity of tenure and freedom from interference. Where a favorable lease can be secured, the problem will turn largely upon the ratio of the price of the land to its rent. Where the price of land is so high in proportion to its rent as to yield an abnormally low rate of interest, it will be better to rent; that is to say, a capable farmer can make his capital yield him a larger return when he invests it in tools, machinery, live stock, etc., than when invested in the land. Where there is a good landlord who understands farming and takes an intelligent interest in the land and his tenants, the advantages of this system reach their maximum. However, the social results of absentee landlordism, where the landowner takes no interest in his land or his tenants except as sources of income, are so disastrous as to leave nothing to be said in its favor. When the safety of the investment and all the other factors are considered, it is seldom in this country that the price of land rises so high in proportion to its rent as to yield an abnormally low rate of interest. It is only where some other motive than the desire for income, such as the desire for social esteem, leads to the purchase of land that the prices reach such abnormal heights. Generally speaking, therefore, in view of the facts that this is still a growing country and land values are still rising, that our laws and customs are not favorable to long leases on satisfactory terms, and that land values are not as a rule abnormally high in proportion to rent, it is safe to say that it is better for the capable farmer to buy than to rent, as soon as he is able to buy.

For the young farmer, however, with limited capital and experience, it is not usually possible to buy land without depriving himself of the means of equipping his farm. For this reason it is the almost universal custom in this country for the young farmer without capital to pass through a series of progressive stages toward the position of farm owner. The first stage is commonly that of a farm hand. After having acquired some knowledge and experience, and having saved up enough money to buy a team and set of farming tools, he begins his career as a renter. If he is a success as a farmer, and his accumulations of capital are not swept away by some of the multifarious calamities which always hang over the head of the farmer, he will eventually become a farm owner, at first with a mortgage on his farm, but finally free from debt.

Cash or share tenancy. During the interval when the farmer is of necessity a tenant, the question as to whether it is better to pay cash or share rent is a practical one. Generally speaking, the reasons are overwhelmingly in favor of cash rent, though there are special circumstances under which share rent may prove more satisfactory. Both methods call, in about equal degree, for carefully drawn contracts and mutual good will. Under the cash-rent system the tenant is more likely to exploit the soil and leave it depleted. Under the share-rent system the tenant is less assiduous in cultivating the soil, especially the poorer parts, the fence corners, or the other parts where the advantage of cultivation is more or less doubtful. In general, it may be said that cash tenancy leads to more thorough farming, but endangers the future fertility of the soil.

There is a fundamental economic reason, aside from the general superiority of cash over share tenants, for the observed fact that cash tenancy leads to more thorough cultivation of the soil than share tenancy. The cash tenant gets all the advantage of his own superior cultivation, whereas the share tenant gets only a share of that advantage. That is to say, after the cash tenant has produced enough to pay his rent, every additional dollar which he can make the farm produce goes into his own pocket, whereas, no matter how much the share tenant adds to the product, he gets only a share of the increase. Under the principle of diminishing returns the cash tenant can afford to increase the intensity of his cultivation up to the point where the additional cost approximates in amount the additional product, whereas the share tenant could only afford to carry the cultivation up to the point where the additional cost would equal in amount *his share* of the additional product. This principle may be illustrated by means of the diagram on the following page.

Let the amount of labor to be expended in the cultivation of the farm be measured along the line OX, and the cost along the line OY, the cost per unit being represented by the distance OA. Also let the curve YHKBX represent the product to be secured by successive applications of labor to the cultivation of the soil. The cash tenant will pay a fixed sum for the farm, represented, let us say, by the figure OYHL, or the whole product of an amount of labor represented by the line OL. After this is paid he gets the whole product of the additional labor, which additional labor is measured in the figure along the line LX.

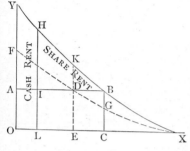

According to the figure he could afford to apply a quantity of labor represented by the line OC, since the last unit of that quantity produces a product equal to its cost, both the product and cost of that final unit of labor being represented by the line BC.

But a share tenant, paying, let us say, one third of the product as rent for the same farm, would get for the successive units of his work only the remaining two thirds of the product, represented by the space below the dotted curve FDGX. If he should carry his cultivation to the same degree of intensity, he would be losing money on a part of his work; that is, if he applied a quantity of labor represented by the line OC, the last unit of his work would cost him an amount represented by the line BC, but he would get in return for it only an amount represented by the line GC. In short, he would find it unprofitable to expend more labor than is represented by the line OE, that being the quantity whose final unit yields him as much as it costs him, namely an amount represented by the line DE. To sum up, under the terms of the diagram a cash tenant would find it to his advantage to expend a quantity of labor represented by the line OC, producing a total product represented by the figure OYBC, whereas the share tenant would find it to his advantage to expend a smaller quantity of labor, represented by the line OE, and producing a total product represented by the figure OYKE. This demonstration proves that cash tenancy is superior to share tenancy as a general economic system, provided the soil can be safeguarded so as to keep the cash tenant from mining or exhausting it during the term of his lease.

Salaried managers. The question as to whether the farm manager should work for a salary or not is merely a personal matter. In general, the reasons are overwhelmingly against it. But there are exceptional men who are really capable farmers, so far as their ability to grow crops is concerned, but who have so little commercial ability as to unfit them for what are called "business dealings." They fall an easy prey to agents of all kinds; they cannot resist the temptation to buy things which they do not need; they can scarcely buy the necessary things without getting cheated; and consequently they are business failures in spite of their skill in the real work of farming. Such a man may do well to accept a salaried position under some landowner, who will himself look after the commercial side of farming. The author has known a number of cases of this kind. But a salaried position is far from satisfactory in the long run for any one who does not need the kind of protection which it furnishes. It leads to nothing, and is likely to leave a person stranded in his old age.

What to produce. The question what to produce is sometimes decided for the farmer by the location of his farm. To be sure, he has to decide first upon the location, and, from his individual point of view, that might be regarded as the most fundamental question of all. But from the point of view of the country as a whole, the land is approximately a fixed quantity and every available piece of it is supposed to be managed if not by one manager then by another. While the manager of any given farm may not have many choices open to him as to what kind of crops to grow, he usually has some alternative. The question which will determine many other problems of management is whether to grow staple products or an agricultural specialty.

Staple products *vs.* **specialties.** The distinction between staple products and agricultural specialties is not always clear, since they shade off into one another by almost imperceptible stages. In general, a staple product is one which will always sell at some quotable price; that is, any product whose price can always be determined by the market quotations — as in the case of grain and hay, beef, cotton, hogs, and cattle — may be called a staple product. Any product, on the other hand, which is not actually classified on the market, and for which there are not and cannot be regular market quotations, but for which there is, nevertheless, considerable sale, sometimes at fancy prices, may be called an agricultural specialty. Fine stock for breeding purposes, fancy saddle and driving horses, where each individual animal has a special purpose and a special price of its own, fancy fruit and vegetables which cater to special tastes, etc., are examples of this class of agricultural products. In the growing of staple products the farm manager's problem is primarily that of reducing the cost of production. Since his products always sell at a quotable price, the problem of marketing is reduced to a minimum. Though important in itself, this problem is relatively less important than that of keeping down the cost of production. But the reverse is the case with the grower of agricultural specialties. His greatest problem is that of marketing, — of getting a fancy price for each individual unit of product. Though the problem of keeping down the cost of production is important in itself, it is relatively less important than that of successful marketing. Success in the production of staple products depends primarily on being a good producer; in the growing of agricultural specialties it depends upon being a good advertiser, a good displayer of products, — in short, in being a good seller. While there will always be a place for the grower of agricultural specialties, yet by far the greater part of the agricultural industry must always be concerned with the production of the staple crops. Hence our interest is primarily with this branch of the industry.

While the geographical and market conditions will often prescribe the principal crop to be grown on each farm, it is not so simple a matter as may appear at first sight. The soil of a certain farm may be admirably adapted to the growing of wheat or beef, but those products can also be successfully grown in regions very remote from markets. If this particular farm is to be devoted to either of these crops, it will have to compete with vast areas of land well suited to their production and not well suited to other crops which require less land and more labor, and which do not stand transportation so well. If, therefore, this particular piece of land is also well suited to some of these other purposes, — to the growing of corn, cotton, potatoes, milk, or garden crops, products which have to be grown in narrower areas or nearer the markets, — it is not only more profitable to the farmer, but more economical of the nation's resources, to have it devoted to some of these purposes.

It is seldom, however, either profitable for the farmer himself, or economical for the nation, to have a farm devoted exclusively to the production of a single crop. Only in rare exceptions, where an agricultural specialty of high value is grown, and where considerable money can be spent for manures and fertilizers, is this profitable. Diversification of crops is and must be the rule for the vast majority of farms.

Reasons for diversification. There are three main reasons for this, though doubtless a multitude of minor ones could be named. In the first place, every crop has its enemies, and these tend to multiply if the land is continually planted to the same crop. The enemies of one crop are not necessarily the enemies of another, though they are sometimes. By changing the crop every year the special enemies of each crop are held in check, even if they are not starved out altogether. According to one theory, in addition to the known enemies of the different crops, such as insect pests and the like, there is a tendency of plants as well as of animals to throw off excreta which are poisonous to themselves. Therefore, after dense crops of the same plant have been grown continuously for several years, the soil becomes unhealthy for that plant, just as the conditions become unwholesome for animals which live in crowded quarters for a long time.

Another reason for diversification is that different crops extract the different elements of plant food from the soil in different proportions. A wise diversification of crops will tend, therefore, to exhaust the soil less rapidly, or rather, to retain for a longer period a proper balance of the various elements which go to make up the soil fertility. A third reason for diversification, and one which, though no more important in itself, appeals to the average farmer much more strongly, is that different crops require labor and attention at different times of the year. Suppose a farmer is located in a corn country. With a given labor force there is a pretty definite limit to the amount of corn which he can plant, cultivate, and harvest. But if he grows nothing but corn, there will be times and seasons when there is no work to do, for example, between corn-plowing and corn-husking time. His labor power is going to waste at these times. If he can find another crop which will occupy his time during these intervals, he can grow it without adding to his labor force and without subtracting from his corn crop. Some form of small grain, preferably spring grain such as oats, or spring wheat where the climate is suitable both for spring wheat and corn, will fit in admirably with his plans. This grain can be sown in the early spring, before it is safe to plant corn, and the harvesting and threshing will come between corn plowing and corn husking.

Competing and noncompeting crops. This situation gives rise to the distinction between competing and noncompeting crops.

Two crops are said to be competing either when they consume the same properties of the soil or when they consume the same portion of the farmer's time; that is, when they demand his time and attention at precisely the same time of the year. Otherwise they are noncompeting crops. Two crops may be competing in one sense and noncompeting in the other. The ideal diversification is, of course, a combination of crops which are noncompeting in both senses. So important is this principle that it may be laid down as a rule that no farm will pay unless it provides steady and regular work for a fairly permanent labor force throughout the greater part of a year. Even dairying, which may be called a highly specialized form of agriculture, is seldom profitable unless combined with the growing of field crops of some kind for sale. The number of men necessary to do the milking evenings and mornings are more than enough to take care of the cows and grow feed for them. Unless some other products are grown the time of the men is not fully utilized. By growing field crops for sale, the cost of producing milk is divided with that of growing these other crops; or, to look at it in another way, these crops are by-products of milk and cost very little. Very little poultry is kept profitably in this country, except on farms where it is in the strictest sense a noncompeting crop or product. Where it is kept in small quantities it forages for itself, consuming mainly waste products, besides destroying insects, and does not exhaust the soil at all but tends rather to enrich it. Again, it does not compete for the farmer's time, being cared for mainly by the labor of women and children. This will help to explain how difficult it is for any one to make a living raising poultry alone in competition with farm poultry, unless one is prepared to go into the business on a large scale and is equipped with thorough scientific knowledge. Where diversified farming means the growing of noncompeting crops, specialization is a long way off.

Rotation of crops. Diversification of crops almost invariably means some sort of rotation. One admirable scheme, though there are many others applicable throughout the greater part of the corn belt, is a three-year rotation of corn, oats, and clover. Where the tillable land of the farm is divided in three parts, each part in turn being put through this rotation, these crops will be found to be noncompeting in both senses of the term. One great obstacle to diversification is the lack of suitable crops to work together in rotation. Thus it is difficult to combine corn, wheat, and clover because of the difficulty of getting fall wheat sown after the corn is harvested, and spring wheat is usually grown farther north than the corn belt. A great obstacle to diversified farming in the cotton belt has been the difficulty of finding a noncompeting crop to go with cotton, which crop is very exacting in its demands upon the farmer's time. Though cotton land is generally good corn land, these two crops demand the farmer's care at about the same seasons of the year. Therefore every acre which he adds to his corn crop subtracts an acre from his cotton crop, and he naturally prefers to give his time to the more profitable of the two crops.

Large-, medium-, or small-scale farming. Another large and fundamental question which the farm manager must determine is the scale upon which he shall carry on his farming operations. Sometimes this question is settled for him by the size of his farm, the amount of capital, and the limit of his credit. But if he is known to be a capable farmer, he can usually rent as much land and borrow as much capital as he can handle effectively or economically. If large-scale farming were distinctly more profitable than small-scale farming, he would have no difficulty in embarking upon large-scale production. It is because large-scale farming is usually less profitable, and because large-scale farmers fail more frequently than medium-scale farmers, that it is difficult to rent land or borrow capital on a large scale.

It is, of course, impossible to draw any hard-and-fast lines between large-, medium-, and small-scale farming. The acreage of the farm is no test, because more capital may be invested and more labor employed on ten acres intensively farmed than upon a thousand acres extensively farmed. For purposes of discussion we shall define large-scale farming as farming where there is land enough, capital enough, and men enough employed to make it economical for the manager to give his whole time to the work of supervision and management, all the manual work being done by employees working under his direction. A relatively small number of men on a cattle ranch covering a wide area and having considerable capital invested in stock would be equivalent to a relatively large number of men on a small acreage devoted to market gardening. That which marks the farm as a large farm is the size of the whole business unit, and neither the number of men nor the number of acres taken separately.

By medium-scale farming is meant that style of farming, more common than any other in this country, where the manager does the greater part of his own work, — that is, he and his family, with an occasional hired man, who usually boards with the family, — and where the acreage is sufficient to employ the reasonable working time of this labor force when equipped with the teams, tools, implements, and machines which are necessary to utilize that labor force to the best advantage. The acreage may be small or large, according to the nature of the crops grown, but it must be large enough to allow the economical use of such machines, tools, etc. as are commonly used in that line of production. In the grain and hay region of our central West anything from one hundred to two hundred acres, say one hundred sixty on the average, would meet this description.

By small-scale farming is meant a type very common among the peasants of certain European countries, and more especially in Japan, China, and other countries of the Far East. This type of farming consists of taking a very small parcel of land which comes into one's possession by inheritance or in some other way, and trying to make a living upon it, not by using methods suited to the economical production of the crop, considered as a crop, but by methods suited to the small size of the farm. Though a reaper or a twine binder is well adapted to the work of harvesting wheat, where the farm is large enough, it is entirely unsuited for the harvesting of wheat in such small patches as these peasants can grow. Though the transplanting of young wheat plants or young rice plants is an uneconomical and unremunerative method of growing those crops, being a pitiful and woeful waste of human energy, yet considering what tiny patches these peasants are able to grow, and the imperious necessity of making such a living as they can off these small patches, this is a method well adapted to this type of farming because it increases the yield per acre. The fact that the cost of growing wheat by this means is high in terms of human labor, as compared with the cost in more favored countries, does not affect these peasant farmers. They have got to make their living off of such land as they have, or they have got to starve. Therefore they are willing to use these laborious methods in order to get as much as they can from their land. Their living depends upon the productivity of their land rather than upon the productivity of their labor.

Superiority of medium-scale farming. The undoubted tendency in this country is toward the medium scale of production and away from both extremes. While manufacturing, transportation, and mining are, generally speaking, tending toward large-scale production, agriculture, the greatest of all our industries, still remains one in which the average man may hope to be self-employed. A few bonanza farms there have been, but they have generally proved less efficient than those of medium size, and the tendency has been for these immense agricultural establishments to break up. There are, to be sure, certain advantages and economies in large-scale production, even in agriculture, but there are also very marked difficulties and disadvantages, and the general experience tends to show that the disadvantages are greater than the advantages.

Advantages of large-scale production. The advantages of large-scale production in agriculture are the same as in any other industry. They are, first, economies of skill; second, economies of equipment; and third, economies in buying and selling. Economy of skill is effected when one who possesses special skill for a particular kind of work is enabled to spend all his time at that work. If there is only enough of this special work to occupy a part of his time, he must either remain idle the rest of his time or spend it doing an inferior kind of work which could be done just as well by a less skillful and cheaper man. On a large farm he is more likely to find enough skilled work to occupy all his time than on a small farm. For example, the farmer himself may be a skilled manager. On a large farm a number of men could work under his direction, and thus the full advantage of his skill would be secured. On a small farm fewer men would have the benefit of his direction. On a very small farm he might have to do all or a part of the muscular labor himself, — labor which a cheaper man could do just as well. However, beyond the full utilization of the skill of the manager, there are comparatively few opportunities for economy of skill in large-scale farming. This particular kind of skill, however, is undoubtedly economized by large-scale farming. As Professor Alfred Marshall points out: [1]

The head of a large business can reserve all his strength for the broadest and most fundamental problems of his trade. He must indeed assure himself that his managers, clerks, and foremen are the right men for their work, and are doing their work well; but beyond this he need not trouble himself much about details. He can keep his mind fresh and clear for thinking out the most difficult and vital problems of his business; for

[1] Principles of Economics (fifth edition), Vol. I, p. 285.

studying the broader movements of the markets, and the yet undeveloped results of current events at home and abroad; and for contriving how to improve the organization of the internal and external relations of his business.

For much of this work the small employer has not the time if he has the ability; he cannot take so broad a survey of his trade or look so far ahead; he must often be content to follow the lead of others. And he must spend much of his time on work that is below him; for if he is to succeed at all, his mind must be in some respects of a high quality, and must have a good deal of originating and organizing force; and yet he must do much routine work.

Economy of equipment is effected when a labor-saving machine can be used to its full capacity. This is much more likely to happen on a large than on a small farm. On a small farm a machine may be used only a part of the time, and on a very small farm, where it could be used very little, it is frequently cheaper to dispense with it altogether and do the work by hand. A twine binder, for example, on a small farm may be used only during the actual harvest season, and where a very small crop of grain is grown it may actually be cheaper to reap it by hand. In the economy of machinery, however, small farmers are sometimes able by coöperation to gain some of the advantages of the large farmer. This is especially true in the threshing of grain in the Middle West.

Economy in buying and selling is sometimes effected by reason of the fact that the large farmer, having to buy in large quantities, can afford to take more pains in looking over the market, besides being able sometimes to buy at wholesale rather than at retail rates. Similarly, in selling, since he has a great deal to sell, he can give more attention to the market and can sometimes get better freight rates when shipping by the carload or the trainload. If he is growing agricultural specialties, — fine stock, choice fruits, etc., — for which a special price is to be had, the large producer can also advertise more effectively and economically than the small producer; but this is of no advantage to the grower of a staple crop, which must be sold at the regular market price, in which case advertising is of little use.

The disadvantages of large-scale farming. The disadvantages or difficulties of large-scale farming may be grouped into three classes, namely, geometrical, seasonal, and temperamental. The geometrical difficulties are due to the fact that farming necessarily requires considerable space or superficial area. Even intensive farming, gardening, etc., where large-scale farming shows most signs of persisting, need more space than most other industries. Large-scale farming, therefore, necessitates large spaces or large areas of land. This means a loss of time and energy in traveling from one part of the farm to another, transporting tools and machinery, seed and crops, to and from different parts, and especially in going to and from work. More than that, it generally increases the difficulty of supervision and direction. The manager cannot get quickly from one part of the farm to another, as is possible in a store or factory, and consequently only a small part of a large farm can be under his supervision at any one time. This necessarily limits very materially the possibility of economizing the only important kind of skill which large-scale farming is capable of economizing, namely, managing skill.

This possibility is still further limited by the seasonal difficulties. In a factory there are certain operations which have to be performed continuously the year round. An employee may be set at one of these operations and he requires no further attention beyond the necessary inspection and accounting, to see that he puts in his full time and does his assigned task in a satisfactory manner. Accordingly one human intellect is capable of managing a large-scale aggregation of such men by the aid of modern business systems, checking devices, etc. When the working force is once organized and put in operation, the work of the manager consists merely in keeping it in effective operation. One intelligent manager is therefore capable of directing a considerable aggregation of men and machines. But what could any human intellect do with an aggregation of several thousand or even several hundred men who had to be reorganized several times during the farming season, as the nature of the work changed with the advancement of the season? It is a very different matter to direct a large body of men who are to do the same kind of work the year round, from what it would be to direct a body of men whose work must change frequently, as it must of necessity change on a farm from month to month, from day to day, and even from hour to hour. Such a change necessitates not only supervision but an entire organization of the working force of the farm, assigning to each and every man a new task. Even the work of supervision becomes much more complicated and difficult by reason of the fact that no mere automatic checking device can be utilized to keep a record of the workman's time or the amount and character of his work. Not only are there normal, seasonal changes of work, but farm management has to contend with abnormal or unforeseeable changes like storms, floods, fires, insect pests, etc. As a result of a sudden shower in harvest time the plans of the day may be upset at an hour's notice, and the whole working force of the farm may have to be reorganized and set at a new task for which there are no precedents or experiences to guide. To direct a score of men under these conditions requires a degree of intelligence, resourcefulness, and executive ability of a very high order. To direct a hundred would require the ability of a military commander, a merchant prince, or a railway magnate, while to direct a thousand effectively enough to be economical, may safely be said to be a human impossibility. When these seasonal difficulties are added to the geometrical difficulties, it is easy to see that farming must always be an industry of small units as compared with manufacturing, mining, transportation, etc. The only apparent exceptions are evidently in those regions where the weather and the seasons are singularly stable and monotonous; that is, on certain grain farms in the semiarid West. Even there, however, large-scale farming is successful only where the agriculture is of a very low grade. But in addition to these difficulties, the farm manager has certain temperamental difficulties to contend with, — difficulties less easily understood than those already mentioned, but important nevertheless. Men who work on farms are, as a rule, more individualistic than men who work in urban industries. Men who long for human companionship, who dislike working in isolation, who herd easily, do not as a rule remain on farms, if there is a chance for them to get work in a town. Inasmuch as the towns are drawing upon the farms for their workmen, it generally results that the men who stay on the farms are those to whom the lure of the city is least attractive. They are the most individualistic, — the most impatient of rules, of restraints, of discipline; in a word, they are harder to manage in gangs. This considerably increases the difficulty of directing large numbers under one management in farming, and gives a corresponding advantage to the small farmer in competition with the very large farmer.

The supreme advantage, however, of the medium scale of production over the large scale is that the work is performed by those who have a direct, personal interest in the result. There are, therefore, no perplexing labor problems, no questions of the hours of labor or of the relation of employer to employee, to be solved. Even if large-scale farming were technically a little more efficient, these social advantages would be on the side of medium-scale production and would enable it to hold its own in competition with large-scale production. Where there are large numbers of wage-earning agricultural laborers, a class feeling is almost certain to develop among them, and an organized effort to resist the plans of the employers to increase output. There will be demands for shorter hours, frequent holidays, and sundry privileges which, all taken together, will handicap the farmer who has to depend on hired labor in his competition with the farmer who does his own work. In view of the fact, therefore, that the technical advantages are not definitely and decidedly on the side of large-scale production, these social advantages on the side of medium-scale production will give it the upper hand so long as we maintain the present social conditions.

There are social conditions, however, which might change all this and give a technical advantage to large-scale production. It is well known that slave labor necessarily means large-scale production. Now slave labor is necessarily of a low grade and cannot be self-directed. It must work under the direct supervision of an overseer or boss. This overseer must be a man of special and somewhat exceptional ability, and must therefore be paid a somewhat special or exceptional salary. It would be a wasteful process to employ such a man to superintend the work of two or three slaves. Even though the plantation owner does his own superintending, he would find it a wasteful expenditure of his time to superintend the work of a small number of slaves. In order to get the full use of the time and ability of the overseer, there must be a considerable number of slaves and sufficient acreage, which means large-scale production. But any situation where there was a large mass of low-grade labor, either slave or free, incapable of directing itself, would produce a similar result; that is, it would necessitate large-scale production. If the mass of the agricultural laborers do not know how to run farms and cannot be even trusted to work alone without direct and immediate supervision, then, of course, they must work under overseers. But an overseer could not economically give his time to superintending the work of one or two free laborers any more than he could that of one or two slaves. The consequence would be that the economic advantages would lie on the side of large-scale production, where men could be worked in gangs, rather than on the side of medium- or small-scale production. But if a high scale of intelligence, efficiency, and initiative can be maintained on the part of the mass of the agricultural workers, there is not the slightest reason to expect that large-scale production will ever become the rule in agriculture. The only chance for the advocate of large-scale production is the importation of masses of cheap coolie labor to fill up our land and crowd out the independent, self-respecting, native farmers.

Dear vs. cheap labor. This reveals one of the fundamental antagonisms of interest among the different classes of our population. The class, small as yet in this country, which owns land but does not work with its own hands, is interested in getting a large mass of cheap labor which will enable it to cultivate the land more profitably and increase the income from it. The class which labors with its hands but does not own land is interested, for obvious reasons, in keeping labor dear or wages high. But the middle class, which both owns land and works with its own hands, is divided in its interests. As owners of land, the members of this class would like to see high rents, but as workers they would like to see labor well remunerated. So long as the mass of the farmers of the country belong to this class there are not likely to be labor difficulties or conflicts between property owners and wage earners.

A large mass of cheap labor would inevitably result in a separation of classes. So long as we have cheap land and dear labor the way is easy from the position of farm hand to farm owner. Wages being high, it is easy for the farm hand to save money. Land being cheap, it is easy for him to buy land. Therefore every farm hand who will practice ordinary thrift and foresight may reasonably expect to become a farm owner. Barring sickness or accident, there is no excuse for him if he does not.

Therefore the number of farm workers who remain permanently in the class of hired laborers is relatively small. Forty years ago one month's wages of a farm hand would buy as much as one acre of land almost anywhere in the state of Iowa, and in some places they would buy two, three, and even four acres. To-day, though wages have risen, land has risen still more, so that it will take at least two months' wages anywhere, and generally three, four, five, and even six months' wages, to buy an acre in that state. Under these circumstances it is not difficult to understand why fewer and fewer men own the land on which they work.

But let the tendency be carried still further; that is, let there be dear land and cheap labor, and a different result will follow. Labor being cheap, or wages low, it will be difficult for the farm hand to buy land. A larger number will fail to make the transition from the position of laborer to that of landowning farmer, and there will be a larger class permanently in the position of hired laborers. This separation of classes will foist upon the country some of the same social problems which are such a present disgrace to our cities. The way to prevent this is to see to it that our agricultural population maintains a high standard of intelligence, of efficiency, of independence, and of power of initiative; or, in other words, that as many as possible of them shall possess sufficient *managing ability* to fit them to become independent farmers, and that every effort to fill up our rural districts with any other class of people be defeated.

Disadvantages of small-scale farming. Before discussing the merits and demerits of small-scale farming let us distinguish a little more sharply than we have done as yet between medium-scale and small-scale farming. A single acre of land, or even less, when devoted to some highly specialized product, such as violets or winter vegetables, may be medium-scale rather than small-scale farming. Such a tract of land devoted to such a purpose may easily require the entire working time of one family even when equipped with all the known labor-saving devices which can be used in that business. But only a limited number can engage in such extreme agricultural specialization as this. The vast majority of farmers must necessarily be engaged in the growing of the great staple products for which there is a large and permanent demand. To try to grow any of these staple products, or to engage in general farming on one acre, or three, or five, or even ten, will usually be small-scale farming. If it uses the best equipment in the way of labor-saving devices, no family can employ all of its time on so small a tract in growing grain, hay, beef, wool, cotton, or any of these great crops.

A great deal has been written in advocacy of small-scale farming under such alluring titles as "Three Acres and a Cow" or "Three Acres and Liberty" (for those to whom the idea of liberty is more inspiring than that of the cow). While three acres devoted to some high-priced agricultural specialty will bring in a handsome income, yet, as already suggested, the mass of our farmers cannot grow agricultural specialties. Three acres devoted to any of the great crops which are necessary to feed and clothe the race is a very poor way to make a living, and as long as laborers can get reasonable wages, they are surely not going to make a stampede to get three-acre lots. Again, while a man of good business ability may undoubtedly make a living off three acres, yet if he has good business ability he is usually not in need of three acres. He can run a bank, a store, or a larger farm, and make a much better living than he could from three acres, even when liberty and a fluent cow are added. There are, however, exceptional cases where this will prove a useful combination. These are well worth our thoughtful consideration, but we must not think that we are solving a great agricultural problem when we are providing for a few exceptional cases.

In the first place there is the army of the unemployed in every large city. It is urged that they be put upon these small tracts of land and allowed to make a living. While this method, even if it would work, is a solution of an urban rather than of a rural problem, being merely a scheme whereby the cities may relieve themselves of a burden of their own creation by shifting it upon the country, yet the rural economist ought to consider it on general philanthropic grounds. Experience has shown, how-ever, that, as *a general rule*, men who cannot get employment or make a living in an American city, with its growing indus-tries and expanding opportunities, will seldom be able to make a living in the country, even if given the free use of a small parcel of land. Occasionally there is a man whose health or whose temperament unfits him for life in a crowded city or for work in a gang under the surveillance of a boss, who could do well under rural conditions, where work is in the open air, and where it can be performed independently. For such men it is a real godsend to be given an opportunity to get back to the land, and the three-acre farm may be the best thing for a small percentage of these, though the majority of them would do better to take positions as farm hands on farms of a larger size. While a majority of those who attempt to make their own living on these minute farms make rather poor livings, even this may prove an attractive alternative in a country where so-cial conditions are bad; that is, where trades are overcrowded and wages low. In general, the worse the social conditions are, the more men there will be to whom the three-acre farm will be an advantage. But so long as wages, especially the wages of farm labor, are as good as they are in this country, the number to whom this type of farming will appeal will remain small.

A larger class who might be benefited by these small farms consists of laborers and artisans having employment in regular trades. They sometimes have a little extra time mornings, evenings, and holidays, which might be spent in their own gardens, if they had gardens, to better advantage than it is now spent. Besides, their children would undoubtedly profit greatly from having some productive work to do during a part of the time outside of school hours. The chief difficulty in the way of the extension of this kind of small farming is the lack of adequate transportation facilities. Even with adequate transportation facilities, however, only a small percentage of the people would really gain anything from this source, because of the lack of the mental and more particularly the moral qualities necessary to make a good farmer or gardener. But out of the millions of laboring people in our cities there would doubtless be many thousands who would find this kind of farming a great help in getting a living for their families, if land were to be had in small parcels and if transportation facilities were sufficiently developed to enable them to get to and from their work conveniently. If one laborer's family in a hundred, or even one in a thousand, were materially benefited in this way, it would be well worth accomplishing. But this type of farming usually reaches a higher development in countries where trades are overcrowded and wages low, than where the demand for labor is fairly good and wages are fairly high. Under these conditions a larger number are driven by necessity to supplement their regular earnings by work in their gardens, utilizing their spare moments and the surplus labor power of their families. But even in a country where wages are relatively high, a wider diffusion of the knowledge of the gardener's art would undoubtedly result in a much wider application of that art by wage workers and their families.

Gardens of this description, sometimes called homecrofters' gardens by English-speaking people, have become prominent features of the environs of European cities such as Paris, London, and Berlin. They have had their highest development in the neighborhood of Paris, where some remarkable results have been achieved on very small areas. More remarkable still, however, are some of the things which have been written about them upon a very small basis of fact. Though they are important as considered by themselves, yet as compared with the great agricultural interests of rural France, these city and suburban gardens are of microscopic importance.

We come now to the question of small-scale farming as a distinctly rural problem and not as a solution of urban problems. This concerns that class of farmers who are farmers and nothing else, and who make their living from very small farms devoted to the production of the great staple crops. A great deal has been written by the admirers of this system of farming, but most of their arguments apply to medium-scale farming better than to small-scale farming. Small-scale farming, as we have defined it, invariably means small incomes for the farmers, though the land is usually well cultivated and yields large crops per acre. There is no reason to expect, however, that small farms will yield more per acre than medium-sized farms, and, as a matter of fact, they do not. A farm large enough to enable the farmer to use adequate team force, with efficient tools and machinery, will usually be quite as well cultivated as a farm so small as to make heavy teams and efficient tools and machinery an unprofitable investment. As suggested in a previous chapter, the French or the Belgian peasant frequently finds it more profitable to dispense altogether with horses, or even oxen, as draft animals, using rather a pair of milch cows, or only a single cow, for such work as he cannot do with his own muscles. This is not due to his ignorance, but to the simple fact that his farm is too small to employ more efficient but more expensive draft animals advantageously. It will take the produce of from three to five acres of hay and grain to feed one horse throughout the year. The farmer with only a ten- or fifteen-acre farm would have very little left for himself if he tried to keep a pair of horses to do his work, unless, as suggested above, he is in a position to produce some agricultural specialty. He would likewise find a reaping or a mowing machine a poor investment. The general result of such small-scale staple farming is necessarily the use of laborious and inefficient methods.

However, a great increase in the agricultural population of the country, which seems so desirable to some people, will necessarily result in either the multiplication of small farms or of agricultural laborers. If we are to have a wholesale increase in the rural population anyway, the former may be, and probably is, the more attractive alternative. It is the desire to escape both alternatives which, more than anything else, explains the movement from the country to the city, though doubtless less commendable motives are frequently mixed with this one. It is this motive undoubtedly which drives multitudes of people from our own rural districts to the Canadian Northwest, where land is still abundant.

In so far as the movement from the country to the city has the result of maintaining medium-scale farming rather than small-scale farming on the one hand, or the formation of an agricultural proletariat on the other, it is a wholly commendable movement, and all efforts to check it or to increase the agricultural population beyond the point where medium-scale farming can be maintained, is wholly and extremely vicious. We must therefore expect the surplus population to continue to leave the rural districts. That is the only way by which a high standard of rural living can be maintained.

That medium-sized farms are more profitable than small farms in a certain section of New York state has been conclusively shown by Professor G. F. Warren of Cornell University, who furnishes the following tables. They form a part of the results of an agricultural survey of Tompkins County, New York.

SIZE OF FARM AND CROP YIELDS

Townships of Ithaca, Dryden, Danby, and Lansing

Acres in farms	Yields per Acre		
	Oats (bushels)	Potatoes (bushels)	Hay (tons)
30 or less	35	117	1.38
30–60	32	111	1.36
61–100	32	119	1.33
101–150	34	114	1.35
151–200	32	127	1.24
over 200	35	113	1.24

Contrary to popular opinion, the medium-scale farms are producing as good yields or crops as the small farms, except in the case of hay. The hay yields are slightly less on the bigger farms.

SIZE OF FARM RELATED TO PROFITS

586 Farms operated by Owners. (Townships of Ithaca, Dryden, Danby, and Lansing)

Acres	Number of farms	Average size (acres)	Labor income
30 or less	30	21	$168
31–60	108	49	254
61–100	214	83	373
101–150	143	124	436
151–200	57	177	635
over 200	34	261	946
Average	. . . .	103	415

These figures help to explain why, according to the census of 1910, the small farms are disappearing. It is also true that the large farms, of 500 acres and over, are disappearing. The tendency is undoubtedly toward the medium-scale farm as the most efficient agricultural unit.

The equipment of the farm. As stated in a previous chapter, the question of the equipment of a farm is partly one of proportion. That phase of the question, however, has been sufficiently discussed already, and we may now consider the kinds of equipment rather than the mere question of the quantity of each kind to use in combination with the others.

Power. The first problem in the equipment of a farm, as well as in that of a factory or a railroad, is the problem of power. Every one is familiar with the facts regarding the revolutions which have been wrought in other industries by the substitution of new sources of power, particularly steam. While there are many other operations upon a farm where power is needed, yet the greatest need is in the treatment of the soil, — turning it, pulverizing it, and making a proper seed bed of it. Next in importance to this is the need for power in the transportation of crops from the fields to the barns, and from the barns to the markets, and of seed, manures, fertilizers, fencing materials, etc., to different parts of the farm. For none of these purposes is a stationary engine available; they all require traction power. Wherever stationary power is needed, mechanical power of some kind is clearly, and beyond all question, cheaper and more efficient than animal power. But where traction is needed, there is no such clear and indubitable advantage in mechanical over animal power, except where there is a suitable roadbed prepared especially for the engine. This is, of course, impossible in most of the farm work. Some of the heavier work of the farm, such as plowing and drawing loads to market, may be done economically with a traction engine, though even here the advantage is sometimes doubtful. And there is a multitude of operations on every farm which cannot be performed efficiently or economically except with animal power. Harrowing, drawing the corn planters, grain drills, etc., cultivating the growing corn, cotton, potatoes, etc., and all similar tasks, demand animal rather than mechanical power, and, so far as we are yet able to see into the future, will continue to demand it.[1] Since it is necessary to have a certain amount of animal power for these purposes on every well-equipped farm, it is sometimes economical to use it for other tasks where mechanical power might otherwise prove more efficient and more economical.

Animal power. Taking the world over, a great variety of animals have been used for this purpose. They include the elephant, the camel, the buffalo, the reindeer, the dog, the ox, the horse, the ass, and the mule. We in America, as well as the nations in western Europe, make use of the last four only. In all probability we shall continue to restrict ourselves to these four, though there are reasons for believing that the camel would prove a useful addition on some of the farms of the arid Southwest, from Texas to southern California, if we could only become accustomed to it and skillful in its management. However, the advantage is by no means certain, and the difficulty of getting used to the camel would be considerable; therefore it is not probable that it will ever come into general use on this continent. In southeastern Europe, however, one frequently sees camels harnessed to plows, harrows, and even to twine binders imported from America.

While the ass is in common use as a draft animal in some parts of southern Europe, particularly on very small farms, its use for such purposes is almost unknown in this country. The ox was formerly found at work on almost every farm, but its use has very greatly declined, particularly since about the period of the Civil War, when farm machinery came into general use. In very recent years, however, there has been a slight renewal of interest in the ox, partly as a result of

---

[1] Prophecy is, however, always hazardous. Since it is not only hazardous but unnecessary, we shall content ourselves with the undoubted fact that at the present time mechanical power has not displaced animal power.

the high price of beef, and partly because of the high cost of horses. But in spite of this apparent renewal of interest, the ox is a relatively small factor in the agricultural economy of the nation as a whole. As a source of animal power the horse stands preëminent among domestic animals in this country, and the mule comes second, but even he is not a close second. According to the census of 1900 there were, on farms in the United States, about 20,000,000 horses and 2,000,000 mules and asses. That census did not take the number of working oxen, but according to that of 1890 there were about 500,000 in the country. In some parts of Europe, however, particularly in central and southern France, in Spain and Italy, and in some parts of Germany, the ox is still a factor of great importance. In parts of France and Italy, in particular, cattle have been bred for work and not exclusively for beef and milk. Hence the oxen of these countries are probably more efficient as working animals than any of the breeds with which we are familiar in this country, except perhaps the Devons, which used to be noted for their excellence as working cattle. When one sees the huge white oxen of Tuscany, with their relatively rapid gait and their prodigious strength, one is prepared to believe that they may be quite as efficient as horses for heavy farm work. As a matter of fact, the author was told by a large Italian landowner, who was also a scientific agriculturist, that he had made careful trials of both horses and oxen and that he had found the latter to be much more profitable. There are reasons, however, as will be shown later, why this might be true in Italy and not true in America, quite irrespective of the difference in the breeds of cattle.

Comparative advantages of horses and oxen. In general the advantages of using oxen are: (1) Their lower cost as compared with horses; (2) their lower liability to disease or unsoundness and their greater ability to stand exposure; (3) the lower cost, both for purchase and maintenance, of yokes and chains as compared with harness; (4) the fact that when they become unfit for work, either through age or injury, they can be fattened and turned into beef.

Stated more favorably, the ox may be worked from the age of three years up to seven or eight, during which time he is gaining in weight, and then sold for beef, his gain in weight and value paying in part the cost of keeping him. There are also certain minor advantages, such as the slight saving of time in hitching and unhitching oxen as compared with horses; the fact that oxen are less nervous and excitable and less inclined to worry when at rough work, such as plowing in stony or stumpy ground; the fact that they may be turned out to pasture, when not in use, with slightly less care and attention than horses usually demand; and the fact that oxen can subsist on slightly coarser feed than horses require.

Over against these advantages are these disadvantages:

1. The slowness of movement of the ox unfits him for any except such heavy work as needs to be done at a slow gait. A horse is more adaptable to a variety of purposes, being able to trot when necessary, to walk rapidly when the nature of the work demands it, or slowly when that gait is required.

2. Most of our farm machinery requires the rapid gait of the horse rather than the slow gait of the ox. This, however, could be remedied by the manufacturers of machinery by the simple expedient of gearing the machinery higher if oxen were in general use. But the fact that this is not done tends to prevent their coming into general use. Therefore there is a considerable social inertia in favor of the horse, even if it could be shown that oxen were more economical.

3. It is probable, though not definitely proved, that the horse is a better machine than the ox for transforming feed into mechanical energy, though the latter may be the better

machine for turning it into flesh. If allowed to take a slower gait, with a correspondingly heavier load, the average ox may be able to pull as many foot pounds in a day as the average horse in proportion to the food consumed. This has not been put to a satisfactory scientific test.

However that may be, there is no doubt that one man, with a good team of horses, will be able to do more work of the general and miscellaneous kinds which come up on a farm in the course of a year than he could do with a yoke of oxen, though he might not be able to do more of special kinds of work, such as breaking sod or plowing heavy ground. In a country such as Italy, where labor is cheap and where it is therefore not a matter of supreme importance to get as much work out of each man as possible, the lower cost of the oxen might easily compensate for the smaller amount of work done. But in a country like the United States, where labor is dear, it is highly important that it be economized and that each man should be enabled to accomplish as much as possible. Therefore it may pay better to equip him with a team of horses than a yoke of oxen, even though the horses cost a great deal more, provided he will accomplish more with them. This is a principle of economy of very wide application. If you are hiring a very expensive man, you must not give him a cheap equipment for his work, provided you can get more and better work out of him by giving him a more expensive equipment. But if you are hiring a cheap man, it may not pay you to give him the expensive equipment. If one cheap man with a cheap equipment is not able to do all your work, it may be cheaper to hire two than to give the one a more expensive equipment. The high price of American labor is the final economic reason for the general displacement of the ox by the horse on American farms, and the low price of labor in southern Europe is the final economic reason why the ox is still used in preference to the horse.

In some parts of France, particularly on the beet-sugar farms in the northeastern section, oxen fit admirably into the peculiar system of rural economy prevalent in that region. Considerable numbers of oxen, usually of the large white or cream-colored Nivernais breed, are purchased every spring and used during the season for the heavy work of the farm, including the carting of the beets to the factories and of the beet pulp back to the farm. After this work is finished the oxen are fattened on the beet pulp mixed with wheat straw, and sold for beef, and a new supply of oxen is purchased for the following year's work.

It has frequently been urged, in advocacy of a return to the use of oxen on farms, that there is great economy in using an animal which can be turned into food after his working years are finished. There is undoubtedly something to be said in favor of this policy, especially when it is reduced to a system like that adopted by the beet-sugar growers of France. The policy, also, of beginning to work oxen at three years of age and fattening them for beef at seven or eight has its merits. But where there are large city markets for horses for street work, the farmer is enabled to take advantage of a similar economy. He can begin working his horses at three years of age and sell them to city buyers at good prices, if they are still sound, at seven, eight, or even ten years of age. At these ages they are seasoned and are ready for the trying work on the city streets. The rapidity with which horse flesh is used up on city streets is such that the average horse will last as long, if he comes to the city at eight or ten years of age, as he would if he came at four, five, or six. In other words, it is not age, but pavements, strains, bruises, and hard work which wear him out. That is why a horse of mature age, if still sound, will sell for more than a younger and less mature animal for work on city streets. The farmer can work his horses, therefore, until they reach this mature and seasoned age, and then sell them to good advantage, thus realizing the same economy as is realized in the use of oxen. However, there is the unavoidable disadvantage that if the horse becomes unsound, particularly in his feet or legs, his value is gone, whereas the ox is still good for beef. Until horse flesh comes into general use as an article of food, this will be a permanent disadvantage to the user of horses.

The mule. The economic differences between the horse and the mule as a source of power are by no means so great as those between the horse and ox. The horse is the larger animal, and will, on the average, by reason of this superior size and weight, exert more strength on a short, sharp pull than the mule. Pound per pound, however, the mule is quite as capable, though it is doubtful if he is any more capable. Some extravagant opinions are frequently expressed regarding the prodigious strength of the mule, but these opinions are not based upon practical tests. On the other hand, the mule appears to have the more endurance. At steady work such as plowing, which does not require short and sharp pulls, but continuous hard work over long hours, the mule will probably do more work in proportion to his weight. Again, it is probable that he will thrive on slightly coarser food than the horse, though the difference in this respect is not so great as is popularly supposed. Pound per pound, he requires quite as much nourishment as the horse, though he may get along with a slightly larger proportion of his nourishment in the form of hay and slightly less in the form of grain. This, however, is not always economical. Certainly it is a mistake to assume that the mule does not respond to good feeding as well as the horse. Again, the mule is less nervous and excitable than the horse, and wastes less of his energy in worry and excitement in trying situations and under unkind and unskillful handling. Finally, the mule is better fitted for very hot weather than the horse. The two qualities last named give him a decided advantage on the cotton and sugar farms of the South, where the work is done largely by negro labor, and where it has to be done under intense heat.

On the other hand, the horse is slightly less expensive to rear. The cross between the mare and the jack shows a lower percentage of fertility than that between the mare and the stallion. Moreover, during the early period of infancy, the mule colt is more susceptible to injury and sickness than the horse colt, though afterwards the advantage is on the other side. Another advantage on the side of the horse, particularly in Northern cities, is his greater size and capacity for drawing heavy loads over paved streets. Again, his feet are believed by many to stand the pounding on stone pavements better than those of the mule. Still another advantage on the side of the horse is the fact that the teamsters of the Northern cities are more accustomed to the horse than the mule, and therefore will generally buy him in preference. This is an important item for the farmer who expects to sell his mature and seasoned animals to city buyers. However, the market for mules in the South is a partial offset to this; but if there were as many mules grown as there are horses, this market would soon be oversupplied. Were it not for the larger market for the horse, it would seem that the patience and steady endurance of the mule would fit him so admirably for farm work, where there are fewer occasions than in cities for short and sharp exertions of great strength, as to cause a great increase of his numbers, particularly in the hay and grain farms of the great central area of the United States.

Mechanical power. As stated above, where stationary power is needed, mechanical power is beyond all question more economical and efficient than animal power. The use of mechanical power for traction also is increasing, and will doubtless continue to increase, but that it will ever completely displace animal power is more than doubtful. Where a suitable roadbed is prepared, mechanical is proving superior to animal power even for traction purposes, and it is very probable that it will eventually displace animal power, or nearly so, on our roads and streets. For plowing, particularly in large fields, it has some advantages also, and may gain in favor as engines are improved, but it will probably be a long time before it displaces animal power completely. Some of the large harvesting machines in use in the Far West have been drawn by mechanical traction, but the experiment has not yet proved such an unqualified success as to cause its general adoption. An interesting combination is being tried, by means of which the dead weight of the harvester is drawn by horse power, but the machinery is run by steam or gasoline engines. This is virtually a stationary engine running the machinery while the traction power is furnished by horses. Eight horses are able to pull the whole machine, as a mere load on wheels, whereas it would take thirty-two to pull it if the traction had to run the machinery also.

For the running of stationary machinery on a farm, water power is undoubtedly the most economical where it exists, but unfortunately those farms are very few. The windmill is an equally economical source of power, and it can be used on almost every farm in almost any place, but it is suitable for only a few kinds of work, such as pumping water, grinding feed, etc., which do not have to be done at definite periods. Where labor is dear it would not prove economical to use so uncertain and so uncontrollable a source of power as wind, for work which required labor as well as power. There would be too many vexatious and unprofitable delays and interruptions. As between steam engines and gasoline, or explosive engines for stationary power, the choice must depend upon a variety of circumstances. Where, as on a dairy farm for example, considerable quantities of hot water are needed, and the same boiler can be used for heating the water and running the engine, steam power is unquestionably more economical. Again, where coal does not have to be hauled too far or does not cost too much, and where considerable power is needed, and needed a good deal of the time, steam is probably to be preferred. But the advantage is clearly on the side of the explosive engine, where only a small amount of power is needed, or where it is needed for only short periods at a time, or where it is inconvenient to give constant attention to the engine. The explosive engine can be started more quickly and does not require so much attention while running.

Attempting to forecast the future is always hazardous because one never knows what new inventions or improvements may change the whole situation. But so far as present indications go, it looks as though mechanical power would be used more on farms, and animal power somewhat less. It is not improbable, moreover, that the work of hauling produce to market or to shipping points will eventually be done almost exclusively by mechanical power, though this will depend somewhat on the state of highway improvement. A farmer who has work enough for his horses on the farm could scarcely afford to use them on the road, or to keep extra horses for that purpose, when auto-trucks come into general use. If the farmer cannot himself own one, he will probably find it more economical to hire some one else to do his freighting for him, just as he now finds it more economical to ship by rail than to do his own transporting. Where, however, the farmer finds that he has to keep more team force than he can conveniently employ on the farm after harvest, he may still find it more economical to do his own hauling with his own teams. Again, the heavy work of plowing will be done more and more by mechanical power. The farmer whose farm is too small to make it economical for him to own a traction engine and a gang plow will, in many cases at least, find it economical to hire some one else to do his plowing, just as he now hires some one else to do his threshing. The general result of these tendencies will be to reduce somewhat the number of work animals kept on farms, or to check their increase somewhat, leaving a larger proportion of the produce of the farms to be turned into money, since a smaller proportion will be used in providing power, that is, in horse feed.

Live stock. It is safe to say that there is no such thing as good farming without live stock, except in the neighborhood of large cities from which abundant supplies of manure can be carted, or where it is found profitable to buy large quantities of chemical fertilizers, to be used in the production of high-priced agricultural specialties. The relation between live stock and good agriculture is partly cause and partly effect. Live stock is a cause of good agriculture in the sense that it is good for the land and good for the farmer; it is an effect of good agriculture in the sense that good farming is necessary before the live-stock industry can reach its highest development.

The benefit which the land receives from live stock may be due in part to factors not well understood, such as the tramping of the soil by the animals' feet; but it is not necessary to give such doubtful reasons when there are at least two that are unquestioned. In the first place, the consumption on the farm of some of its vegetable products and the removal from it of only the refined products, or products combining great value with little weight, such as butter, cheese, wool, eggs, and meat, removes comparatively little fertility from the soil; that is to say, the greater part of the value, for fertilizing purposes, of the food consumed by live stock is left on the land in the form of manure. In the second place, live stock, particularly sheep and goats, have a liking for many of the noxious weeds, grasses, and shrubs with which the farmer has to fight incessantly, and they prove effective allies of his in his efforts to keep them down; that is, they help to " keep the farm clean." Even poultry plays its humble part in this work, and wages war not only on weeds but on insects as well. Any one familiar with the farms of the Middle West will have had occasions to notice some remarkable object lessons of this kind. In a grasshopper year, for example, when pastures are generally suffering from these pests, one farmer will occasionally be found whose pastures show very little injury from that source, the reason being that he has a large flock of turkeys roaming over his pastures, literally sweeping their path clean of grasshoppers as they go. Our orchardists have probably not yet begun to appreciate the help which they may get from poultry in their efforts to fight the multifarious insect pests which always threaten them with ruin.

That live stock is good for the farmer as well as the farm is due primarily to the fact that they require constant attention and train him in habits of thrift, economy, and foresight. They are thus a source of education in the virtues which go to make the good farmer. The farmer who sells his hay, grain, or cotton crop and has no continuous business interest to occupy his time and thought during the interval between the sale of one crop and the planting of another is, on the average, more likely to fall into habits of wastefulness and shiftlessness. The fact of his having a herd of live stock helps to keep him alert. Again, animals are more interesting than plants, being a higher form of life, and are more likely to create in the mind of the farmer an interest in themselves. When he develops a kind of love for his animals as animals, in addition to his interest in them as a source of profit, he has a double motive for care and industry in their behalf, and this tends to make a more careful, painstaking man of him in every respect. However, in some exceptional cases this has the unfortunate result of leading a farmer to spend more care and attention on his live stock than on his family.

That good farming is necessary to the highest development of the live-stock industry is shown historically by the fact that it was not until after the introduction of clover and root crops into England, and the superior type of farming which resulted from it, that the great English breeders began to develop the modern English breeds of live stock. The reason was that for the first time these crops furnished winter feed in sufficient quantities to enable the flocks and herds to be brought through the year in good condition. In America, however, up to the present time, this principle has not been so apparent because we have always had a frontier where cattle could be grown cheaply on open land or ranges. When these range lands are exhausted and our supply of cattle has to be produced on our cultivated farms, it will be found necessary greatly to improve our characteristic systems of culture, particularly in the management of pastures, where there is probably greater room for improvement than in any other branch of agriculture. The introduction also of superior forage crops, such as alfalfa, is likely to have a profound reaction upon our live-stock industry. Again, sheep husbandry is an impossibility in any community whose moral and intellectual condition is such as to permit the common cur dog to multiply freely and prey upon the flocks of the would-be enterprising farmer.

Tools. As already suggested, the question of the kinds and quantities of the tools, machinery, etc., to use will depend partly upon the size of the farm. It will depend also upon the social and economic conditions in the community surrounding the farm, partly upon the character of the labor to be had, and particularly and primarily upon the price which has to be paid for that labor. A machine is, of course, a labor-saving device. Whether it pays you to use it or not, will depend upon whether the machine costs less or more than the labor would cost which it enables you to save. If the labor costs less than the machine, obviously it will not pay to use the machine. The extensive use of agricultural machinery is most economical, and will therefore prevail principally where labor is dear and hard to get. At the same time, this extensive use of machinery requires a higher kind of labor than that which can be utilized where muscular strength is employed. This required superiority of labor is both moral and intellectual, but primarily moral; that is, greater steadiness of habit, reliability, and resourcefulness are required.

Buildings. One of the greatest causes of waste energy on the average farm is the lack of proper buildings and the bad arrangement of those already erected. It is easy to condemn farmers in a new country for their slipshod methods, particularly for the somewhat prevalent custom of allowing tools and machinery to remain exposed to the weather when not in use. It is not always so easy, when you come to try it, to show them, in dollars and cents, just how they would save money by building houses to shelter their implements. The high cost of building materials and labor in a new country, the lack of capital and the high rate of interest, together with the rapidity with which tools deteriorate even when kept under shelter, furnish an explanation of, even if they do not justify, the absence of buildings. But these difficulties are of course outgrown in an older country, and farmers are no longer thus reproached for carelessness.

The bad arrangement of buildings, necessitating a great many extra steps in the perennial job of doing chores, is a problem not so easily solved as that of the mere absence of buildings in a new country. It is too intricate a problem to discuss at length here, even if the author had the necessary knowledge, which he has not. It may prove suggestive, however, to merely mention characteristic arrangements which are to be seen in different countries. One of the most interesting is that found throughout northern France, particularly in Normandy and Picardy. All the farm buildings, including the dwelling, are built solidly around a central square or farmyard, and all face inward. This masses everything in this central court, which serves as front yard, barnyard, and poultry yard, and into which open the stables, the wagon and tool sheds, the granaries, etc. In this square is also the inevitable *fumier* or manure heap. Altogether it is a convenient arrangement, but it does not make an attractive front yard for the dwelling house. In Holland one frequently finds everything in one building, — the dwelling in the front, stables in the back, and the haymow and grain bins in the middle. Among people who are so scrupulously clean as the Dutch this is an excellent arrangement. In parts of Italy one sees occasionally a farm building, fairly large and commodious, built of stone and roofed with tile, in which the ground floor serves as stable, granary, etc., while the upper stories serve as a dwelling house. Outside of New England, many people in this country do not know that in this section the characteristic arrangement is to have the barn and house connected, with the wood-shed, tool house, and possibly a carriage house serving as the connecting link. This is both convenient and economical, in that it gives more room for less cost than could be got from several disconnected buildings, and enables one to pass under shelter from the house to the barn. It also serves as a spur to cleanliness, since it would be unpleasant to have a foul and odoriferous barn in such close proximity to the house.

Problems of supervision and administration. The problems of supervision and administration cannot be discussed at length in a treatise of this kind. Nothing but actual experience and training will fit a man for the actual direction of the farm work from day to day and from hour to hour. There is probably no other business enterprise of equal size which demands of its manager such resourcefulness, such decisiveness, such energy and "push" as a farm. The seasonal character of the work requires a constant and incessant changing of plans and solving of new problems. One thing, however, needs to be said with the greatest emphasis, and that is, that good accounting is the key to all successful administration, whether in farm, store, factory, or transportation company. This is a fact which farmers have been slower than other business men to accept. Good accounting means, of course, much more than mere keeping of cash accounts, or a record of receipts and expenditures. It means such a record as will enable the farmer to tell exactly at the end of the year how much every part of the farm enterprise has cost him and how much it has brought in. By this means only will he be able to determine just where the losses have occurred and just where the profits have been made. Until he knows this he is in constant danger of one of the commonest mistakes, — that of losing as much on one product as he makes on another.

Scientific management. Every farmer in the corn belt is familiar with the different ways of reducing such a simple operation as the husking of corn to a system. Each expert corn husker has his own favorite system by which the number of motions involved in the husking of an ear of corn and throwing it into the wagon is reduced to an absolute minimum. In the old days when the binding of grain was done by hand, every expert binder had his favorite system by which the motions involved in the binding of a sheaf of grain were also reduced to the minimum. Such examples as these furnish a basis, or a beginning, for the scientific study of farm management on a broader scale. The same problem is involved in the harnessing, hitching, unharnessing, and unhitching of teams, in the handling of hay and grain, in the arrangement of farm buildings, in changing from one kind of work to another. The problem of the manager must always be that of reducing the number of motions to a minimum and of saving every second of time possible in the performance of any of these operations. There is a vast field of study here and endless opportunities for the exercise of the ingenuity, originality, and scientific precision of the farm manager.

This kind of economy, that is, the kind which economizes labor and muscular energy, is more important in this country, where wages are high, than in any other country where wages are low.

Problems of buying and selling. As suggested above, the problem of buying and selling grows in importance as farming develops from the self-sufficing to the commercial stage, and still further as it develops from the growing of staple crops to the growing of agricultural specialties. Aside from the fundamental problem of the buyer, namely, what to buy, there are three problems of general importance, — from whom to buy how to buy, and with what to buy.

The middleman. The first of these problems involves some study of the commercial organization of the country, for the problem is really whether to buy from middlemen or, as far as possible, from producers. Fundamentally, the purpose of the middleman is to save trouble for both the producer and the consumer. If the producer is to take time finding a consumer for his product, that time is lost to the work of production, since he is thereby prevented from producing as much as would otherwise be possible. The middleman, who saves him that trouble and enables him to devote all his time to the work of production, is therefore performing an important service and is entitled to some profit on a transaction to pay him therefor. A like service is, of course, performed for the consumer. So long as the profits of the middleman are no more than sufficient to reward him for the services performed, neither the farmer nor the consumer of farm products has any right to complain. It sometimes happens, however, that the market becomes so overorganized as actually to make work for the middleman and to put the consumer more or less within his power ; for goods in the process of transition from producer to consumer are practically forced by the organization of the market to go through certain special channels, and all other channels are virtually closed. The middlemen who control these channels are able to levy a rather heavy toll upon goods which pass through them. In order to prevent abuses of this kind it is important that as many channels as possible be kept open between the producer and the consumer ; in other words, it is desirable that they should have as many opportunities as possible to deal directly with one another, even though they may not always find it profitable to do so. It is extremely improbable that any scheme by which consumers could buy directly of producers and producers sell directly to consumers would eliminate the middleman altogether. He will always be in a position to save trouble to both the producers and the consumers. And yet if producers and consumers always have an opportunity to deal directly with one another, the result will be that the middleman can only charge for his services what they are actually worth. If he attempts to charge more than they are worth, that is, if his charges are such as to make it cheaper for producers and consumers to deal directly with one another, they will dispense with his services. But if such opportunities are closed and the producers and consumers are compelled to deal through the middleman, he will find himself in a position to levy a toll in excess of the real value of his services.

Parcels post. For these reasons it is highly important that such opportunities should be kept open as are furnished by public markets in our large cities. Again, it would be highly advantageous if a parcels post could be established. Under this system, if it were properly administered, it would be possible in a great many instances for consumers to order poultry, eggs, and certain of the less bulky farm products by mail from producers. This would not mean that any considerable proportion of the business would actually be transacted through the post office, but it would serve to keep open the channel of communication between producer and consumer, and thus to restrict the middleman to such profits as would compensate him for the real service he would perform.

How to buy. The next question, namely, how to buy, involves such possibilities as coöperative buying as compared with individual buying. Students of the labor problem of our cities have come to lay great stress on what is known as collective bargaining. By collective bargaining is meant the process by which a whole body of laboring men, acting as a unit, bargain through their representative for wages. It is held that this method gives them greater bargaining power. A similar principle is involved in what is known as coöperative buying on the part of consumers. It is not always possible for the farm manager to enter into a coöperative alliance with other farmers, because of bad social conditions. It is not too much to say that one of the worst drawbacks to American farming is the extreme individualism of many of our farmers, constantly showing itself in the form of unwillingness to coöperate with their neighbors for their mutual advantage. A few coöperative stores have been run successfully, but by far the greater number of those which have been attempted have failed. This is, of course, not entirely due to lack of the coöperative spirit. It has frequently happened that a coöperative store has been started where there was no occasion for starting one, where the local merchant was doing a fair and legitimate business and charging no more than his service was actually worth. To undertake a coöperative store in competition with such a merchant is to invite failure, for the excellent reason that such a store ought to fail. Nevertheless a certain kind of coöperation in the buying of such products as can be graded and sold at standard prices, such as fertilizers, standard farm machinery, lumber, and the like, can be done to advantage if farmers will only agree among themselves to coöperate and will not be held apart by suspicion. The advantage comes not so much from saving the local merchant's profit as from placing large orders. Sometimes, however, these large orders might as well be placed through the local merchants as through coöperative organizations pure and simple.

Credit. The question, with what to buy, involves the question whether to buy always with cash or to make a judicious use of credit. What advice to give farmers in general on this subject is an exceedingly delicate question. The farmer who has not a very keen sense of values or is not in the habit of keeping accurate accounts, who does not understand the importance of charging for deterioration, etc., would better avoid the use of credit as he would the plague. If he never makes use of it, he will probably not achieve a large degree of success as a farmer; but if such an unbusinesslike farmer does make use of it, he is pretty certain to become bankrupt. But the farmer who has a keen sense of values, who understands business methods, who keeps accurate accounts and knows what to charge for deterioration, and who at the same time is a successful manager in the sense that he is able to grow good crops and to sell them to advantage, should not hesitate to make a large use of credit. By means of it he saves time. He can secure fertilizers, farm machinery, live stock, etc., much earlier than would otherwise be possible. If he is very wise in his purchases or skillful in his management, he will make enough from the use of the credit he has borrowed to pay the interest and leave a handsome profit besides. This profit, that is, the sum which he makes from the purchases over and above enough to pay principal and interest, represents the advantage of making use of credit.

Sometimes the political and social conditions are such that capital cannot be borrowed except at exorbitant rates or under very unfavorable conditions. Under such circumstances the honest and capable farmer is a victim of his bad social surroundings. Therefore one of the most valuable things for the honest and capable farmer is a good system of credit by means of which he can reap a larger advantage from his own superior managing ability than would otherwise be possible.

A state of society where the sense of financial responsibility is weak, where debtors are in the habit of dodging their obligations, where the general sentiment of the community sympathizes with and encourages them in their dishonesty, where lenders and so-called "moneyed men" are unpopular and cannot get justice, there we have an invariably backward community. Such a community is an unfavorable location for an honest and capable farmer, because money and credit are invariably scarce, interest rates high, and prices low. Men with capital to invest, men of enterprise and forethought, who make the prosperity of a community, will avoid such surroundings. When such men are lacking, and there remain only those without any sense of financial responsibility, men who hate every one more prosperous and progressive than themselves,— such a community is doomed to remain, for a period at least, unprosperous, unprogressive, a reproach and a byword among more enlightened neighborhoods.

There are four kinds of credit commonly made use of by farmers,— individual credit, store credit, bank credit, and co-operative credit. Individual credit is where an individual farmer borrows from an individual lender on such terms as the two can agree upon. This is the simplest form of credit, and if both parties to the transaction are honest and wise, it is the most satisfactory of all. However, it is limited in its application. It is similar to the case of a consumer buying directly from the producer, which is an excellent system but not always possible.

Store credit. Store credit is made use of more or less in every rural community. In many cases it merely consists in buying from the local storekeeper those goods necessary to keep the household running, and paying for them after the crop is harvested. In other cases this system has undergone such a development as to dominate the whole rural life. A large part of the business of a local storekeeper, in such cases, consists in the management of the credits which he gives rather than in the buying and selling of goods. Where this system prevails, nearly every farmer arranges at the beginning of the season for a certain amount of credit at the store, giving a mortgage or lien on his crop. This puts the storekeeper in a position to dictate as to the kinds of crops to be grown, and sometimes he even specifies the method of cultivation. He is compelled to do this in order to protect himself, that is, in order that his mortgage or his lien may be worth something. In return for the credit, he only advances ordinary household supplies, horse feed, seed, fertilizers, tools, implements, etc. While not bad in itself, this system has worked disastrously in many cases, particularly in the cotton states of the South, sometimes because of the thriftlessness and incapacity of the farmers with whom the storekeeper has had to deal, and sometimes, also, by reason of the unscrupulousness of the storekeeper himself, and sometimes by reason of both combined.

Bank credit. Generally speaking, the credit system works better where it is not mixed up with something else like storekeeping, that is, where the credit institution is purely one of credit and nothing else. In other words, bank credit is generally a better system than store credit. In the first place, when one borrows of a store he does not borrow money, does not receive money, and has, moreover, no liberty to buy where he chooses. He only borrows credit and must, furthermore, make use of it in buying at the store where he borrows. But when he borrows of a bank he either receives money or the right to draw it when he needs it. He is thus at liberty to buy with that money at whatever store or in whatever way he chooses. This puts him in a position of greater independence than he enjoys when he makes use of store credit. Where the banking system is well developed and there is competition among banks to get business, it is not likely that the rate of interest charged will be exorbitant, though it is never low. The bank is virtually a middleman, performing much the same function, and entitled to a reward for the same reason, as a merchant. So long as a borrower can borrow directly from the lender, the bank's profits can be saved; but where it is difficult for the borrower to find a lender, or a lender to find a borrower, or where the personal relations are such as to prevent dealing in a personal way with one another, the bank performs a real service. They who have money to spare can deposit it in the bank, and they who need money can always find it there. Both are saved the trouble of finding one another.

Again, the bank generally deals impersonally and according to fixed rules, which it will not vary for personal considerations. In such delicate transactions as borrowing and lending this is a matter of greater importance than farmers commonly realize. Probably no one thing has worked so much disaster in farming neighborhoods, or produced more bitterness of feeling or more financial loss, than making use of personal considerations in matters of credit. In every neighborhood all over the Middle West there are men who remember to their sorrow transactions of this kind, where they were induced by personal appeals to lend money or indorse the personal notes of friends. There is probably not a farmer above threescore years of age, who has had a reputation for business capacity and integrity, who has not been burdened more than once because of his reputation. Such men are always acceptable as indorsers of notes for their less scrupulous neighbors. In times past they have continually been besieged by requests for favors of this kind, and he may regard himself as exceedingly fortunate who has never lost money in this way. One of the chief advantages of a good banking system is to protect men of honor and integrity against appeals of this kind.

Coöperative credit. Coöperative credit has not had a high development in this country. In European countries, particularly among the smaller peasant farmers, it has played a great part in recent years. Three distinct types of coöperative banks have been developed. The first is known under the name of the Raiffeisen system, the second is known as the Schulze-Delitzsch system, and the third is not known by any special name, but consists of a group of men joined together for the purpose of borrowing a considerable sum on their joint security, each one securing his own share of the sum borrowed, and assuming his equal responsibility for the payment of the whole sum. This system does not require any special organization of credit nor does it require an institution known as a bank to carry it into operation. Any group of farmers, say ten, who wanted to borrow $1000 each for a period of five years could sign a joint note for $10,000. By this means they could borrow at a lower rate of interest than any one of them could. Inasmuch, however, as there is joint responsibility, this method could be adopted only by a group of men who knew one another thoroughly and had confidence in one another's honor and solvency.

The Raiffeisen system. The Raiffeisen system, named after Herr F. W. Raiffeisen, its founder, originated in Germany after the famine years of 1846 and 1847. Herr Raiffeisen had witnessed the sufferings of the peasantry under the hard conditions imposed by the money lenders. After several attempts he succeeded, in 1849, in establishing at Flammersfeld, a coöperative loan bank. The object of this bank was to loan money at a low rate of interest, for productive agricultural purposes only, to such peasants as would comply with the rules laid down in advance. The plan succeeded, and other banks were subsequently formed in different sections. The principles on which these banks were organized are as follows : first, every individual that goes into the scheme becomes responsible for all the capital borrowed, that is, there is unlimited liability ; second, money is loaned to a peasant for an agricultural purpose only, and the purpose must meet with the approval of the representatives of the bank. They will not lend to any one until they know what he wants to do with the money and are satisfied that it will pay *him* to borrow; that is, they will decide whether or not the purpose for which he wants the money is likely to prove profitable and enable him to pay back the sum borrowed and leave a surplus besides. Under these conditions a sense of solidarity and mutual responsibility is developed among all the members, and practically nothing has ever been lost through loans of this kind. A third feature of the organization is that, after the first organization, new members are elected by a vote of those who are already members. A fourth feature is that these organizations are small and are restricted to narrow areas, in order that only near neighbors shall be in the same organization. This is made necessary by the fact that every member is responsible for loans made to other members. In the fifth place, the bank's management is absolutely democratic, the final authority on all local questions being the general meeting in which every member has one vote. The books of the bank are open to all members for inspection.

The Schulze-Delitzsch system. The Schulze-Delitzsch banks originated at about the same time as the Raiffeisen banks, but differ from them mainly in that they deal with a somewhat wealthier class of people, a large part of their loans being for commercial and industrial purposes. They do not always insist upon unlimited liability. They raise their funds sometimes by the issue of shares. They pay salaries to their officers and sometimes make use of collateral security.[1]

A system of coöperative credit resembling the Raiffeisen system, in some particulars, has had a remarkable development in recent years in Denmark and Ireland, where it has been an

[1] An excellent account of both these systems of credit may be found in an article by Professor E. W. Kemmerer, in Bailey's Cyclopedia of American Agriculture, Vol. IV, pp. 269–276. See also Henry W. Wolff, People's Banks.

important factor in the agricultural rebirth of these two countries. In Denmark, where it has had its highest development, it is based upon a remarkable spirit of friendliness and mutual helpfulness among the farming population. A group of neighbors will organize a coöperative bank, electing a president and a board of directors. The only one to receive a salary is the one who is responsible for keeping the accounts. He usually receives $150 a year. This salary and the necessary office expenses are paid out of the profits of the bank. These profits are simply the difference between the rate of interest which the bank pays for the money it borrows and the rates which it receives from the money which it lends. Since expenses are very low, one half of one per cent difference in these two rates is usually sufficient. If anything is left over after paying the necessary expenses, it is spent for some common or public purpose. The bank is open to receive deposits and to make loans on regular dates, usually twice a month. On these days some member of the board of directors is present, but these directors serve without compensation.

It is the opinion of those experts most closely acquainted with the Raiffeisen and the Schulze-Delitzsch systems that neither is specially adapted, without considerable modification, to conditions in the United States. It is possible that the Raiffeisen system might be of use in a few cases where there are very poor and struggling farmers. But the principle of unlimited liability would absolutely prevent its being even seriously considered by fairly prosperous, property-owning farmers. That is to say, a farmer who owns considerable property would not enter into any scheme where all his property would be liable for the debts of the organization should it become insolvent. Among a few very poor farmers, no one of whom owns more than a very few hundred dollars' worth of property, and all of whom are about equally wealthy (or poor), the principle of unlimited liability is essential in order to secure credit on favorable terms, and is no serious drawback from the standpoint of the individual farmer. But there is no reason why coöperative credit associations, with limited liability, should not have considerable development in this country.

Problems of selling. The problem of selling the farm crops involves some of the same questions as the problem of buying; whether, for example, to sell directly to consumers or to middlemen, whether to sell individually or coöperatively, and other similar questions, involve the same considerations as were mentioned in the discussion of the general problem of buying. As already pointed out, the problem of selling is a relatively simple one, so long as the farmer grows only staple crops. For such crops there is always a market at some price, and the price is always quotable. But the grower of agricultural specialties must look for a special market. Where such a special market exists he may succeed in getting a special and highly remunerative price, but unless he succeeds in finding a special market he may not be able to sell his product at any price. Therefore everything depends on a special market and the farmer's special skill as a seller.

In the selling of farm crops, either staple or special, there are certain general considerations of importance to the student of economics and incidentally to the farmer as well. There are, for example, four well-recognized methods of selling: first, selling by individual units; second, selling in bulk; third, selling by sample; and fourth, selling by grade or standard. These four methods may be illustrated as follows: In the sale of a horse, particularly a blooded horse, the first of these methods is alone possible. Each individual horse has his own individual qualities and his own individual value. Each individual is therefore a unit and is sold as a unit. In the selling of beef cattle or hogs the whole bunch will be sold at a specified price per pound or per hundredweight, but the whole bunch must be seen by the buyer and the price agreed upon. This is selling in bulk. Among the agricultural specialties, or even in the sale of fruits and vegetables, the method of selling by sample is frequently adopted. The whole quantity is not inspected, but samples are shown and the price is fixed on the basis of these samples. On the large produce exchanges, such as the Chicago Board of Trade, however, such standard products as wheat, pork, etc., are graded by responsible authorities, and the buyer then merely buys so many bushels or pounds of a certain grade. He is indifferent as to what particular bulk he gets, so long as he gets the requisite quantity of the required grade. He does not even see a sample. This is selling by grade or standard.

The first of these methods is the most expensive, and the last is the least expensive method of sale, but the last is possible only in a few cases. Wherever it is possible, a good deal of social energy may be saved by its adoption, and, moreover, the margin between what the producer gets and what the consumer has to give is much smaller than it is in any of the other cases. The middleman is enabled to handle products in very large quantities; therefore a very small profit on each unit of the product enables him to pay the expense of his business and to leave a profit for himself. Where this method is not possible the dealer must do a great deal of inspecting, and this involves a great deal of dickering on the market. Every such expenditure of time and energy has to be paid by the producer or by the consumer, or by both. This larger payment shows itself in a wider margin between what the producer gets and what the consumer pays than is necessary where the fourth method of selling is practiced. The difference between selling by sample and selling by grade or standard is well illustrated in the cases of cotton and wool. The former can be easily graded but the latter cannot. Accordingly the former is sold by standard or grade, whereas the latter is sold by sample.

Speculation in farm crops. There is also a question when to sell. Is it best to sell as soon as the crop is harvested or to hold for a rise in price, or may it be better to sell before the crop is harvested? Either to sell before the crop is harvested or to hold for a rise in price involves speculating on the market. As a general rule, it is safer for the farmer to stick to his work of farming and to leave speculation to those who make a specialty of it. This is a principle well recognized by successful business men in other branches. The successful miller, for example, avoids speculation as far as possible. If in order to get business he must contract long in advance, there is a speculative risk involved. This risk he uniformly covers by buying his wheat in advance. That is to say, suppose a miller has contracted to deliver 1000 barrels of flour per week for the next six months at a fixed price. He knows what the price of wheat is, but he does not know what it will be three months from to-day. If the price should go up, and he should continue to buy from week to week in order to fulfill his contract to deliver flour at the price agreed upon, it might wipe out his profits, though, of course, these would be increased if the price of wheat should fall. But of course his business is that of milling, and that requires all the attention and energy which he is capable of expending. He has no time nor energy, therefore, to expend in studying market conditions and determining whether to speculate or not. To render himself perfectly safe he buys to-day, at a fixed price, wheat enough to last him for the whole six months and to enable him to carry out his contract. By this process he may know where he stands. While it looks like speculation, it is in reality a means of avoiding speculative risks.

Again, a miller who has not a contract for delivering flour at a specified price, but who expects to be able to sell his flour at some price as fast as it is manufactured, may decide, in order to be sure of a constant supply of wheat, to buy in advance a sufficient supply to last him for the season. If the price of wheat should rise, the price of flour would probably rise also, and he would gain ; but if the price of wheat should fall, he would lose in this process of buying wheat in advance. In order to eliminate this speculative risk, he pursues another method. He sells or agrees to sell in advance the same quantity of wheat which he has bought. By this method he avoids all risk. If the price of wheat goes up, he gains as much on what he sells as he loses on what he has bought; if it goes down, he gains as much on what he has sold as he loses on what he has bought. By this method, also, he knows where he stands, and he can go on with his business of manufacturing flour, giving all his attention to the problems involved in his own business, and leave to the professional speculator the business of studying the market and prognosticating the course of prices. There are, of course, a good many conspicuous cases of farmers who have gained by holding their crops for a rise in price, but these cases are canceled by those of farmers who have lost by the same process. Taking one farmer with another, one year with another over a period of time, the chances are that not enough is gained by holding crops in this way to pay the cost of storing, insurance, interest on the money tied up, etc.; and therefore the farmer who sells as soon as the crop is harvested will do just as well in the long run as the farmer who tries to hold his crop for a rise in price. This conclusion, however, assumes that it is a crop the market for which is well organized and for the handling of which middlemen are well equipped with warehouses, elevators, etc. In such cases the chances are that the middleman will do the storing and the handling cheaper than the farmer can do it. In all cases, however, where the market is not highly organized, and where middlemen have not equipped themselves to handle the crop efficiently and easily, this advice does not apply. In all such cases as this, there is a wide opportunity for coöperation among the farmers. Coöperative storehouses, elevators, etc., coöperation in the hiring of selling agents, etc., will prove highly profitable to those who are willing and able to coöperate. Numberless illustrations could be found in support of this conclusion. The potato growers of Aroostook County, Maine, began growing potatoes before there was a well-developed system of handling their crop through private enterprise. By the coöperative building of storehouses and the coöperative selling of their crops they succeeded in getting the advantages of a highly organized market without waiting for private enterprise to develop a system of handling the crop.

The growers of agricultural specialties have two well-recognized methods of selling their products. One is judicious advertising and the other is the exhibition of their products before the eyes of prospective purchasers. The question of the economy of advertising has been discussed a great deal by economic writers, and much can be said against it from the economic point of view. It is urged that, though advertising may be a means of attracting trade from one dealer to another, it really serves no social purpose, since one loses as much as another gains. When two rival grocers or manufacturers advertise the alleged merits of their respective brands of soap or codfish, it is difficult to see what social purpose is fulfilled. It is not probable that any more soap or codfish are bought than would be bought if there were no advertising. If that be true, all such advertising is a waste of social energy and is therefore undoubtedly and unqualifiedly wrong. But these objections cannot apply to the reasonable advertising of an agricultural specialty. Such advertising is informational and is a real service to the buyer as well as to the seller. An agricultural specialty, being something for which there is no well-organized market, no constant and calculable demand, and no quotable price, it is not always easy for the seller and the buyer to get together. Reasonable advertising informs them of one another's whereabouts and enables them to transact business. Suppose, for example, that A has a specially trained saddle horse for sale and feels that he ought to get a special price. B may be looking for just such a horse, but may not know where it is to be had. A notice in the advertising columns of a reputable paper gives him the information he needs, and both buyer and seller are benefited. There is nothing in this argument, however, to justify the extravagant advertising which sometimes disgraces the pages even of some of our reputable papers, where impossible horses of prodigious size and action are represented in connection with the tallest kind of mendacity as to the telescopic merits and microscopic prices of the animals which the advertiser has to sell.

Markets and fairs. Whenever possible, the ideal method of selling agricultural specialties is that of exhibiting them. Regular periodic markets, where such things can always be found, and where buyers are always present, have been proved in all old and highly developed countries to be the most effective way of bringing buyers and sellers together. This method has not had a high development in this country for the reason mainly that our farmers have generally been more interested in staple crops than in specialties, and also because the organization of our national economy has tended to produce a wide geographical separation of the producers and consumers. The western, sparsely settled areas have produced for the eastern, densely settled areas. This wide geographical separation has tended to place producers and consumers in a position of dependence upon commission merchants and other middlemen. When our population is more uniformly distributed, and each center thereof becomes more closely dependent upon its immediate surroundings for its agricultural products, there will doubtless be a revival of interest in periodic open markets where buyers and sellers, producers and consumers, can meet together.

Too much must not be expected in this direction, however. Any careful observer of the public markets and fairs of the Old World must have been impressed by the great waste of time involved in a system which requires so many people to sell a given amount of produce. Among people with a low standard of living, whose time is worth very little, this waste does not seem to be a great burden; but so long as American farming remains prosperous and American farm wages high, it will probably never seem like a wise economy of energy for the producers to spend their time on market days trying to sell their products. When population becomes more dense and labor becomes cheaper in consequence, the wasting of labor will not seem quite so unprofitable.

Aside from their purely educational purposes, the county and state fairs and other agricultural exhibitions have served the purpose of facilitating the buying and selling of agricultural specialties. This is particularly true of live stock. As a matter of fact, it is this reason rather than the hope of winning prizes, which induces the average farmer to place his products on exhibition.

CHAPTER V

DISTRIBUTION OF THE AGRICULTURAL INCOME

The income of the agricultural classes. By the agricultural income is meant that portion of the gross product of the farms which goes, as compensation or income, to those who are directly connected with them. In other words, it is the total farm value of all products after deducting the cost of all such factors of production as commercial fertilizers, tools, machinery, etc., which are not themselves produced on farms. More specifically, this agricultural income includes the wages of farm labor, the rent of farm land, the interest on the capital invested in live stock, tools, machinery, etc., employed on farms, and the profits of farming. It is obvious that the agricultural income includes more at one period than at another. At one time, for example, all the labor involved in the growing of crops was performed on the farms. Now a part of it is performed in the shops where farm machinery is made.

Though it is customary in the United States for the functions of laborer, landowner, capitalist, and manager to be combined in the same person, yet it is possible, even in such cases, to divide the farmer's income into the four parts just named. The farmer sometimes hires all his manual labor, frequently a part of it; sometimes rents all his land from another, frequently a part of it; and sometimes borrows all his capital, frequently a part of it. In view of the wide variations of practice in these particulars, it is simpler and less complicated to divide the whole farm income into four parts, — wages, rent, interest, and profits, — even when they all go to one and the same person.

I. Wages

The wages of a farmer who does all or a part of his own work may be considered to be the amount which he saves in his wage bill by reason of the fact that he works himself. The rent of a farmer who owns all or a part of his land may be considered to be that amount which he saves in his rent bill by reason of the fact that he is using his own land; and the interest of a farmer who owns a part or all of his capital free from debt, as that amount which he saves in his interest charges by reason of the fact that he uses his own capital. Another way of stating the same thing is to say that such a farmer's wages are the amount that he could get by hiring out to some one else, that his rent is what he might get by renting his land to some one else, and that his interest is what he might get by lending his capital to some one else. If, when he adds these sums together, he finds that they exceed his actual average income, then he is making no profit, but is sustaining a loss instead. In that case he would do better — at least he would make more money — if he would rent his land, lend his capital, and hire out to some one else. But if he finds that his average total income exceeds the sum of these three special incomes, then he is making a profit as a farm manager, that is, as an independent farmer.

Value. The problems of wages, of rent, and of interest are special phases of the general problem of exchange value and price. A concrete individual article, such as an egg, a loaf of bread, a horse, etc., has value [1] only because it is wanted; and the more it is wanted in comparison with other things, the more value it will have; that is, the more of these other things will be given in exchange for it. Other things equal, if there are available a great many other eggs besides the one in question,

[1] In this discussion exchange value is always to be understood when the word "value" is used.

that one will be less wanted than it would be if eggs were scarce. The same proposition might be repeated with respect to the loaf of bread, the horse, or any other article of exchange which one might have in mind. This is the simple mental fact which lies back of the great and well-known law of demand and supply.

In order to understand fully the reason for this fact we must recall the distinction made in a previous chapter between consumers' and producers' goods. Consumers' goods, it will be remembered, are goods which are wanted for their own sake and not for the sake of some other goods which they help us to get. They include such things as food, wearing apparel, household furniture, etc. Producers' goods, on the other hand, are not wanted for their own sake, but for the sake of other things which they help us to get. They include such things as plows, harrows, reapers, fertilizers, etc.

With respect to consumers' goods, the reason why each unit of a large supply of a given commodity is, other things equal, less wanted than each unit of a small supply is found in a rather simple physiological fact known as the satiability of wants ; that is to say, every want is satiable, and the more nearly it reaches the point of satiety the less intense it becomes. Stated in language so simple and obvious as to appear almost ridiculous, this simply means that if you give a man all he wants of a certain thing, he will not want any more ; and the more nearly he comes to having all he wants, the less intense will be his desire for more. This applies to every person in the community. When there is a large supply of a given article of consumption, the desires of its consumers in general are more nearly satisfied than when there is a small supply. Consequently the desire for each unit becomes less intense, that is, the average consumer does not want more than he has with quite the same intensity that he would if he did n't have so much already. Simple as this may seem, it is the sum and substance of the whole theory of value, in so far as it applies to consumers' goods. It is the basis also of all our moral and æsthetic values.

With respect to producers' goods, or productive agents, however, the case is not quite so simple. Since the desire for a productive agent is based on the desire for the thing which it helps to produce, it would follow that if the thing produced becomes more abundant and the desire for it less intense, then the desire for the thing which produced it would also become correspondingly less intense. Since one result of an increase of the supply of a productive agent would be to increase the supply of its products, we have one very good explanation of the reason why the desire for each unit of it diminishes as the supply increases. But there is another reason more important than that one, which may be found in the law of diminishing returns. Under this law, if the supply of one factor of production increases relatively to the other factors, each unit of this one factor becomes less productive.

Let us see how this principle applies to the price of such an agent of production as farm labor. If the number of laborers increases while the land and the tools remain the same, or if the number of laborers should increase more rapidly than the land and the tools, then there would be less land and fewer tools for each laborer to work with. Unless, at the same time, the laborers have learned something new about farming, they will, ordinarily, not be able to produce so much per man with less land and capital as they could with more. Since the product of each unit of labor is cut down by this relative increase in the number of units, and since the employer's desire for labor is based upon its product, it follows as a matter of course that the employer's desire for each unit of labor diminishes as the number of units increases relatively to the other factors of production. When the employer's desire for each unit diminishes, the price which he is willing to pay for it diminishes also. Thus we have the clearest possible reason for the observed fact that abundance of labor makes low wages. Vice versa, if the number of laborers should diminish relatively to the land and capital, there would then be more land and more and better tools for each laborer to work with. Unless, meanwhile, the laborers had forgotten something about farming or otherwise become less efficient, this would increase the product of each one. By a process of reasoning similar to that just given, we arrive at the best possible explanation of the observed fact that scarcity of labor makes high wages.

But this principle can be carried still further. It is not enough to show why wages are high when labor is scarce, and low when it is abundant. If it were possible, it would be important to know just what proportion of the agricultural income would go to labor, or take the form of wages, under different conditions. Such exact information is probably unattainable in the present state of human knowledge, but the principle which determines wages is fairly well understood. To this principle is given the name "marginal productivity," which means the productivity of the marginal unit of labor or the last unit of labor employed on a given area of land.

Marginal productivity. Let us assume, for the sake of an illustration, that one man working alone on a certain farm can produce, on the average, $1000 worth of product, and that two working together on that farm can produce $1600. This shows diminishing returns, the average product being only $800 when two men are working as against $1000 when only one man is working.

But the marginal product is quite different from the average product. In this case, while the average product is $800, the marginal product is only $600, this being the sum *added* to the total product by the coming of the second man. This is the maximum which the owner of the farm, if he knew his business, would pay for the services of the second man. Since two men produce, in this case, only $600 more than one man, two men are obviously worth $600 more than one man. If, however, wages in the community are only $400 per year [1] or for the farming season, it would certainly pay the farmer to hire a second man, if a second man is to be had, since he would make $200 by the process.

Such a large profit as this would lead him to consider whether it might not pay him to hire a third man also. Now suppose that three men on the same farm could produce $2000 on the average and in the long run. This gives a marginal product, under the terms of the illustration, of exactly $400; that is, the third man *adds* $400 to the product over and above what two men could produce. If, as we have assumed, $400 is also the cost of the third man to the employer, it is a matter of indifference to the latter whether two men or three men are employed, since he neither gains nor loses by the employment of the third. If, however, the marginal product were even one dollar greater than the cost of the third laborer, it would pay the farmer to hire the third man, though the profit would be only one dollar.

Now suppose that in the country, generally, there were so few laborers that, in a normal distribution, there were only two for every such farm as the one we are considering, the tendency would be for wages to be fixed at $600, or the marginal product of labor. If the wages were more than $600, every farmer who knew his business would dispense with one man. This would leave a good many of the existing supply of men out of work, and they would begin to offer to work for less. If wages were less than $600, then every farmer who knew his business would want to hire an extra man, and every man would be employed. If wages were very much less than $600, then a good many

---

[1] Under wages are included everything which the laborer receives for his work, including board, lodging, washing, and other privileges.

farmers would want to hire still more men, and there would not be enough men to go around. This would again force up wages approximately to the average marginal productivity of labor.

Of course no farmer can tell in advance just what the marginal product of labor is going to be, because he cannot tell what the season is going to be like. Nevertheless, they who show the best judgment in the matter will, other things being equal, succeed best, and they who show the poorest judgment will succeed least, or become bankrupt most frequently. In the long run, the farms will get into the hands of those who succeed best, and thus it will happen, eventually, that those farmers who remain in business will actually be hiring as many men as will, on the average, one season with another, produce a marginal product approximately equal to their wages. To hire more or fewer men would be to lose profits.

There are very definite mathematical laws, for example, determining the course of a rifle bullet. A good marksman may not know anything about these laws. He merely aims at the mark, gauging his sights on the basis of his experience. Nevertheless, whether the theory of projectiles be understood or not, the best marksmen will actually conform their practice, knowingly or unknowingly, to that theory. If we could imagine a competition in which there were a limited number of rifles and a great many men seeking to own them, and where ownership was to be secured only by showing superior marksmanship, then it would happen that the rifles would fall into the hands of men who conformed most closely, knowingly or unknowingly, to the theory of projectiles. Under such conditions one could safely say that, in actual practice, the rifles were being used in accordance with the theory of projectiles. Since there is just such a competition for the ownership or possession of farms, and since they who conform most closely to the laws of economics will succeed best in that competition, it will happen that farms will be managed in the end or in the long run in accordance with economic laws. It is for this reason that one may feel safe in saying that wages will actually tend to conform to the principle of marginal productivity. Those farmers who depart most widely from this principle will fail, and those who conform most closely will succeed and remain in control of the business of farming.

II. Rent

The law of demand and supply, which in its application to productive agents is, as we have just seen, based upon the law of marginal productivity, applies as well to the rent of land as to the wages of labor. But there are certain peculiarities in the supply of land which need to be taken into account. In the first place, the supply of any particular kind of land is almost a fixed quantity, whereas the supply of any kind of labor is variable. In the second place, land is immovable, whereas labor is movable and can be brought from places where it is less wanted to places where it is more wanted. The fixity and immobility of land make it more difficult to adjust the supply to the demand than is the case with an agent of production whose supply may increase or diminish, and which may be moved from one place to another in response to changes in demand.

By reason of the first of these peculiarities it happens that certain tracts of land, possessing special qualities which cannot be reproduced, acquire a sheer scarcity value. Again, since the supply of land is always a fixed quantity, its value always tends to rise higher and higher as the population increases more and more. But the second of these two peculiarities is by far the more important of the two. By reason of the immobility of land, a tract which is favorably located may acquire a pure site or situation value, independently of its physical or chemical fertility. Two laborers of equal energy, intelligence, and skill will tend to get the same wages, even in different neighborhoods, for the simple reason that if the demand for labor is greater in one neighborhood than in another, laborers will migrate from the one where the demand is less to the other where the demand is greater. Unless there are artificial restrictions in the way of their getting employment in the one neighborhood, or unless the two neighborhoods are so wide apart as to involve an expensive journey, wages for the same kind of labor will be the same in different localities, and labor will not command a mere site value. But two acres of land may be only a few miles apart and their real fertility may be equal, but one may be, by reason solely of its location, worth many times as much as the other. Site value is, as a matter of fact, an element of greater or less importance in the total value of almost every acre of land. In cities it is almost the only element.

However, when the farmer is considering the question of renting or buying a parcel of land, his question is what it will enable him to produce over and above what it will cost him to cultivate it. Then there is the question of how much land he shall use. Will it pay him better to cultivate a large tract or a small tract? This brings in the question of the marginal productivity of land. In order to cultivate a larger rather than a smaller tract, he must either employ more labor and capital or use the same labor and capital as he would use on the smaller tract, but spread it more thinly, that is, cultivate the large tract less intensively. Assuming, even, that he has or can get the use of indefinite quantities of capital, and that he can hire indefinite numbers of laborers and buy or rent indefinite areas of land, there would still be a limit to the quantity of land which he could handle economically, owing to the increasing difficulties of oversight and supervision. The productivity of the land would decline under his management acre by acre as he approached the limit of his capacity as a manager, not, of course, through any physical change in the land, but through his sheer inability to handle it efficiently. When he has already such a quantity under his management that to undertake the management of a few more acres would divide his attention and cause a slightly less efficient management of the whole, the question for the farmer is, Will the additional acres *add* as much to the total product of his whole business as they will cost? This is different from the question, Will these acres themselves produce as much as it will cost to cultivate them? The former question alone relates to the marginal productivity of his land.

The case is even clearer when we assume that the farmer has a fixed quantity of labor and capital at his disposal and is debating the question whether to rent (or buy) a few more or a few less acres. If he uses more land he will spread his labor and capital a little more thinly, that is, he will cultivate his land a little less intensively, which will ordinarily result in a slightly smaller product per acre. This may be more than counterbalanced by the larger number of acres, *but* the *addition* made by the few additional acres will not be their total product. It will be the product of the whole farm when these acres are added, minus the product of the whole farm when these acres are not included. For example, if the farmer with labor and capital at his disposal can grow 50 bushels of corn per acre when he cultivates 40 acres, and only 42 bushels per acre when he cultivates 50 acres, with the same labor and capital, the additional 10 acres are worth at the outside only 100 bushels a year to him, that being the amount added to his total crop by the additional 10 acres. If by spreading his labor and capital over 60 acres he gets only 36 bushels per acre, the last 10 acres are worth, at the outside, only 60 bushels, that being the amount by which his total crop is increased by the addition of those acres. Again, if by spreading his capital and labor over 70 acres he succeeds, on the average and in the long run, in getting a crop of only

30 bushels per acre, then the last 10 acres are worth 60 bushels less than nothing to him because the addition of this new area actually reduces his total crop. Now when land is so abundant in a certain community, relatively to the number of farmers and the quantities of labor and capital, as to allow 70 acres on the average to every such farmer as the one assumed in the foregoing illustration, or a proportional amount to other farmers with different equipments, it is evident that land would command no rent at all, *assuming that the land is all equally desirable*. Even if he could get his land absolutely free of rent, it would not pay any such farmer to cultivate as much as 70 acres. Therefore, if land were free, some of it would be allowed to lie idle, and no owner would be able to rent his land for a price so long as these conditions remained.

The differential law of rent. If, however, the land were not all equally desirable, — and it never is all equally desirable in any community, — then the more desirable acres would command a price or a rental. So long as there remained any free land anywhere in the community, the rent of any special piece would normally represent the preference of the renter for it as compared with land which he might have for nothing. The poorer or more difficult of access this free land is as compared with the special piece in question, the higher the degree of preference for the latter, and the higher its rent will rise. This is one phase of the famous differential theory of rent which has played so prominent a part in the economic discussions during the last century. It is, beyond all question, a true theory, the only question being whether it is so significant as many economists have supposed.

Rent as determined by marginal productivity. Some are now contending that the larger and more fundamental principle is that of the marginal productivity of land. For every farmer the real and immediate problem is how much he can produce when he has the use of a certain piece of land, over and above what he could produce if he did not have the use of it. That is what determines the price he can afford to pay for it. The presence of free land and the possibility of substituting some of it for the land which he is considering, is only one, and that not the most important, factor in the larger and more immediate problem of how much it is worth for use.

One special difficulty with the differential theory of rent, as commonly stated, is that the same piece of land is worth different sums to different men. To take an extreme case, an acre of land is worth very little to an Indian who is not yet civilized, and who uses it principally for hunting. By such a method it takes hundreds of acres to furnish a rather meager living to an Indian family. To a white farmer the same acre is worth a great deal more than it is to the Indian hunter, and for this reason the former can afford to pay the hunter more than the land is worth to him and still make a very good bargain.

But, for the same reason, the same acre of land is worth a great deal more to a highly skilled scientific farmer than it is to a shiftless, unbusinesslike farmer. Since the former can make an acre produce so much more than the latter can, and at lower cost, the former can pay more for the land than the latter can. If the unskillful farmer is already in possession, it is only necessary to offer him as much as or a little more than the land is worth to himself. This the more skillful farmer is easily able to do, either as renter or purchaser. Thus the land tends to pass into the hands of the more skillful farmers.[1]

Again, there are great differences in the ways in which various kinds of land respond to skillful and scientific treatment. Land which does not respond to such treatment may be worth very little more to the scientific or successful than to the

[1] Cf. an excellent article by Henry C. Taylor, "The Differential Rent of Farm Land," in the *Quarterly Journal of Economics* for August, 1903.

unscientific or mediocre farmer. Consequently it may remain for a considerable period in the hands of poor farmers. But land which makes a more vigorous response to skillful treatment attracts the skillful farmer. To him this land in particular is worth more than it is to the unskillful, and consequently he will get possession of it by offering more for it, either as rent or as purchase price, than the unskillful can afford to offer. Thus there grows up a territorial distribution of agricultural skill, the more capable farmers gaining possession of the better lands, and the less capable remaining on the poorer lands, though the least capable tend to be crowded out altogether.

Another phase of the differential theory of rent, not less important but more difficult to explain than the last, is based upon the law of diminishing returns from labor and capital applied to land. Under this law, since the marginal product of labor and capital diminishes when increasing quantities are applied to the cultivation of a given piece of land, if intensive cultivation be carried far enough, the marginal product from this piece of land, however fertile it may be, will eventually fall to the level of that of the poorest land in cultivation. That is to say, if intensive cultivation be carried far enough on a piece of fertile land, the point will eventually be reached when another unit of labor and capital added to that already applied to its cultivation will add so little to the total product as to make it a question whether that unit produces as much when thus applied as it would if applied to the cultivation of some of the free land.

The relation of rent to the price of products. One of the least-understood questions in economics is that of the relation of the rent of land to the prices of agricultural products. It is a very common opinion that high rents are a cause of high prices. In reality that is putting the cart before the horse, high rents being the effect rather than the cause of high prices. When prices are high farmers make money, and this increases their desire for land. This increasing desire for land makes rents and land values high. The logical order is as follows : A scarcity of good land makes a scarcity of agricultural products relative to the demand for them. A scarcity of agricultural products relative to the demand for them makes high prices. High prices for agricultural products make farmers prosperous and increase their desire for agricultural land. This increased desire or demand for land and the scarcity of its supply make high rents. In other words, the price paid for the use of a piece of land, like the price of anything else, is an indication of its desirableness ; and the desirableness of a piece of land depends in part upon how much one may make from its use, and this in turn depends in part upon the price of its products.

The single tax. In the minds of certain social reformers, known as "single taxers," the rent of land is not earned by the landowners. In justification of this position they begin by distinguishing very sharply between land and improvements on it. Land, in the sense of the original and indestructible properties of the earth's surface, is not at all the product of any man's labor, frugality, or forethought, but is a free gift of nature. It becomes the property of a man not because a man makes it, but because he appropriates it. Having appropriated it, and being protected by others, that is, by society, in its possession, it becomes his legal property and he can thereafter exclude others from its use or exact a payment from them therefor. This payment which he exacts becomes an income, which is not a payment for any service which he has rendered to society or to the world. It is otherwise with the improvements upon the land. When the land is drained and thereby made more productive, the man who does the draining is rendering a service. As a result of his work the world has something which it would otherwise not have had, but the naked land was there anyway, and the world has nothing new by reason of his having appropriated it. That part of the owner's income which comes from the improvements which he puts upon his land is virtually his own product, but that part which comes from the original properties of the land is not his own product: it is the result of his appropriation of a natural resource and not the result of his own productive work.

By way of illustration let us assume that a certain farmer has an average income, over and above all expenses, insurance, deterioration, etc., of $2000; that he and his family are doing work which, on the market, would bring in $1000, and that he has spent $10,000 in buildings, in improving his land and stocking it with tools, machinery, teams, etc. If interest is 5 per cent, then $500 of his income would be interest. Under these assumptions the farmer's real earnings would be $1500. The remaining $500 would not, under the assumption, be payment for his work during that year, — the $1000 covers that. Nor would it be payment for previous work in improving his land, erecting buildings, etc., — the $500 covers this year's share of that. What, then, is the extra $500? It is the rent of the land, or the income which comes to him by reason of the fact that he is in possession of a small section of the earth's surface. Therefore, say the single taxers, while he has obviously earned his $1500 he has not earned this other $500.

The question at once arises, Suppose that the farmer has bought the land from some one else, paying $10,000 for it, besides another $10,000 for the buildings, improvements, stock, etc. Is not the $500 interest on the investment in the land as much his rightful income as the other $500 interest on the investment in improvements? It would seem so. At any rate, the single taxers have never been able to satisfy a majority of the voters that this is not true. The most that can be said is that this farmer has made a mistake in paying another man $10,000 for land which the latter never produced. This man, the seller, has secured this large sum of money without having earned it. The present purchaser, having paid for something which he ought not to have paid for, is, according to some of the more extreme and partisan single taxers, entitled to no consideration. The $500 which represents the rent of the land ought to be taxed away, even though this would virtually confiscate the $10,000 which had been paid for the land. Some of the more moderate single taxers, with a somewhat keener sense of justice, propose either to compensate the present owners or to tax away only the future increases in rent, exempting entirely from taxation any value which is due to improvements which the owner has made or shall hereafter make upon his land. It is difficult to find any valid objection to this more moderate program aside from the difficulty of applying it, which is, after all, probably less than that of applying any system of taxation now in existence.

It is so startling as to be almost unbelievable, and yet it is a demonstrable truth, that if the government had pursued from the beginning the policy of taxing only the rent of land, we should have had a practically burdenless tax. The farmer in the above illustration would not have had to pay $10,000 for the naked land, for the naked land would never have had any particular selling value. Whatever value it had would have gone to the government in the form of taxation. On the other hand, every improvement placed upon the land by its owner would have escaped taxation altogether. The result would have been that this farmer instead of paying $20,000 for the farm, that is, $10,000 for the land and $10,000 for the improvements on it, would have paid only $10,000 for the improvements. Having saved $10,000 as the purchase price of the farm, he would be able to pay the taxes with the interest thus saved; that is to say, if he had $20,000 in cash, he could pay $10,000 for the farm and put the other $10,000 at interest.

This interest would pay his taxes. If, on the other hand, he had to borrow money to pay for his farm, he would need to borrow $10,000 less than would have been necessary if there had been no tax. He would save the interest on this $10,000, and this saving of interest would just equal the tax which he would have to pay. This farmer would thus be just as well off if the rent had always been taxed, as he would if it had never been taxed at all. Instead of paying the previous owner a large sum of money for something which he did not produce, this farmer would be paying the interest on that sum to the government in the form of a tax ; and this tax would pay, or help to pay, the necessary expenses of the government and thus relieve it of the necessity of taxing things which have been produced by labor, which is the same as taxing labor.

III. Interest

One of the most difficult and elusive problems in the whole field of economics is that of interest. Interest is the income derived from the ownership and use of capital. The problem is to explain just how that income arises and how it is determined. This problem is simple enough when we consider the simplest possible case, namely, that of a man who makes a tool for himself and then uses it in production. The increased production which results from the use of that tool might then be regarded as interest, though it would not ordinarily be distinguished from wages. The increased production resulting from the use of the tool, however, needs to be clearly understood. The time and labor used in making the tool might have been used in the production of other goods. After the tool is made and put to use, it presumably increases the quantity of other goods produced. If the quantity of this increase is no greater than the quantity which might have been produced by the time and labor spent in making the tool, then there is no real net advantage in making the tool. The apparent income from its use is not a real income since it only pays off the principal. But if the total apparent income from the tool is greater than the quantity which might have been produced by the time and labor spent in making it, there is a real net advantage in making the tool. This surplus is, in other words, the real increase in production resulting from the use of the tool, and this surplus alone is interest.

If, instead of using the tool himself, the owner hires it to some one else, the distinction between wages and interest becomes a little clearer, but is not yet as clear as it might be. In so far as the income which the owner receives only reimburses him for the time which he spent in making the tool, it is wages, or deferred wages, to be perfectly accurate. If the total income is more than sufficient to reimburse him for his time, or to give him the quantity of goods which he might have produced with the time and labor spent upon the tool, this surplus is interest. If, instead of making tools himself, the owner hires other men to make them for him, and then hires these tools to other men, it is clear that he gets no interest from his tools unless his receipts are more than sufficient to reimburse him for the wages he has paid out to his own workmen. Or again, if in the making of the tools he has incurred other expenses than wages, he must be reimbursed for all these expenses before he can be said to get any interest. All the surplus would be interest.

Let us now consider another case. Suppose that instead of hiring men to make tools for him and then hiring the tools to some one else, he buys them outright of the man who made them and then uses them himself. Buying them outright of the man who makes them probably means paying outright a sufficient sum to cover all the costs of production, including wages. Unless each tool enables him to add to his production, over and above what he could produce without it, enough to more than cover the price which he paid for it, it is of no advantage to him to have purchased. In other words, it yields him no interest; but whatever it brings him in excess of the purchase price is interest. Again, let us suppose that instead of using the tools himself, he hires them to some one else. That which he receives for their use in excess of the price which he paid for them, and that alone, is interest. Finally, let us suppose that he employs other men to work with the tools which he has bought, which is the case of a modern capitalist employer. Wages must, of course, be paid for the labor that uses the tools. The total combined product of the laborers and the tools must therefore cover not only the wages of the laborers employed, and all the other costs of operation, including risk, etc., but also the original cost of the tools, before any interest accrues to the owner. If any surplus remains, it may be regarded as interest. A careful management of the business, with accurate accounting, will enable the owner to set aside a certain sum each year for maintenance and depreciation, which is to set aside each year that year's share of the original cost. If anything remains each year, it may be regarded as that year's interest, and thus the owner may receive interest every year from the very beginning of his enterprise.

All the cases which we have thus far considered are fundamentally alike, the difference being incidental to the different stages of industrial development under which they are found. They are all alike in that interest accrues by reason of the fact that the increased product resulting from the use of tools is greater than the product used up or given up in making or gaining possession of them.

The case is complicated somewhat, but not materially changed, when money is introduced into the transaction. Since money is simply general purchasing power, or a general claim on the community for a share of the commodities on sale in the community, the lending of money is virtually the lending of tools or other goods. When he lends his money he transfers that power to the borrower, which is virtually the same as transferring the tools to the borrower. When the borrower pays interest to the lender he is, therefore, virtually paying for the use of tools. From this point of view the case becomes almost identical with those considered above, where no money intervened.

But how does it happen that a tool or any productive agent will sell to-day for less than the whole of its future product? If a certain tool will enable me to produce $10 a year more than I could without it, and if it will last for a period of 10 years, why should I not be willing to pay $100 for it? If I do, then the toolmaker gets in cash the whole future value of the tool, and I get no interest. In the course of 10 years I merely get back the principal, that is, the original price of the tool. Or, why should the toolmaker be willing to sell such a tool for less than $100? If he is willing to sell it for $90, and I am willing to pay that for it, then he is willing that I should gain $10, that is, $1 per year for waiting. That is interest, — a very low rate to be sure, but interest nevertheless. If I am unwilling to give $100 for such a tool, but insist upon getting it for something less than this amount, then I am insisting on interest. Men generally act in just this way, though some of them inconsistently disapprove of interest (in theory) at the same time, their disapproval being based upon a misunderstanding of the problem of interest.

The reason why such a tool does not sell for $100, or why any piece of capital will not sell for its whole future value, is simply that men do not like to wait. They would rather have something now than have the same thing or its exact equivalent in the future. Since waiting is as necessary as working, and since men do not like to wait any better than they like to work, it follows that they must be paid for waiting, just as surely as they must be paid for working. Waiting is involved whenever one purchases a tool and whenever one spends time in making a tool. If you purchase a tool, you give up the purchasing power which would have enabled you to buy some article of consumption. You do not want the tool for its own sake ; you want it only because of the things it will enable you to get in the future, but you must wait for them. If you spend time and labor in making a tool, you use up energy which you might have spent in play, or in getting some article of consumption, and waiting is involved just as though you had purchased the tool. If, after you have made the tool, some one else buys it of you, he thereby relieves you of further waiting, while he, having paid for it, must therefore wait for its products to recompense him. You will ordinarily be so glad to be relieved of further waiting as to sell it at a price which will enable him to realize a surplus eventually. That surplus is interest. If, however, you have yourself used other tools in making that tool, you will have already done some waiting, and part of the price which you get for the tool will pay for the labor which you have put into it, and part for the tools which you have used. This in turn will in part recompense you for the original cost of these tools, and in part pay you for having waited. This last sum will be interest.

Waiting. Waiting is, of course, merely another word for "saving." This analysis has been given primarily to show the exact nature of the process by which capital originates and interest arises. Though certain mistaken reformers are nowadays trying to teach the contrary doctrine, this analysis will help to show how well grounded is the common-sense view that thrift and saving and forethought are economic virtues second only to industry itself. If there is one lesson more than another which the American people need to have dinned into their ears until they learn it thoroughly, it is that the man who saves is a public benefactor and the man who spends needlessly is not. Rich and poor alike need to learn this lesson, because both are led sometimes to ignore it; but the evil results of this ignorance weigh most heavily upon the poor, and they, therefore, have the best reason for knowing this truth, which is, in a most literal and material sense, the truth which shall make them free. The falsity of the proposition that lavish expenditure makes work, and thus benefits labor, has been demonstrated more frequently, probably, than any other economic fallacy, and yet it is still occasionally heard. This is so clear as to leave no room whatever for doubt or discussion in the mind of any one who will follow the demonstration through.

If I have a dollar to spend, and I decide to spend it for some trifling luxury, I do, it is true, set labor to work producing that luxury, or, more accurately, I encourage the industry which produces it; but if I spend it for a tool instead of a luxury, I set labor to work, to the same extent, producing the tool, or I encourage the toolmaking industry. Therefore the two cases are equal up to this point. There is this difference, however, when we carry the analysis further: when I have bought the luxury and consumed it, it is gone forever. I may get some ephemeral satisfaction out of it, but it is destroyed as effectually as if it had been burned or cast into the sea, so far as the rest of the world is concerned. If, however, I buy a tool to help me in my work of production, I am thereafter enabled to produce more and to contribute more to the wealth and satisfaction of the rest of the world. The rest of the world is to that extent the gainer by my frugality and owes me accordingly.

Even though I do not myself use the tool, but allow it to be used by somebody else, the world's production of wealth and satisfaction is thereby increased, and the new income which I receive for the use of the tool is merely a partial return for the contribution which I have made to the increased productivity of the world. This contribution is partially neutralized if I then consume my new income lavishly; but if I, in turn, invest this increased income in more and better tools, the world is the double gainer by my frugality. The sum of the whole matter is that in proportion as my economic life is a long series of expenditures for luxuries, I direct a fraction of the productive energy of the world into the production of luxuries which serve me alone. On the other hand, in proportion as my economic life is a long series of investments in tools of various kinds, I turn a certain fraction of the productive energy of the world into the production of tools which serve the world as well as me,—which, in fact, must serve the world in order that they may serve me.

It ought not be difficult to see that the same results follow when I deposit my dollar in a savings bank as when I spend it myself. In case the savings bank lends my dollar to some one who buys a luxurious trifle with it, the results upon the rest of the world are the same as though I had myself bought the trifle. It is a matter between us two alone. I have virtually loaned him the trifle. But in case the savings bank lends my dollar to a man who spends it for tools, this also is the same, so far as the rest of the world is concerned, as though I had myself bought the tools. This man is able by means of the tools to produce more for some one else, and some one else pays him for that additional service. He, in turn, pays me for the use of the tool. They who receive the service must prefer it to the price which they pay for it, otherwise they would not buy it. He must get more for the extra service than he pays me for the use of the tool, otherwise he would not borrow it of me. There is thus a profit all around.

These considerations are more important to-day than they ever were before in the history of the world, and they are growing more important every day. The reason is that capital is coming to play a more and more important rôle in industry. This, in turn, is the inevitable result of our own inventiveness, which is responsible for the ushering in of this age of machinery.

There was a time when a farmer could succeed with very little capital, for the simple reason that nobody used a great deal. He was as well equipped as his competitors in the industry and could produce as cheaply as they. But in this age of labor-saving devices he must be as well equipped with these devices as his competitors, otherwise he will not be able to produce cheaply enough to sell his products at a profit. But to equip himself with all these modern machines and implements is to possess a large amount of capital as compared with the farmer of a century or even a generation ago. Capital does not rain down from the sky, nor does it come into existence in any other mysterious way. It comes into existence through the simple process of saving and investing. So long as I spend all my income for consumers' goods I shall never become a capitalist. Every time I spend a dollar for a productive tool rather than for an article of consumption, I become a capitalist to the extent of a dollar. If I spend a great many dollars in this way, I become a great capitalist, and that is all there is to it. It is true, as pointed out already, that I may spend my dollars for tools directly or I may spend them indirectly through the medium of savings banks or other credit institutions.

Since capital is coming to be a more and more indispensable factor in industry, it follows that the man who supplies capital, that is, who spends his income for tools rather than for consumers' goods, is coming to be a greater and greater benefactor. He supplies a thing which is needed more than it was ever needed before, and which is coming to be more needed every year. Society usually pays highest for what it most wants. That is the simple and logical explanation of the fact that the capitalist is coming to be a more and more important personage in every progressive society. This is as simple and logical a result as it was that the soldier should have been the most important personage in an age when society needed soldiers more than it needed anything else. They who once understand this situation will cease to inveigh against capitalists as such, but will begin to become capitalists as rapidly as they can. They will then have the double satisfaction of knowing that they are not only benefiting themselves, but are benefiting society as well. They will be supplying what society needs more and more in proportion as inventions increase, and because they supply what society needs they will be rewarded by society.

There is need, however, of the most careful discrimination between genuine productive capital and spurious or acquisitive capital. Genuine capital consists of productive tools, implements, and improvements of all kinds which add to the productive power of the world. There is a kind of possession masquerading under the name of capital which is directed toward the impoverishment rather than the enrichment of the world. Devices for the beguiling of innocent people into the purchase of shares in fraudulent mining and other corporations; lottery companies which sell for a dollar, tickets whose mathematical value, based on the theory of chances, is less than twenty cents; gambling establishments of various kinds; trusts and other monopolistic organizations whose single purpose is to cause two dollars to emerge from other people's pockets whence one had emerged before; patent-medicine establishments; devices for the adulteration of goods; counterfeiters' outfits; "gold bricks" of various kinds, and a multitude of other similar forms of "business" enterprise using "business capital" belong under this general heading. Rural people of the more ignorant sort seem to be the peculiar prey of these forms of predatory enterprise, all of whose homes are in the city. If these forms of deception resulted in the speedy starvation and death of those who are deceived, there would be at least the result of ridding the country of fools as a partial compensation for the filling of the city with knaves; but since they are not thus exterminated, but left to breed more of their own kind in order that future generations of knaves may have a plentiful supply of fools to prey upon, we shall continue to have abundant crops of both fools and knaves to afflict us, unless something is done about it. When modern states awaken to the full significance of the distinction made in Chapter I between the economic and uneconomic ways of getting a living, and try to suppress all uneconomic ways as effectually as they are now trying to suppress some of them, such as stealing, forging notes, counterfeiting, etc., the problem will be solved. Meanwhile we must depend upon the education of the people, especially the rural people, against the methods of knavery in order that they may avoid being victimized.

However, there is comparatively little spurious capital employed in agriculture; therefore there is less need of qualification in our commendation of the rural capitalist than there is in the case of the urban capitalist. With practically no qualification, one may say that he who increases the supply of agricultural capital, by spending his income for tools rather than for consumers' goods, is rendering a service to society and is therefore earning whatever income he gets from his tools. If he invests unwisely, that is, if he buys tools which do not add to his productive power, he does not render any service, nor does he get any income from the use of his tools. In proportion as his tools do actually add to his production, in that proportion does he increase his serviceableness to society, and in that proportion also will he be rewarded by a larger income. This larger income is interest. In agriculture this looks simple enough. There are not many socialists in the country. In the city there are so many uneconomic forms of capital, "spurious capital" as we term it, that it requires considerable judgment and discrimination to see the inherent value of real capital and the real capitalist. There are a great many socialists in the city.

IV. Profits

As already indicated, the profits of farming are what is left of the farmer's annual income after allowing himself wages for his own labor, rent for his own land, and interest for his own capital. It is, of course, by no means certain that there will be any profits unless the farmer is a good manager. In fact, it is doubtful whether half the farmers of this or any other country make any profits at all, while it is certain that the poorest of them do not. In the growing of staple products, where there is little opportunity for selling at fancy prices, profits accrue mainly to those who are able to reduce the cost of production below that of their less efficient competitors. In the growing of agricultural specialties profits may result from reducing the cost of production, but they result mainly from the production of a fancy product which will sell at a fancy price, and from skillful selling, which is necessary to secure the maximum price.

It is, of course, a question whether profits as thus defined should not be classed as a part of the wages of the farmer's own labor. If the grower of a staple product is able to secure profits only by reason of the superior management whereby he increases his product above that of his competitors, or reduces his cost of production below theirs, his labor is of a superior order and would ordinarily command a superior salary on the market. If such a farmer allows himself a superior salary corresponding to his superior managing ability, would he have anything left in the way of profits, averaging one year with another? Or in the growing of an agricultural specialty, where profits depend partly upon good salesmanship, if the farmer allows himself a superior salesman's salary, will not this cover all that is commonly called profits?

There is one thing which the independent farmer does, whether he be a grower of a staple crop or a specialty, which is difficult to bargain for on the market, and which would scarcely be included under wages, rent, or interest. He acts as an insurer of the landowner from whom he rents land, of the capitalist from whom he borrows capital, and of the laborers whom he hires. That is to say, if he rents land and pays cash rent, the landlord's income is assured, even though there be a partial crop failure. A complete failure may render the payment of rent impossible, and in an extreme case of this kind the landlord's income may be cut off also. But if the farmer has anything with which to pay rent, it must be paid whether he has any income left for himself or not. Thus the landlord is in a safer position as regards crop failures, etc., than the farmer is. Similarly with the capitalist from whom the farmer borrows his capital. Interest must be paid, whether there is a crop failure or not, so long as the farmer has the wherewithal to pay. By this arrangement the lender of capital is in a safer position than the farmer who uses it, because the farmer loses all his income before the lender loses any of his. Again, the farm laborer's wages must be paid whether there is anything left for the farmer or not. The farm laborer bears none of the ordinary risks of crop failure, of loss of live stock, etc., and nothing but the complete and irretrievable bankruptcy of the farmer will cut off his wages. He is thus in a safer position than the farmer so far as the ordinary risks of farming are concerned. Thus we see that the independent farmer bears the burden of these innumerable and unforeseeable risks. He stands between the other three classes and these risks, and so long as he is able to stand up against the blows of misfortune they are protected. These blows fall upon them only after the farmer has been completely knocked out.

Because of the greater risk which the farmer assumes, and because of the relative safety which the landowner who rents out his land, the capitalist who lends his capital, and the laborer who works for wages, all enjoy, the farmer is entitled to a surplus profit somewhat analogous to that of an insurance company.

The real reward of the insurer, whether he be a farmer or a chartered insurance company, is to be found in the excess of gains over losses. In the case of the insurance company it is the total premiums received for assuming the risk minus the losses consequent upon assuming the risk. Here the question arises, How does there happen to be a difference? Why will the patrons of an insurance company pay it more than their total losses, thus leaving the company a profit? Evidently because the risk to the insurer is less than to the insured. In the case of fire insurance, for example, the loss to the insurer in case of fire would include only the money value of the buildings and goods destroyed; but in the case of the insured it would also include shrunken credit and crippled business. Having capital of his own, his credit is good for a certain amount in addition, but a part at least of that credit vanishes with his capital. More important still is the effect of a large and sudden loss as compared with small annual payments upon his consumption. These annual sums are paid, as it were, out of the last and least necessary part of his income. In order to make these payments he gives up only the enjoyment of those things which he can best get along without. But a large and sudden loss may deprive him of even the necessaries for a time. This can be illustrated by means of the diagram on page 318.

Let the income of a certain farmer be measured along the line OX, and the utility to him of the various parts of that income along the line OY. That is to say, if his income were represented by the line OF, its marginal utility would be represented by the line EF; but being in fact, let us assume, represented by the line OB, its marginal utility is represented by the line CB. Now let us suppose that he suffers a loss of $1000 by fire once every 55 years on the average. He could well afford to pay a premium of $100 every 5 years for the sake of being insured.[1] A hundred dollars paid in any one year would cost him in the way of sacrifice an amount of utility represented by such a parallelogram as HCGB. In eleven payments, each cover-

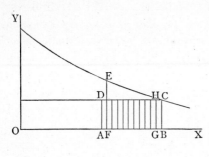

ing a period of 5 years, he would have paid $1100, which would make a total sacrifice represented by the parallelogram DCAB. But the loss of $1000 in any one year would involve a sacrifice represented by the irregular surface ECFB. Since this surface is larger than the parallelogram DCAB, he would lose less in the way of real utility by paying $1100 in 55 years than by losing $1000 in any one year.

In the case of ordinary insurance the shifting of the risk from the insured to the insurer does not diminish the number of losses to be borne, but it diminishes the amount of risk because the loss can be more easily borne by those upon whom it is shifted; it bears less heavily upon the insurer than it would upon the insured. It is for this reason that the insured can afford to pay in premiums more than enough to enable the insurer to meet the losses. This familiar principle of insurance explains how it happens that there are profits in the insurance business.

It is evident that in the case of the farmer, as was shown to be true in the case of the insurance company, so much of his gross income as is necessary to cover his real risk, or to make

[1] The premium of $100, if we take interest into account, might be reduced to the sum which, principal and interest together, would equal $100 in 22½ years, that is, the average time between the payment of the premium and the loss by fire.

good his losses, is not to be classed as profits. Only that which he wins because of favorable changes in the market over and above what he loses because of unfavorable changes can be so classed. How does there happen to be a surplus in this case? It must be, as in the former case, because the risk to him is less than it would be to those whom he relieves of it. As compared with the laborers, it is probable that a given loss would affect him less seriously than it would them. The loss of any considerable part of their wages, which would frequently happen if they bore their own risk or took their own chances with the market for their products, would mean serious deprivation. But there is no reason for believing that a given loss would, on the average, affect the farmer less seriously than it would the landlord and the capitalist of whom he hires his land and capital. They are usually in as good a position to bear a loss as he is. But there are reasons for believing that the skillful farmer will experience fewer losses than would be experienced by those whom he relieves of risk, whether they be laborers, landlords, or capitalists. This is due to no actuarial principle, as in the case of the insurance company, but to the farmer's superior foresight and skill in avoiding losses. That is a part of his special function, and in the performance of it he can be assumed to develop special skill. This part of his income is, therefore, due to the fact that he is able to avoid losses more effectively than the others whom he relieves of their risks. Even if he pays them what they might be expected to earn on the average and in the long run, — counting the losses with the gains resulting from fluctuations of the market and other fortuitous circumstances, — by so managing the business that the losses are reduced and the gains increased, the farmer will find himself in the possession of a surplus without having robbed or outbargained any one. This means that this part of his surplus is due to the fact that he is able to reduce the risk which he assumes below that which the others would have had to carry if he had not relieved them.

But even if the farmer is not able to avoid losses more successfully than the others whom he relieves of risk, he may still secure an income through his function as a risk taker. The owner of any factor of production will ordinarily accept as hire something less than its average marginal product, on condition that he be relieved of risk. The loss of a given sum out of one's customary income is a matter of more concern than the gain of an equal sum in addition to one's customary income. Almost any one would therefore accept an assured income in preference to an uncertain one, even though the chances were that the uncertain one would average, in the long run, something more than the assured one. Assured wages, interest, or rent, for example, of $1000 a year, would be accepted by the average man in preference to the uncertain earnings of business, even though these uncertain earnings might be expected in the long run to average as high as $1100 a year. By taking advantage of this tendency in bargaining for labor, land, and capital, the farmer will therefore find himself in the possession of a surplus, provided he does not fail through sudden losses before he has had time to profit by the average of the "long run."

Let us suppose that a given fund of labor, land, and capital can, on the average and in the long run, produce $1000 a year. That is the amount which these factors would receive if they worked together on the coöperative plan instead of being hired by some farmer. But owing to crop failures, fluctuations of the market, and other fortuitous circumstances, their product varies from year to year, some years rising as high as $1500, and again falling as low as $500. Rather than take their chances with these ups and downs, the laborers, landlords, and capitalists will ordinarily be willing to accept a stipulated income of something less than $1000, say $950, provided any one is able to make them such an offer with a good prospect of being able to carry out his contract. In that case the farmer will, in the long run, have an income of $50 a year in addition to the earnings of his own labor of management, or of his own land and capital.

If, in addition, he is able to develop special skill in prognosticating the conditions of the market so as to reduce slightly the losses, thereby increasing the annual product to $1010 a year, he will have an average income of $60. Then if he also succeeds in outbargaining some of those from whom he hires the factors of production, he will find his income still further increased. In addition to all these methods he may, as already pointed out, so organize and manage the factors as to make them turn out a larger product than they otherwise would, in which case he will secure a still larger income. But the amount which he earns in this way really belongs under the wages of superintendence rather than under profits. It is earned by the productive labor of the farmer, and by a kind of labor which can be, and frequently is, hired at a stipulated salary. When it is so hired, its earnings clearly belong under wages rather than profits, and there is no good reason for placing it under a different head when it happens to be earned by the farmer himself. But the function of risk taking cannot be turned over to an employee working for a salary. It is essentially the function of the farmer himself, and he cannot shift it to any one but another independent farmer. The farmer is essentially an enterpriser, or an *entrepreneur*, as he is sometimes technically called.[1] It is the reward of this special function which, together with the results of superior bargaining, constitutes the peculiar income of the independent farmer,— such an income as is never earned by any one in agriculture except a farmer who undertakes risks.

[1] Cf. the article by F. B. Hawley, on " Enterprise and Profit," in the *Quarterly Journal of Economics*, November, 1900. Also Mr. Hawley's book on the same subject.

That part of a farmer's income which is due to his ability to reduce his risk by his superior skill in guessing at the weather and the probable conditions of the market is closely akin to his wages of superintendence and might almost as well be placed under that head as under profits. But inasmuch as it is so closely related to the function of risk taking, it seems better, on the whole, to include it under the latter head. It is the peculiar reward of the speculator, — in the better meaning of that term, — whose special skill, if he has any, consists in knowing better than others when to buy and when to sell. Every farmer is a speculator in the sense of being compelled to make expenditures in advance when it is uncertain what the crops or the market will be, and he is the one who gains or loses by such transactions. In so far as this is a necessary part of every business, including that of farming, the income secured by special skill in this direction must be regarded as earned.

Speculation in the purely commercial sense, which consists simply in buying things when they are believed to be cheap and holding them for a rise, without any industrial purpose whatever, is not a wholly barren function, though there are few communities in which it is not overdone. Wherever it is necessary that goods should be produced a long time in advance of their consumption, it is also necessary that some one should hold them during the interval. This consists not only in housing or storing them, but also in waiting to get the value out of them, or to get one's money back, as it is sometimes expressed; and waiting, as we saw in the discussion of interest, is burdensome when carried too far. The producer must wait a long time for his reward, or the consumer must buy a long time in advance of his needs, unless some one else will come forward and relieve them both of the necessity of waiting by buying the products of the producer when they are produced and holding them for the consumer until he needs them. The reward for waiting is interest, but in addition to waiting there is the risk of losing. It is as necessary that some one should risk his capital as it is that some one should wait. But no one is likely to do this unless he is tempted by the hope of a profit. Whoever does it under such an inducement is to that extent a speculator. To be sure, he may be several other things besides; he may be the storer of goods, as in the case of the owner of a warehouse, and a distributor of goods, as in the case of a merchant; but in so far as he is merely a buyer of goods when they are cheap and a seller when they are high, he is a speculator.

Let us suppose, as an extreme illustration, that no one were willing to hold any part of a wheat crop from the time of its harvesting until such times as it was most needed. The whole crop would then have to be used up at once, and in order to be so used it would have to be put to very inferior purposes, or used in the satisfaction of very inferior wants. Consequently its utility or want-satisfying power would be very low. During the remainder of the year there would be a scarcity of wheat, and many important wants would have to go unsatisfied. By holding a part of the crop till it is needed more than it is immediately after harvest, its utility would be greatly increased and the well-being of the community enhanced. Whoever does this holding, whether it be the farmers themselves, the millers, or a special class of speculators, is serving the community by increasing the want-satisfying power of some of the goods in its possession. Whatever in the way of profits is secured by this process may be regarded as payment for this service.

But much that goes on under the name of speculation does not deserve that name, in spite of its opprobrious sound. Gambling is a better name for those transactions which pretend to be buying and selling, but which consist really in betting on the course of the market. It is quite as easy for a couple of men, either in or out of the stock market or the board of trade, to bet on the state of the market at some future time as it would be to bet on the state of the weather; and one kind of betting would serve about as important an economic purpose as another, even though the one was done under the form of buying and selling without any real transfer of goods. However, so long as it is impossible to distinguish for legal purposes between legitimate speculation and gambling under the form of buying and selling products, it is generally considered best to allow them both to go on together, since the one serves an important economic purpose and the other affects only the parties who participate, and does no one else any harm.

Certain fallacies regarding the influence of speculation upon prices have been given currency, not only on the popular platform, but even in the halls of Congress. The opinion is expressed, for example, that the custom of "short selling" as it is called, that is, of selling wheat on the board of trade when one has no wheat to deliver, has the effect of depressing the price of wheat. Since more "wheat" is offered for sale than there is in existence, this inordinately large supply of fictitious wheat must, it is argued, have some of the influence of an oversupply of real wheat. The difficulty with this argument is that it overlooks the fact that for every fictitious sale there is also a fictitious purchase. One might argue, on the opposite side, that the purchasing of more "wheat" than there is in existence must have some of the effect of a real demand for real wheat, and thus raise prices. As a matter of fact, these two processes counteract each other. Perhaps it would be better to say that they have no more influence on prices than would result when two gamblers merely bet on the probable price of wheat at some date in the future. While this betting would be reprehensible, it would have no influence whatever upon the course of prices.

What is known as a "corner," however, is quite a different thing. If one of the gamblers in the foregoing illustration took measures to win his bet, these measures might be effective, while the mere fact of betting unaccompanied by such measures would have no effect whatever. If the gambler who had bet that the price of wheat would go up should set about quietly to buy all the real wheat there was to be had and then refuse to sell to anybody, he might, if his money should hold out, actually force the price high enough to enable him to win all his bet. But this is a very difficult thing to accomplish because it can easily be prevented by his opponents if they see through his game in time. As a matter of fact it is never accomplished successfully more than once in a lifetime. The man who tries it almost invariably fails and bankrupts himself as the result of his folly.

It should be observed that there are no profits of gamblers as a class, for what one makes another loses. But in the business of real buying and selling there is a margin of difference, on the average and in the long run, in favor of those who buy at opportune times — say just after a wheat harvest — and sell when the article is more wanted than it was when it was bought. This margin is due to the fact that the speculator relieves the other classes of the disadvantages and uncertainties of waiting, enabling them to realize a certain price at once, which they will generally prefer to an uncertain price in the future, even when the chances are that the future price will be slightly higher than the present one. The speculator furnishes a kind of insurance by relieving others of a share of their risk.

It is not to be inferred, however, that all risk is burdensome. The gambling instinct is so strong in some people that they will eagerly hazard their wealth on chances which they know to be against them, purely for the excitement of the hazard. Different individuals differ greatly in this particular, but in general it will be found that small sums will be risked on the chance of winning large ones more readily than large ones will be risked on the chance of winning small ones, even when the chances in the latter case are more than proportionally superior. So great is the preference for the former class of hazards that a great many men — one might almost say the majority of men — will risk $1 on the chance of winning $1000, even when it is well known that there are 2000 chances to 1 against their winning. That is why lotteries flourish where they are not suppressed by law. But very few will risk $1000 on the chance of winning $1, even if they knew that there were 2000 chances to 1 in favor of their winning. If a company should offer to sell 2000 tickets at $1000 each, only one of which was a blank, all the rest drawing prizes of $1001 each, it would be making a better offer than any lottery ever has made or ever could make ; but it would not be able to induce many individuals to buy tickets. And yet such a company would be offering a good risk, as risks go, and any one who would continue buying such risks would gain in the long run, though he might lose all his money on the first venture.

Outside of mining and of a few extra-hazardous enterprises, industrial and commercial risks belong in the class where relatively large sums must be hazarded on the chance of small gains. This is preëminently true of the risk taken by the independent farmer. Such risks do not appeal to the gambling instinct, and consequently they do not attract men except where the chances are good in the long run, that is, where the gains on the whole exceed the losses. Those who embark intelligently on such enterprises will, in the long run, receive profits. But in such extra-hazardous enterprises as appeal to the gambling instinct, by the chance of large gains from small investments, men are so over-anxious to invest that the losses on the whole exceed the gains, and there are no profits for such men as a class, though of course a few win large prizes. It is in the former class of enterprises that the " irksomeness of the risk " deters men from embarking, reduces competition, and improves the chances of those who have the foresight or the hardihood to enter.

For the sake of illustration only, let us assume that two men are trying to sell lottery tickets ; one is trying to sell tickets of the common kind and the other is trying to sell a kind which no lottery ever thought of offering. The first has a box containing 2000 tickets, all of which are blanks but one, but that one will draw a prize of $1000. The second has a box containing 2000 tickets, only one of which is a blank; all the rest will draw prizes of $1000. Suppose, also, that these two men are equally energetic and skillful as salesmen ; that each is to sell his own tickets all at a uniform price, but that that price is to be determined by the willingness of purchasers to buy. What is the *highest* price at which each will be able to dispose of *all* his tickets ? Mathematically, the first man's tickets are worth exactly 50 cents each ; that is, the total prizes ($1000) divided by the total number of tickets (2000) gives 50 cents. But if the experience of lotteries is any guide, there is not the slightest doubt that the first man would be able to sell all his tickets at more than 50 cents apiece. The buyers *as a class* would then lose more than all of them together gained. But the second man's tickets would be mathematically worth $999.50 ; that is, the total prizes ($1,999,000) divided by the total number of tickets (2000) leaves that sum. It is so probable as to amount to a practical certainty, that he would *not* be able to sell his tickets at that price, but would have to take a much lower price. In that case buyers as a class would gain by buying ; that is, their total gains would exceed their total losses. For some psychological reason, which need not be discussed here, men evaluate these different kinds of risks in this way.

Now it happens that industrial and business risks are unavoidable, and if production is to be carried on, some one must be induced to assume them. But these risks are associated with investing in enterprises of various kinds. When the enterprise is such that small sums may be risked, and the profits, though very uncertain, are very large, the gambling instinct will lead men to invest freely. Shares in such enterprises can be sold at a price so high as to make it certain that investors as a class will lose, just as the buyers of the first box of tickets, in the foregoing illustration, are sure to lose. But when the enterprise is such that large sums must be risked, and the profits, though small, are *fairly* certain, men are so reluctant to invest that the price which has to be paid (for the farm, for example, or the farming equipment) is so low as to make it certain that they who do invest will gain as a class, just as the buyers of the second box of tickets, in the foregoing illustration, will gain as a class.

There is a certain parallelism between the risk theory of profits and the abstinence theory of interest. In the discussion of interest it was seen that the necessity of waiting for the product of a piece of capital tended to reduce its present value somewhat below the sum total of its future earnings. The one who buys it at its present value and waits for its earnings to mature will, for this reason, secure a surplus in the form of interest. In a similar way, the risk connected with carrying on any enterprise under unstable conditions *may* reduce the present value of the equipment, including the labor employed, somewhat below the probable value of its product, even after allowance is made for interest. Those who undertake such enterprises may be expected, in the long run, to secure a surplus in the form of profits.

But we saw in our discussion of the interest problem that not all waiting is equally burdensome, some being done without any hope or expectation of reward in the form of interest. Similarly, not all risk is equally burdensome, some being undertaken for the sake of the excitement of the hazard. In the case of an enterprise which appeals to the gambling instinct, the eagerness of men to buy the risk will give it a selling value somewhat greater than it is really worth, so that they who persist in buying such risks invariably lose in the long run more than they win, though they may win on some of their early ventures.[1] But in the case of an enterprise which does not appeal to the gambling instinct, men are so reluctant to buy the risk that its market value is usually less than its real worth, and men who persist in buying such risks inevitably gain if they continue long enough and are not ruined by early losses.

In the former class of enterprises there are no profits, but losses instead, for the adventurers as a class, though an occasional fortune is won. In the latter class of enterprises there are profits for the adventurers as a class, though occasionally an individual becomes bankrupt.[2]

What becomes of the price paid by the consumer. Another important problem in distribution is that of finding what part of the price paid by the consumer of farm products goes to the farmer, and what part goes to the various agencies which take part in bringing the products of the farmer to the consumer. Unfortunately this problem cannot be reduced to general principles, but must be solved for each particular product for each particular locality. A full and complete answer to this question would therefore require elaborate investigations in many localities, and the tabulation of the results of these investigations in voluminous tables. Some indication as to the nature of such an investigation and its results may be gathered from the following table, the facts for which were gathered by the members of the author's class in agricultural economics in Harvard University in the spring of 1911.

[1] This is invariably true of lottery tickets. It is believed by most men of sound judgment to be true also of mining risks.

[2] Cf. the author's Distribution of Wealth (New York, 1905), pp. 270–285.

PRODUCT	WHERE PRODUCED	WHERE CONSUMED	PRICE RECEIVED BY PRODUCER	PRICE PAID BY CONSUMER	DIFFERENCE
APPLES . . . . . . No. 1 Baldwin	Marlboro, Mass.	Boston	$2.25 (bbl.)	$7.50 (bbl.)	$5.25
APPLES . . . . . . Extra fancy Jonathan	Wenatches Valley, Wash.	Chicago	1.45 (box)	8.00 (box)	6.55
APPLES . . . . . . Best No. 1 Baldwins	Maine	Liverpool	4.00 (bbl.)	6.42 (bbl.)	2.42
APPLES . . . . . . Jonathan	No. Yakima, Wash.	Boston	1.66 (box) (90–100 apples)	3.60 (box)	1.94
APPLES	Maine	Portland	2.00 (bbl.)	6.00 (bbl.)	4.00
BACON . . . . . . Home cured	Western Mass.	Boston	.08 (lb.)	.19½ (lb.)	.11½
BEEF . . . . (per hundredweight of steer)	Western ranges	Boston (?)	4.25 (cwt.)	6.475 (cwt.) [1]	3.79
BUTTER . . . . . . "Worcester Co. Best"	Worcester	Boston	.20¾ (lb.)	.25 (lb.)	.0425
BUTTER	Ashfield, Mass.	Boston	.25 (lb.)	.36 (lb.)	.11
CORN	Middle West	Boston	.40–.60 (bu.)	.60–.80 (bu.)	.12–.20
CORN TO ALCOHOL .	Pekin, Ill.	Pekin, Ill.	(station price) .40 (bu.)	.81 (bu.)	.41
SUGAR CORN	Hightstown, N. J.	Philadelphia	.425 (basket)	1.15 (basket)	.725
DWARF BROOM CORN	Kansas	East	85.00 (ton) (85 brooms)	344.25 (ton)	259.25
EGGS	Taunton, Mass.	Boston and vicinity	.18 (doz.)	.25 (doz.)	.07
EGGS	Vt. and N. H.	Boston	.20 (doz.)	.28 (doz.)	.08
EGGS	Indiana	Boston	.12 (doz.)	.25 (doz.)	.13
HAY	Maine	Boston	20.00 (ton)	23.00 (ton)	3.00
HAY, TIMOTHY . . .		Cambridge	8.00 (ton)	26.50 (ton)	18.50

[1] For meat to retailer, and $1.5675 for guts, etc., to packer.

WHERE DOES THE DIFFERENCE GO?

Picking, $0.25; barrel, $0.25; freight, $0.25; commission, $0.25; sorting, $0.15; labeling, carting, etc., $0.10; storage, $0.50; wholesaler, $2.00; retailer, $1.50

Growers' Association, $0.10; railroad rate to Chicago, $0.50; wholesaler, $2.45; retailer, $3.50

Barrel, $0.35; freight, commission to exporter, salesman, etc., $1.00; retailer, $1.07

Growers' Association, $0.09; freight, $0.50; refrigerating, $0.10; expressage, $0.03; wholesaler, $0.12; retailer, $1.10

Broker, $0.50; commission man, $1.50; retailer, $2.00

Freight, $0.002; dressing, $0.012; packing, $0.008; shipping, $0.01; wholesaler, $0.048; retailer, $0.03½

Feeder, $2.25; freight, $0.50; killing and chilling, $1.25; packer on meat, $1.45; wholesaler, $2.85; retailer, $0.4885 (all per hundredweight of steer)

Freight, $0.0025; wholesaler, $0.01; retailer, $0.03

Creamery, $0.03; expressage, $0.008; retailer, $0.072

Local dealer (elevator man), $0.02–$0.04; commission house, $0.04; direct to jobber from local dealer, $0.0075; freight, $0.005; retailer, $0.05–$0.10

Local freight, $0.02; elevator, $0.02; manufacture of 5 gallons of alcohol from a bushel, $0.31; for slop from 1 bushel, $0.06

Railroad rate, $0.05; commission, $0.025; wholesaler, $0.25; retailer, $0.40

Freight, $12.00; manufacturer's cost, $77.25; his profit, $42.50; grocer's profit, $127.50

Expressage, $0.01; commission, $0.01; breakage, advertising, etc., $0.03; retailer, $0.02

Expressage and delivery to wholesaler, $0.015; wholesaler, $0.04; delivery to retailer, $0.005; retailer, $0.02

Storekeeper (who assembles), $0.02; transportation in Indiana, $0.01; Indiana commission man, $0.0017; railroad rate from Indiana, $0.025; carting, $0.001; commission man in Boston, $0.0075; retailer, $0.0685

Pressing, $2.50; hauling, $1.00; carting, $1.00; freight, $8.00; jobber, $2.00; wholesaler, $1.00; retailer, $1.00

Product	Where produced	Where consumed	Price received by Producer	Price paid by Consumer	Difference
Milk	Montgomery Co., Pa.	Philadelphia	.03⅝ (qt.)	.08 (qt.)	.04⅜
Milk	Middlesex and Worcester Co., Mass.	Boston and vicinity	.04 (qt.)	.10 (qt.)	.06
Milk	Worcester Co., Mass.	Boston	.02¾ (qt.)	.08 (qt.)	.05¼
Cal. Oranges Alta Crestæ (navel)	Bonita, Cal.	Boston	1.612 (box)	3.50 (box)	1.888
Cal. Oranges Ruby Bloods	Bonita, Cal.	Boston	Loss .068 (box)	2.00 (box)	2.068
Oranges (navel)	California	New England	1.07 (box)	3.00 (box)	1.93
Peaches	Paonia, Cal.	Denver	.245 (box)	.75 (box)	.505
Peanuts	Virginia	Boston	.04½ (lb.)	.18 (lb.)	.135
Potatoes	Aroostook Co., Me.	Cambridge, Mass.	.50 (bu.)	.90 (bu.)	.40
Cal. Potatoes Oregon stock	California	San Francisco	.70 (sack) (2 bu.)	1.50 (sack)	.80
Dressed Poultry (Broilers)	Eastern Mass.	Boston	.33 (lb.)	.55 (lb.)	.22
Dressed Poultry (Roasters)	Eastern Mass.	Boston	.19¼ (lb.)	.33 (lb.)	.13¾
Poultry (Capons)	Eastern Mass.	Boston	.22$\frac{3}{7}$ (lb.)	.35 (lb.)	.12$\frac{4}{7}$
Poultry (Fowls)	Eastern Mass.	Boston	.16 (lb.)	.28 (lb.)	.12
Rice	Arkansas	Boston	.40 (bu.)	4.16⅔ (bu.)	3.76⅔
Strawberries, No. 1	Georgia	Boston	.08–.14 (box)	.15–.25 (box)	.07–.11
Tomatoes	Florida	Boston	.35 (crate)	2.10 (crate)	1.75
Tomatoes	Mt. Holly, N. J.	Philadelphia, N. E. section	.3775 (basket)	.80	.4525
Dressed Turkeys	Northern New York	Boston	.25 (lb.)	.38 (lb.)	.13
Milk (in spring)	Cooperstown, N. Y.	New York City	.025 (qt.)	.08 (qt.)	.055
Potatoes	Mass.	Cambridge	.55 (bu.)	.90 (bu.)	.35

Where does the Difference go?
Freight, $0.00⅜ ; retailer, $0.04
Freight, icing, bottling, $0.00⅝ ; wholesaler, $0.02⅜ ; retailer, $0.01 ; delivery, $0.02
Transportation, $0.00½ ; contractor, $0.02¾ ; peddler, $0.02
Picking, packing, etc., $0.50 ; freight, $0.828 ; auction commission, $0.06 ; retailer, $0.50
Picking, packing, etc., $0.50 ; icing, $0.21 ; freight, $0.828 ; auction commission, $0.03 ; retailer, $0.50
Packing and selling, $0.40 ; freight, $0.83 ; half-refrigeration, $0.10 ; local dealer, $0.60
Commission, $0.045 ; cost of box, paper, and packing, $0.14 ; wholesaler, $0.20 ; retailer, $0.12
Freight, $0.002 ; wholesaler (including packing), $0.018 ; retailer, $1.15
Bagging, $0.01 ; freight, $0.12½ ; wholesaler, $0.064 ; hauling to Cambridge, $0.03 ; retailer, $0.17
Freight, $0.10 ; commission agent, $0.26 ; wholesale and retail dealer, $0.44
Shipping and selling commission, $0.05 ; wholesaler (including cost of dressing, shrinkage, etc.), $0.07 ; retailer, $0.10
Shipping and selling commission, $0.04¾ ; wholesaler (including cost of dressing, shrinkage, etc.), $0.04 ; retailer, $0.05
Shipping and selling commission, $0.03 4⁄7 ; wholesaler (including cost of dressing, shrinkage, etc.), $0.04 ; retailer, $0.05
Wholesaler (including cost of dressing, shrinkage, etc.), $0.07 ; retailer, $0.05
Milling, $0.23¾ ; miller's profit, $0.21¼ ; wholesaler's expenses, $0.15 ; his profit, $1.00 ; retailer's expenses, $0.16⅔ ; his profit, $2.00
Cost to land them in Boston, $0.03 – $0.05
Railroad rate, $0.62 ; cartage, $0.03 ; shipper, $0.10 ; commission merchant, $0.05 ; packing, boxing, etc., $0.35 ; jobber, $0.15 ; retailer, $0.45
Freight, $0.05 ; commission agent, $0.0225 ; wholesaler, $0.15 ; retailer, $0.20
Local agent, $0.01½ ; boxing and packing, $0.01 ; railroad rate, $0.01 ; big dealer, $0.01½ ; retailer, $0.08
Local haul, $0.001 ; shipping, $0.009 ; freight, $0.005 ; wholesaler (who is also the distributor), $0.04
Packing, $0.02 ; commission, $0.03 ; railroad transportation, $0.05 ; retailer, $0.25

CHAPTER VI

PROBLEMS OF RURAL SOCIAL LIFE

The rural population. No other problem is even second in importance to that of maintaining the native quality of the rural population. The rural districts are the seed bed from which even the cities are stocked with people. Upon the character of this stock, more than upon anything else, does the greatness of a nation and the quality of its civilization ultimately depend. If the native vigor, physical and mental, of the people should decline, nothing could save its civilization from decay. Not even education itself can permanently arrest such decay when the inborn capacity to be educated is disappearing. Every horseman believes in careful training as a preparation for racing, but no horseman, no matter how excellent his system of training might be, would expect to maintain or improve the speed of his stable if he bred mainly from scrub stock. Nor should any country, however excellent its educational system, expect to maintain the capacity and productive efficiency of its people if the most capable and efficient of them multiply least rapidly, and the least capable and efficient multiply most rapidly.

But what is really meant by capacity and productive efficiency in a people? There is a story of an aged savage who, having lived most of his life among civilized men, returned in his old age to his native tribe, saying that he had tried civilization for forty years, and that it was not worth the trouble. A great deal of the philosophy of civilization is epitomized in this story. To a savage mind civilization is never worth the trouble, for the reason that taking trouble is distasteful to the savage mind. Only those races which have the capacity for taking trouble, or to whom taking trouble is not painful, are capable of becoming civilized. Civilization consists largely in taking pains. To some people it is too much trouble. They prefer to remain barbarians, even though they live in civilized surroundings. Other people have so much mental energy that they do not mind taking pains ; in fact they rather enjoy it. They are the builders of our civilization. Individual genius was once defined as the capacity for taking infinite pains. The genius of a race or of a nation, and its capacity for civilization, may be defined in precisely the same terms.

Efficient agriculture requires forethought, planning for next year, and the year after, and the year after that; putting in a great deal of careful, painstaking work to-day, with no prospect of seeing a tangible result for years to come; looking after an interminable number of details day by day, week by week, month by month, and year by year, in expectation of returns so distant in the future as to lie beyond the vision of lesser minds. Only the men or the races which possess this kind of capacity are capable of efficient agriculture or of efficient industry of any kind. Whatever other admirable qualities the savage may possess, — and he may possibly boast superiority over the civilized man in many respects,—lacking these qualities, he will remain a beaten race. Similarly, whatever admirable and amiable qualities an individual of our own race may possess, lacking these he will be a beaten man. It is idle for either a race or an individual to complain, or to say that in some other kind of a world it would not have been beaten. This happens to be this kind of a world, and in this kind of a world it happens that success comes to those races which possess in the highest degree the economic virtues of industry, sobriety, thrift, forethought, reliability, knowledge of natural laws, and mutual helpfulness. These are the qualities which bring success to a race or a nation, and the possession of these qualities constitutes, therefore, what we call capacity and

efficiency. We may persuade ourselves that we like other qualities or people who possess them, but nature pays very little attention to our likes and dislikes in such matters. However much
we may like other qualities, the peoples who lack these qualities will fail; and however much we may persuade ourselves that
we despise the sober, homely, economic virtues, the peoples who
possess them will succeed and eventually dominate the world.

The problem of maintaining the capacity of the rural population for civilization will depend upon two questions : (1) Is it the
most or the least capable individuals who marry earliest and have
the largest families ? (2) Is it the most or the least capable individuals who leave the farms and migrate to the cities ?

Ideally it would seem as though the most capable young men
should arrive first at a position of independence, where it would
be possible to marry and settle down to the work of building up
an estate and a family. Where social ideals are sound this is
doubtless the case ; but where they are unsound it is otherwise.
Where the social ideals are such that it is regarded as an honorable ambition — as the most honorable ambition, in fact — to
found a family, with a family estate to support it, or to perpetuate a family already honorably established, and to maintain its
standards and traditions, the capable young men will be guided
by this ideal, and the most capable of them will succeed best
in realizing it. But where the end and aim of economic life
centers in the gratification of the senses or of individual vanity,
in attracting public notice because of individual achievement in
fashionable society, in art, literature, or scholarship, or in any
other of the so-called polite pursuits, the family ideal is lost from
sight. Under such circumstances, there is a tendency to look
upon achievement in some of these directions as an end in itself,
rather than as a means of family building ; to assume that an
honorable ambition is realized when success along these other
lines is attained, regardless of the fate of the family ideal. Such

perverted social ideals are likely to prove disastrous to the race, because they lead the capable young men and women to follow those other ambitions and to abandon that of the family builder.

The family builder. The general abandonment of the ambition of the family builder will prove disastrous to the race for several reasons. In the first place, it leads capable and ambitious young men to choose their wives for other reasons than their capacity as mothers. The man whose ideal of life centers in individual gratification will, if he is successful enough in an economic sense to give him some opportunity for choice in the matter, choose a wife on the ground of her capacity to minister to his vanity or to his sensuality; to choose one, for example, who will help him in fashionable society, whose face will please his fancy, etc. The man whose dominant ambition is to found a splendid family, or to achieve immortality by leaving behind him a family of capable children, well trained and disciplined for the battle of life, and dominated by high ideals of morality, patriotism, etc., will choose a wife who is capable of helping him to achieve that ambition. She must be sound physically and capable of bearing and nursing healthy children; she must also be possessed of unusual mental power, and therefore capable of transmitting that mental power to her children; and, finally, she must be dominated by high ideals of morality and social service, in order that she may give her time and strength unsparingly to the task of training her children for good citizenship. When the family-building ambition dominates the people, this is the kind of woman who will be most sought after in marriage, who will least frequently remain unmarried and childless, who will marry earliest and therefore have the longest child-bearing period, and who will get the most capable and vigorous husbands; and therefore bear the most capable and vigorous children. Where different ideals prevail, a different type of woman will be most sought after in marriage. Women weaker physically, mentally, and morally may satisfy other desires better than the type just described; consequently the stronger type of women will be more likely to remain unmarried and childless, or to marry later and therefore have a shorter child-bearing period, or to get less capable and vigorous husbands and therefore bear less capable and vigorous children. In addition to all this, where other than the family ideal dominates marriage, there will be more childless marriages.

The country which maintains the soundest ideals and ambitions in the way of family building will be the country peopled with the strongest and most capable citizens. The country with the strongest and most capable citizenship will be the strongest and the most prosperous country. Since the citizenship of the country is, in the end, recruited mainly from the rural districts, it is especially important that sound ideals should predominate there. To fail in this respect is, eventually, to fail in everything. Therefore there need not be the slightest hesitation in saying that the most important ambition which can be cherished in the country is the ambition of every capable man and woman to found or perpetuate an honorable, capable, and vigorous family. The aim of successful agriculture should be to enable the successful agriculturist to maintain a family estate for the support and perpetuation of such a family. Nothing could be more disastrous than the idea that successful agriculture, or a rich farm, was an end in itself, or that it was a means to any such end as sensual gratification, personal vanity or ostentation, or more luxurious ease.

Rural migration. Next in importance to the character of the family ideal as a factor in race building is the character of rural migration. If it should happen that the most vigorous, capable, and enterprising youths should continually leave the country for the city, there to become sterilized, as is usually the case, through the pursuit of sensuality, vanity, or false ambition, only one result would be possible. The less vigorous, capable, and enterprising youths being left in the country, there to marry and bring up families, and the same process of selection going on generation after generation, the quality of the rural population would inevitably deteriorate. This would happen as certainly as it would if a horse or cattle breeder should follow the practice of selling his best animals and keeping the inferior ones for breeding purposes. If such a breeder should continue this practice, he would eventually have no first-rate animals to sell. Similarly, if the rural population should degenerate, there would eventually be no superior men and women to send to the cities, and the cities themselves would then degenerate. But if it should happen that the best, the strongest, the most intelligent, and the most enterprising youths should stay in the country, and the inferior ones should be sent to the cities to be sterilized by false ambitions, then it would follow that the quality of the rural population would improve. So long as the rural population is improving there is no danger of national decay or weakness, or of a decline of civilization. It is therefore of great importance that the farms shall retain at least their fair share of the talent of the country.

In order that young men and women of talent and capacity may be induced to remain on the farms, rural life must be made attractive to them. Farm life cannot be attractive to such men and women unless it offers opportunities for a liberal material income, for agreeable social life, and for intellectual and æsthetic enjoyment.

An adequate income. The problem of securing an adequate income to the farmer's family is partly a problem of securing an adequate supply of land and capital for them. There is very little in the peasant type of farming, where the farmer is so inadequately supplied with land as to make efficient agriculture impossible, and where even machinery and good teams are unprofitable, to attract men and women of high spirit and enterprise. This is the type of farming, however, which would be forced upon us if the agricultural population should increase in such a way as to bring about a continuous *morcellement*, or subdivision of farms into smaller and smaller units. Such an increase in the number of the rural population would therefore inevitably result in a decline in its quality, because such petty farming, being unattractive to men and women of capacity for larger things, would drive them cityward and leave in the country only the type fitted for small affairs.

This presents a phase of the problem of rural depopulation which is too frequently overlooked. Where the decline in numbers comes about as a result of a readjustment of agricultural methods, it may be, in the end, a good thing. Where the farms have proved too small for the most efficient agriculture, and where therefore the owners of small farms find them so unprofitable as to be induced either to buy out their neighbors or to sell out to them, the result is larger farms and a smaller number of farmers. If the change results in making farming more attractive to men and women of capacity, and in keeping such people on the farms, the decline in numbers is compensated for by a permanent improvement in quality. They who believe that quality is more important than quantity must approve the change.

Fortunately the transfer of land is so easy and inexpensive in this country as yet, especially in the newer states, that there are no serious obstacles in the way of this process. Where the farms are either too small or too large to secure their highest value, they tend to be combined in the former case, or to be subdivided in the latter, until they approximate the size which gives them greatest value. The reason why this process does not go on in the same way in some of the older countries is because of the difficulties in the way of transferring land. The long history of a given title, the vast number of complicated legal rights and claims which may have accrued, the ridiculously pious care with which even the most remote rights of distant relatives are guarded by the courts, make the process of transferring a piece of land a formidable task.

Where, however, rural depopulation results in the sheer abandonment of the land and allowing it to go to waste, the problem is somewhat different. Even though the land is so poor as to attract only a poor grade of farmers, it may be better to have it occupied by a low-grade population than not to have it occupied at all, though even that is open to question. It is a mistake to assume that all unoccupied land is going to waste. In New England it speedily grows up to timber, and in some cases that is the most productive use to which land can be put. The essential thing to remember is that a dense agricultural population, if that density means a small income per family, invariably means, under modern conditions, a low-grade population, because men and women of spirit and capacity will not stay. They will leave the country districts in the possession of people who can do no better anywhere else, and who are therefore content to remain and accept a low standard of living. But a relatively sparse population, if it means a large income per family, will generally mean a high-grade population, because such conditions will help to attract and hold men and women of spirit and capacity. If we once understand this, we shall not be alarmed over a decline in the rural population until we know the reasons and the results.

Still more important as a means of securing adequate incomes for intelligent farmers is the existence and accessibility of exact scientific knowledge to those who have the capacity to acquire and apply it. Our agricultural colleges, the experiment stations, and the agricultural literature which they are publishing and distributing, all combine to give to the farmer of intelligence a higher differential advantage over the ignoramus. Only the man of intelligence is capable of understanding and applying the results of scientific study and experiment. He is the man who will profit most, therefore, and who will in the end be able to buy out his ignorant neighbor and send him off to town to work under a boss. Such an improvement in our rural population augurs well for the future of the republic.

An agreeable social life. Quite as important as the question of an adequate income is that of an agreeable social life as a means of attracting a superior type of men and women to the farms. Few people realize how much more dependent the farmer is than any one else upon his social surroundings. A business man in the city can choose his neighbors without changing his place of business, for the reason that his residence and his place of business are entirely disconnected. If he does not like one neighborhood as a place of residence and a place in which to bring up his family, he can move to another without disturbing his business relations. The farmer must live on his farm and must bring up his children there. Whatever the social surroundings of the neighborhood are, he must accept them or else sell out and move, thus upsetting all his business relations and hazarding his business prosperity on the chance of improving his social relations. Again, the man in the city is usually within easy reach of a great variety of schools, churches, and other social agencies. If one does not suit him, he can make use of another without great inconvenience. In the country, where all such things are farther apart, it would ordinarily be a great inconvenience to send his children to any other school than the one belonging to his own district, or to take his family to another church than one of those of the neighborhood. Again, even though the city man does not choose his place of residence wisely, he is not dependent upon his neighbors for his social life. Where the neighborhood idea does not prevail, as it usually does not in the city, one may ignore his own neighbors and still have an agreeable social life among the members of his class, trade, occupation, or club. This is probably, in the end, a vicious tendency, but it does, at any rate, help to make the city man relatively independent of the social conditions of his immediate neighborhood. But the farmer cannot pick and choose in this way. Perhaps it is well that he should not, but this at least shows that he is dependent upon his neighborhood. As a result of this dependence he is compelled, more than any other class of men, to take an interest in neighborhood affairs. The safety and well-being of his own family depend upon his having good neighbors and good moral and social conditions within his neighborhood. This is doubtless a good thing in the end, because it forces him, if he is interested in his family and the future careers of his children, to give time and energy to the work of neighborhood improvement. But temporarily it may be a hardship to the man of clean habits and sound principles, because, before he can get the neighborhood cleaned up, his family may have suffered from the lack of a wholesome social life.

Whatever may be said upon that point, it can scarcely be denied that the farmer, more than any one else, has reason to take an active interest in the local church, the school, the grange, the library, local sports, and every other agency which may contribute to the social life of the neighborhood. If he allows these things to degenerate, it will profit him little to have come into possession of broad acres, to have grown big crops, and to have built big barns to hold them.

The country church. Among the agencies for the building up of a wholesome social life in the country the rural church deserves first mention ; if for no other reason, because it is the oldest. Unfortunately there has been a close parallelism between the practices of the rural churches in America and the type of agriculture which has prevailed. In the pioneering stage agriculture has consisted mainly in harvesting the soil, and very little attention has been paid to soil building. Similarly, the pioneering churches have too generally followed the plan of harvesting a membership by revivalistic methods and have given too little attention to membership building. A certain pioneer preacher, of picturesque fame, was once reported to have opposed the education of men for the ministry on the ground that there were plenty of well-educated men to be had, and if the Lord wanted an educated minister all he needed to do was to seize upon one of these educated sinners and shake him over the pit until he came to his senses and agreed to preach the gospel. Fortunately this argument did not prevail; but it has looked, at times, as though some of the more popular churches have relied upon a similar policy for the recruiting of their membership. They seem to have relied more upon the making of converts from among mature reprobates than upon the training of successive generations of boys and girls into good, mutually helpful neighbors; into productive, efficient, prosperous farmers; in short, into good substantial citizens such as build up a community, increase the productivity of its farms, and make it a desirable place in which to live.

However, things are improving in one respect at least, and the pioneering stage of church activity is giving way to a more permanent and constructive form of church activity. The transition period, however, is a critical one, and in many cases there appears to be an inability on the part of the country church to live through it.

One serious danger, against which the warning cannot be made too strong, is the snare of a sentimental type of spirituality, a kind of spirituality which wastes itself in mere æsthetic or emotional enjoyment — a kind of spiritual Sybaritism. The church which yields to this temptation, and cultivates a form of religious emotionalism as an end in itself, will fail; and it will deserve to fail because it will be of no use to its members or to the world. The church which realizes that its spirituality must meet the practical test of productivity; that its members must be made better farmers and better citizens generally by reason of their spirituality; that the more religious they are the better crops they will grow, the better stock they will keep, the better care they will give it, and the better neighbors they will be, is the church which will deserve to succeed and in the end will succeed.

It may be laid down as a general law of rural economy that the productive land in any farming community will tend to pass more and more into the hands of those who can cultivate it most efficiently, — that is, into the hands of the most efficient farmers, — unless it is prevented from doing so by some kind of military force exercised by an aristocratic ruling class, or by an expensive and cumbersome system of transferring land titles. In a democratic country like the United States, where there are few impediments in the way of the free transfer of land, we need look for nothing else. The men who can make the land produce the most will be able to pay the most for it, and in the end they will get it and hold it. This looks simple enough, no doubt, and may not at first seem to signify much, but it is weighted with consequences of the most stupendous and far-reaching character, — consequences which it would be suicidal for the church to ignore.

It means simply and literally that the rural districts are never to be thoroughly Christianized until Christians become, as a rule, better farmers than non-Christians. If it should happen that Christians should really become better farmers than non-Christians, the land will pass more and more into the possession of Christians, and this will become a Christian country, at least so far as the rural districts are concerned. The first result would probably be to paganize the cities, since the non-Christians displaced from the rural districts by their superior competitors would take refuge in the towns. But since nature has a way of exterminating town populations in three or four generations, and the towns have therefore to be continuously recruited from the country, the Christianizing of the rural districts would eventually mean the Christianizing of the towns also. But, vice versa, if non-Christians should become the better farmers, by reason of some false philosophy or supercilious attitude toward material wealth and economic achievement on the part of the church, then this would eventually become a non-Christian country for the same reason.

But if, as a third possibility, there should be no perceptible difference between Christians and non-Christians as to their knowledge and adaptability, or as to their general fitness to survive and possess the earth, — fitness, that is, as determined by nature's standard rather than by some artificial standard of our own devising, — the result would be that Christians would remain indefinitely a mere sect in the midst of a non-Christian or nondescript population. The only way of avoiding this rather unsatisfactory situation would be to force the whole population into a nominal Christianity by military force. But, assuming that physical force is not to be used, and that the ordinary economic forces are to operate undisturbed by such violent means, then the contention will hold. This is what is likely to happen if certain religious leaders should succeed in identifying Christianity with millinery, with emotionalism, with abstract formulæ respecting the invisible world, or with mere loyalty to an organization, rather than with rational conduct. By rational conduct is meant that kind of conduct which conserves human energy and enables men to fulfill their mission of subduing the earth and ruling over it, which enables them to survive in the struggle with nature. This is the essence of all genuine morality.

If the significance of this law is once clearly understood, there is little danger that the church will make the wrong choice or hesitate long in making the right one. It would at once decide to make better farmers of its rural members than nonmembers can possibly become, since nonmembers would lack the stimulating influences which go with membership. The only danger is that the churches, some of them at least, will fail to see the point, or refuse to see it, and continue to hug the delusion that they are under the guidance of a higher power than political economy, and may therefore safely ignore its laws. That would be a delusion, because a law is a law, and the words higher and lower have no application. To believe that there may be a conflict between divine law and physical law, or between divine law and economic law, is to believe that this is an irrational universe, at war with itself. Moreover, we must form our conclusions as to the will of God and the duty of man on the basis of the observed facts and uniformities of the world of actual experience ; and the laws of political economy are among these observed uniformities. Our only way of knowing that we are in tune with the Infinite is by observing that we are in tune with the finite ; and we cannot possibly be in tune with the finite unless we act in harmony with known physical and economic laws.

There may be some excellent people who hold that it should not be the mission of the church to make good farmers, but to convert to Christianity those who are already good farmers. Reliance upon the process of conversion may appeal to some as the right policy for the church to pursue ; but unless conversion means increased efficiency, greater adaptability, greater fitness for the struggle for existence, better conservation of human energy, the church can scarcely hold the ground which it wins by that process, but will be continually losing ground through economic competition with the more efficient non-Christians.

But if this is a rational universe, must we not conclude that any religion or any religious movement, however attractive it may seem, is proved a false religion or a misdirected religious movement, which does not increase the capacity of its followers to control the forces of nature, to dominate the earth and to rule over it, which does not increase their adaptability, which does not make the nation which adopts it a prosperous nation? Conversely, must we not conclude, assuming still a rational universe, that that is a true religion which, if adopted by a whole community or a whole nation, would increase the adaptability of that community or that nation and enable it to subjugate the earth and to outgrow both in power and wealth, in comfort and prosperity, the nation which does not adopt it? The alternative to this conclusion would seem to be to fall back upon the concept of an irrational universe, on the belief that this world is Satan's world, in conflict with God's law, instead of God's world in harmony with itself.

This doctrine is not so revolutionary as it may seem. Indeed, it is so old-fashioned as to be positively reactionary, and that is why it may seem new and revolutionary to those who have forgotten certain old truths. If it be correct to say that the rural districts will become Christianized only in proportion as Christians become better farmers than non-Christians, it must also be true that whatever permanent success the rural church has had in the past has been due to the same reason, except where force or some other noneconomic factor has intervened. Such is, as a matter of fact, the case. In spite of the emphasis of the church upon spirituality, or because of its emphasis upon a sane and wholesome kind of spirituality, men have usually become better farmers under its influence. For, along with certain formalities of belief and conduct, there has generally been, for one reason or another, considerable emphasis upon the plain economic virtues of industry, sobriety, thrift, forethought, and mutual helpfulness. Wherever there has been a pure and elevated type of Christianity, there Christians have exhibited these virtues in somewhat greater degree than non-Christians. This simply means that they have wasted less of their energy in vice, dissipation, brawling, or in riotous living, than their non-Christian neighbors. Economizing their energy, they were able to prevail over those who wasted theirs. Sometimes, however, war and persecution have been resorted to, to check this economic growth. At other times Christians themselves have resorted to these noneconomic methods of gaining ground. But where economic forces have been allowed to work unhindered, and where Christianity has been of a type worth preserving, there it has grown strong by reason of these economic forces alone, and it has not needed to appeal to physical force or to the state to spread itself.

But is not agricultural competition itself a form of war? Certain misinformed philosophers have fallen into the habit of saying so. There is this difference. In war success depends upon the power and the willingness to destroy. In agriculture success depends upon the power and willingness to produce. In war they win who inflict the greatest pain and injury. In agriculture they win who render the greatest utility or service; and to a sober mind this must appear to be a real difference.

But why confine these observations to agriculture and rural economy? Are not the conditions of economic success the same in the city as in the country? And must not religion prevail over irreligion in the city as well as in the country, provided religion secures a greater conservation of human energy than does irreligion? In a certain very broad sense, or in the long run, — with a great deal of emphasis on the word "long," — that is probably true. But the conditions of individual economic success in cities are so complex, and there are so many opportunities for

> " ways that are dark
> And for tricks that are vain,"

as to obscure though not to obliterate entirely the working of this law under which success depends upon productive service.

In agriculture one must wrest a living from nature, and nature cannot be tricked or deluded. But a large element of our city populations — and generally they are the dominant element — get their living out of other people; and people are easily deceived. Instead of laboring to make two blades of grass grow where one had grown before, their business is to make two dollars emerge from other people's pockets where one had emerged before. Neither impudence, nor a smooth tongue, nor a distinguished manner, nor lurid rhetoric ever yet made an acre of land yield a larger crop of grain; but they have frequently made an office, a sanctum, a platform, and even a pulpit yield a larger crop of dollars. They who get their living out of other people must, of necessity, interest those other people; and men are so constituted that queer and abnormal things are more interesting to them than the usual and the normal. They will pay money for the privilege of seeing a two-headed calf, when a normal calf would not interest them at all. The dime-museum freak makes money by showing to our interested gaze his physical abnormalities. He is an economic success in that he makes a good living by it, but it does not follow that he is the type which is fitted to survive, or which religion ought to try to produce. Other men, going under the names of artists, novelists, or dramatists of certain nameless schools, make very good livings by revealing to interested minds their mental and moral abnormalities. They, like the dime-museum freaks, are economic successes in that they make good livings, but it does not follow that they are the type of man fitted to survive, or that religion ought to try to produce. This type of economic success is an urban rather than a rural one, and it flourishes under urban rather than rural conditions. So long as it flourishes there is no reason why religious men who conserve their energies for productive service should succeed in crowding them out of existence. The only chance of attaining that end will be for religion to give people a saner appreciation of things, teach them to be more interested in normal calves than in two-headed calves, in normal men than in dime-museum freaks, in sane writers than in certain degenerate types now holding the attention of the gaping crowd. If this can be brought about, then it will result that the religious type of man, even in cities, will more and more prevail over the irreligious, provided the religion itself is worth preserving, — that is, provided it becomes a positive factor in the conservation of human energy.

As has already been suggested, there is a great deal more involved in the making of a good farmer than in the teaching of scientific agriculture. Mr. Benjamin Kidd, in his " Social Evolution," has done well to emphasize the importance of moral qualities as compared with intellectual achievements. In the first place, intellectual achievements, or their results, can only be utilized where there is a sane and wholesome morality as a basis. In the second place, the results of the intellectual achievement of one race or of one man may be borrowed freely by the rest of the world, provided the rest of the world have the moral qualities which will enable them to profit by so doing ; whereas moral qualities cannot be borrowed from one race by another. Japan, for example, could easily borrow from European nations the art of modern warfare, together with its instruments of destruction ; but she did not borrow, and could not borrow, that splendid courage and discipline which enabled her to utilize so efficiently the inventions which she borrowed. So one nation can easily borrow farm machinery and modern methods of agriculture, but it cannot borrow the moral qualities which will enable it to profit by them. Saying nothing of mental alertness and willingness to learn, which might be classed as mental rather than moral, it could not borrow that patient spirit of toil, nor that sturdy self-reliance, nor that stern and unrelenting sense of duty, nor that forethought which sacrifices present enjoyment to future profit, nor that spirit of mutual helpfulness, all of which are essential to any effective rural work. Again, a nation cannot easily borrow a sane and sober reason, a willingness to trust to its own care in preparing the soil rather than to the blessing of the priest upon the fields ; nor can it borrow a general spirit of enterprise which ventures out upon plans and projects which approve themselves to the reason. And, finally, it cannot borrow that love for the soil, and the great outdoors, and the growing crops, and the domestic animals, which marks every successful rural people. These things have to be developed on the soil, to be bred into the bone and fiber of the people, and they are the first requisites for good farming. After them comes scientific knowledge. In the development of such moral qualities as these the church has been, and may become again, the most effective agency.

Because of such moral qualities as these, the Puritans were able to subdue the New England forest and to build up a great rural civilization on the basis of a sterile soil and an inhospitable climate, and without any great amount of scientific knowledge, though as compared with other communities their knowledge of agriculture was not inferior. They took their work seriously, as befitted those who had such a task before them as the building of a wilderness empire. Their unbending sense of duty and their thrift and foresight have become proverbial, as have their keenness, their alertness, and their humor. But their mutual helpfulness, though less proverbial, is attested by their logrollings, their house raisings, their husking bees, and the like, making even their pleasures bring them useful results, both material and social, — material in the sense of having something more substantial than headaches to show for their festivities, social in the sense of having the strongest of all bonds of social sympathy, namely coöperative labor, as the basis of their social enjoyment.

It is said that the great problem of the country church to-day is that of an adequate support of the ministry. How can the ministry be adequately supported? One obvious answer is to reduce the number of churches, where there are too many churches for the community to support. This is a good answer; perhaps that is the easiest way, but it is the second-best way. Another way is to build up the community in order that it may furnish adequate membership and adequate support for all the churches. This may be a harder way, but where it is not impossible it is the best.

There was a time when the finance ministers of European governments were hard pressed to provide a revenue for the expenses of the state. They eventually found that the best way to get adequate support for the state was to increase the prosperity of the country. When they began studying how to make the country prosperous, the science of national economy, or political economy, was born. When they who are charged with the task of raising money for the support of the churches and the ministry awaken to the fact that the best way to secure adequate support is to make the parish more prosperous, the science of parish economy will be born. This will be, for our rural churches, as fortunate an event as the birth of political economy was for modern governments.

Of course there should be continued emphasis, in the teachings of the church and the pulpit, upon the plain economic virtues of industry, sobriety, thrift, practical scientific knowledge, and mutual helpfulness; but much more emphasis than heretofore should be placed on the last two. Practical scientific knowledge of agriculture and mutual helpfulness in the promotion of the welfare of the parish are absolutely essential, and unless the churches can help in this direction they will remain poor and inadequately supported. For those who think that the church should hold itself above the work of preaching the kind of conduct that pays, or the kind of life that succeeds, the economic law stated above is the strongest argument.

If the kingdom of God is a kingdom of service, these efforts are quite consistent with the mission of the church. If it will seek to serve the community in this way, seeking *first* to be of service, all the other things — that is, sufficient wealth, membership, esteem, etc. — will be added unto it. If, however, it seeks first merely to make proselytes, to increase its membership, or to get money, it will have no reason to expect or deserve permanent success.

Organized efforts in the churches for the study of parish economy, for gaining more and more scientific knowledge of agriculture, for the practical kind of Christian brotherhood which shows itself in the form of mutual helpfulness and coöperation, in the form of decreasing jealousy and suspicion, in the form of greater public spirit, greater alertness for opportunities of promoting the public good and building up the parish and the community, in helping young men and young women to get started in productive work and in home building, in helping the children to get the kind of training which will enable them to make a better living *in the parish*, — efforts of this kind will eventually result in better support for the churches themselves, because the community will then be able to support the church more liberally, and, what is more important, it will then see that the church is worth supporting.

This ideal of a church which makes itself a factor in building up a community, even in material things, is not an impossible ideal. It has been realized in the past and it can be realized again. An illustrious example is that of Jean Frédéric Oberlin, the pastor of the Steinthal. Numberless other examples can be found in the religious orders of the medieval church, — examples of communities which were made rich and prosperous by the teachings and the example of self-sacrificing leaders. This ideal will, however, never be realized by a church which affects to despise this world and the things of this world, which regards the world itself as lost, and conceives of its own mission as consisting in saving as many individual souls as possible from the wreck.

If the church will assume that the world is not going to perdition, that it is going to last for a long time, and that it will eventually be a Christian or a non-Christian world, according as Christians or non-Christians prove themselves more fit to possess it, — according as they are better farmers, better business men, better mechanics, better politicians, — then the church will turn its attention more and more to the making of better and more progressive farmers, business men, mechanics, and politicians.

What is social service? Much is being said nowadays about social service as the mission of the church. That is, in itself, an excellent thing ; but there is a tendency to take too narrow a view of social service, just as there was formerly a tendency to take too narrow a view of spirituality. The result is that as much cant is being preached in the name of social service as ever was preached in the name of spirituality. This is to be expected of those who do not realize that all productive work, such as growing corn, wheat, or cattle, to feed the world, or growing wool or cotton to clothe the world, is social service ; and that the best social service which the average man can perform is to do his regular work well, — to grow good crops if he is a farmer, and to bring up his family in habits of industry, sobriety, thrift, reliability, and mutual helpfulness ; that anything, in short, is social service which builds up the country and makes it strong, powerful, progressive, and prosperous. The church which preaches and teaches social service in this broad and constructive sense will become a powerful factor in the progress and prosperity of the country, and is not likely to lack for adequate support.

The dependence of the farmer upon his social surroundings, as previously pointed out, gives the country church a unique opportunity for real service outside the field of agricultural production. The organizations which can supply the farmer and his family with an agreeable social life will supply one of the greatest needs of rural people and will deserve their support. If the church can do this, there need be no rival organization spring up to divide the loyalty and support of the people. If the church does not do it, some other organization will. The need is too great to be left unsatisfied, and will create the means for its own satisfaction.

In order that the country church may contribute its share toward supplying opportunities for a wholesome and agreeable social life, it is not necessary that it undertake an elaborate program of entertainments, concerts, gymnastic classes, etc., though all these things are good in their places. One thing, and only one thing, is essential, though it is sometimes difficult to attain and is always capable of infinite variation. It is essential that people with a common interest should occasionally be brought together, that is, within speaking distance of one another. If that can be done, social life will take care of itself. But it is not always easy to find a common interest. In some times and places theological speculation, in others political or scientific speculation, has so occupied men's minds as to give them an all-absorbing theme of common interest. When they came together their common interests made them agreeable company for one another and gave them ample opportunity for high converse on great themes. Where there is no common and absorbing interest of this kind something must be found or created, otherwise conversation will revolve interminably around such themes as the weather and crops.

But it is not at all necessary that conversation should center in speculative themes, either theological, political, or scientific. Problems of parish or neighborhood economy, of rural beautification, are large enough to occupy the time and attention of several generations. The problems of the beautification of rural roads, bridges, schoolhouses and grounds, church grounds, etc., are enough to occupy the spare time and attention of rural America for a hundred years to come. A neighborhood which becomes possessed with a common passion for beautification will never lack for social life. The church which can arouse such an interest as this, or any other equally noble interest, will have gone a long way toward solving the problem of a wholesome and agreeable social life in the country.

But the well-known and regularly established means of social grace must not be overlooked. Most people like to eat and drink, and when they can be brought together around a common table, they have, in a small way at least, every essential of social life; that is, you have your people together with a common interest. From this as a beginning there is possible a vast widening of the social life. It can scarcely be regarded as profane to suggest that we have, in this elementary social principle, one of the great facts of life which are symbolized in the Holy Communion. Again, there are the common social amusements and recreations. Of particular value for rural communities is choral singing, the highest form of social amusement known to man. Where a group of people sing together for their own delectation, rather than for that of an audience, we have one of the best possible solvents of private differences and idiosyncrasies, and one of the highest possible means of promoting a sense of brotherhood and solidarity, as well as one of the oldest and most primitive forms of social communion. Even dancing is not to be despised as a means of grace, where it can be carried on in the proper spirit.

The example of Denmark. The most remarkable example of agricultural regeneration in modern times is Denmark. In 1864 she was facing national ruin. As the result of a disastrous war, itself a heavy drain upon the country, she had lost some of her best provinces. In addition to this she was obliged to pay a heavy war indemnity. Finally, and worst of all, her German market was cut off by the German tariff wall. But as one result of this accumulation of calamities there was developed an intense feeling of national patriotism and solidarity. Out of this feeling grew a number of coöperative measures for the rebuilding of the country, especially in the field of agriculture. Within fifty years Denmark became the most prosperous country on the continent of Europe, and stands to-day as a monument to the efficiency of the spirit of intelligent coöperation. It is a coöperation not forced upon the people by a government, but a spontaneous coöperation growing out of a general spirit of patriotism and mutual helpfulness. Every student who is intimately acquainted with the history of this movement agrees that the popular recreations and festivities have been powerful factors in creating this spirit, and that the popular songs and hymns, and the habit of singing them together on all occasions, have given to these recreations and festivities a patriotic and religious character which is to be found nowhere else to-day on so large a scale.

Every college student is familiar with the fact that when a body of students unites upon a common interest, like an athletic contest, there is not the slightest difficulty in getting them together, and when they do get together there is not the slightest difficulty in keeping things going. Even singing seems to be a perfectly natural and fitting form of expression. Precisely the same principle has been seen in operation on a larger scale by any one who has lived through a great national crisis, like a war. When the people are intensely interested in the same thing their gatherings are never dull. Singing together is a natural way of expressing the common feeling, and no one questions its propriety.

The Danish people have demonstrated that it is possible for a whole people to become as thoroughly united and as enthusiastic upon the common interest of agricultural production and national upbuilding as it is for a body of college students to become upon the subject of an athletic contest, or for a nation to become on the subject of war. The church which can give its people or its neighborhood a great and noble enthusiasm like this will have no difficulty in creating a vibrating social life. Then it will not seem out of place, or bad taste, for the people to sing whenever they get together.[1] The absence of any common enthusiasm means a disunited, egoistic, disintegrating social life, compared with which even war, horrible as it is, may be the lesser evil if it results in uniting the people in a common interest and a common cause. Since Denmark has shown that a people may develop a common enthusiasm for the arts of peace, it ought to furnish a basis for a constructive faith in its possibility elsewhere. If the church is not to be the conservator of that constructive kind of faith, where shall we look for it?

The country school. The country school, though a younger institution than the country church, is regarded by many as the more powerful and influential of the two. It has certain manifest advantages, chief among which is the fact that it belongs to the whole community instead of a part of it. Therefore it can be made the center of the life of the whole neighborhood more easily than the church can, especially where denominational differences tend to divide the community. On the other hand, the fact that the school is a territorial institution — that is, that it belongs to all the people living within a certain territory — puts it at a disadvantage as compared with the church in a neighborhood where the majority of the voters are unprogressive and unenlightened. In such a neighborhood the school is likely to be of little use, except in so far as it is compelled by

---

[1] Incidentally it may be mentioned that many of the oldest recorded hymns of the Indo-European branch of the human race, those of the Rig Veda, are agricultural hymns.

higher state authorities to fulfill its function properly. But if the church, being a voluntary institution, should happen to have in its membership the more enlightened and progressive part of the community, it may begin a work of social regeneration which would be impossible for the school. But, of course, if the church should be in the control of the least intelligent and least progressive part of the community, as is sometimes the case, it possesses all the disadvantages and none of the advantages of the school.

The country school is, of course, primarily an educational institution, and as such must give its attention mainly to instruction in certain conventional subjects which the world has come to regard as the necessary basis of an education, or as the essentials of a preparation for life. Remembering always that every kind of productive work is social service, we need have no difficulty in seeing that the first duty of the school is to fit its students for individual success in some line of production, and that the line for which the rural school is best fitted to prepare its pupils is agricultural production. But inasmuch as our present purpose is not to discuss the general problem of rural education, but only to consider how the rural school may be made a factor in developing a more wholesome and agreeable social life in the country, we need not consider the rural-school curriculum.

There is already an admirable interest in the school as a means of developing patriotism. The flag raisings, the celebration of national holidays, the reading of patriotic literature, the memorizing of national classics, all are excellent, and show how thoroughly awake our people are to some of the broader aspects of the problem. Much remains yet to be done, however, in giving definiteness and concreteness to the patriotic sentiments which we are trying to develop. It is one thing to develop patriotism as an abstract virtue ; it is quite a different thing to develop it as a passion for a definite, concrete, national achievement. At all times and in all lands the desire for victory in war has been the most powerful stimulus to patriotism. That gives the people something definite to strive for, — a concrete achievement around which patriotic sentiments may crystallize. That " peace hath her victories no less renowned than war," we doubtless believe in a general sort of way ; but until our belief becomes particular, and we come to center our desires upon some definite productive achievement in the arts of peace we shall never be able to arouse the patriotic passion as effectively in peace as in war. This ought to be especially clear to students who will have observed that school loyalty, merely as an abstract virtue, is difficult to develop without some definite achievement like an athletic contest or a debate, or even a spelling match, to be carried through. For our country schools, as well as for every other social agency in the country, one great problem, therefore, must be to particularize the patriotic sentiments of the community and give them a definite, productive aim.

People generally get what they want most. When a common or universal passion for productive achievement is once definitely aroused in a community, the achievement will follow as a matter of course. Any community can have as beautiful a countryside as it wants, provided it wants it seriously enough, and with sufficient unanimity, to spend the time and energy necessary to beautify it. Any community can have as moral a community or as prosperous a community as it wants, under the same conditions. Conversely, the lack of a common desire or a common social interest means failure in the arts of peace as surely as in those of war.

The desire to make the village the most beautiful village in the world, or to make one's township the most beautiful township, or to make it the greatest corn- or cotton- or wheat- or potato-growing township, or to make its schools the best in the world, or to produce the finest cattle or horses or hogs in the world, — any really useful purpose, in fact, if it will unite the people and call out a common and universal enthusiasm, — will do more to dignify the social life of the village or township than all the purposeless social entertainments that could be invented. A social life is not created by merely saying, Go to, now, let us be sociable. It is created by having a common purpose, worthy enough to commend itself to all right-minded people, and large enough to demand their attention, their time, and their hard work. The young men and women in particular, of our race, have never yet failed to respond to a call to hard work and self-sacrifice, when the work and the sacrifice were for an object of common good which they really thought worth achieving.

Next to a common interest and enthusiasm, the most important factors in the creation of a wholesome and agreeable social life in the country are opportunities for meeting and ease of communication. Aside from all the purely religious services rendered by the church, the mere fact that it brings people together in the room once a week is of immeasurable value. The most civilizing influence in the world is contact of man with man. Men cannot habitually meet together and look into one another's eyes without developing some kind of a sense of unity ; nor can they live entirely separate and apart from one another without becoming suspicious, morose, and unsympathetic. The school, likewise, in addition to its purely educational functions, renders a service by the mere fact that it brings the juvenile population together day after day.

In addition to these regular occasions for meeting, there are the extraordinary occasions, such as national holidays and special rural festivities. Unfortunately we have, in this country, failed to live up to our opportunities in the way of rural sports and festivities. In earlier days the corn huskings, barn raisings, quiltings, and a multitude of other occasions of the same general description supplied the need for wholesome recreation. Now we have outgrown the need for those precise forms of social gathering, and have not, as yet, developed anything satisfactory to take their place. We may say distinctly, therefore, that here is one of the unsolved problems of American rural life, though a partial solution has already been found in some sections of the country. In the old-fashioned Southern barbecue, which still survives in certain favored communities; in the Old Settlers' Day, which is celebrated in some communities of the central West; and in the Old Home Week of New England, we have examples of rural festivities which illustrate what may be done in any community where the whole countryside turns out for a holiday. Doubtless there are numerous other examples in other parts of the country. In some of the older countries the number and character of these festivals constitute an attractive feature of rural life.

The tough neighborhood. One difficulty with us is that we are not yet far enough removed from the backwoods stage to have entirely eliminated the rowdy element from our rural population. This element is frequently so much in evidence on these occasions, especially in backwoods neighborhoods, as to keep the more decent and self-respecting element away, thus destroying the value of the festival. A few generations of severe competition will doubtless give the advantage more and more to the sober, steady-going, self-respecting element, especially where the land is highly desirable. The restless, turbulent, rowdy element being crowded out, one of the greatest drawbacks to a wholesome social life in the country will have disappeared. This process is noticeably taking place in the best farming regions, where there is something to attract a more progressive class of people. It has not yet shown itself so clearly in poorer regions, where there is little to attract a superior type of men and women.

In fact, it is an open question whether the poorest land is not destined to remain ultimately in the possession of a poorer type of man. A selective process seems to be going on, which tends to bring about such a result. Where the land is fertile and the opportunities for agricultural enterprise are good, the intelligent and progressive youths are induced to remain on the farm. They will be able to beat the less intelligent in competition and to buy the land away from them. At the same time, such lands attract the more intelligent and progressive farmers who are looking for a place in which to locate. An unintelligent and unprogressive farmer stands a poor show in such a place. The other class will offer so much for land that he will not be able to buy it. If he owns it already, they will offer him so much for it that he will generally yield to the pressure sooner or later, and sell out. On the other hand, where the land is poor and opportunities meager, the more capable of the growing youths tend to move away, so long at least as there are better opportunities to be found elsewhere. Again, the men who are crowded off the richer lands will sometimes drift toward those cheaper lands where they do not have to bid against competent, but only against incompetent, farmers. Eventually, however, it is possible that the competition even here may become so severe as to drive out the undesirable element.

The standard of living. The suggestion that the best lands tend to get into the hands of the best farmers needs qualification. It sometimes looks as though they tended to get into the hands of the farmers with the cheapest standard of living. It has often been noticed and remarked upon that foreign-born farmers are buying out our native American farmers, not because the foreigners are better farmers, but because they can live more cheaply and thus accumulate capital for investment more rapidly. This, it is claimed, is merely a triumph of a lower over a higher standard of living, and indicates a tendency toward keeping farm life on a low level.

Against this pessimistic view there are two arguments. In the first place, during the entire latter third of the nineteenth century agriculture was relatively unprofitable in this country. This is the period when the displacement of American-born by foreign-born farmers was so noticeable. For an American of good education and business capacity, who was therefore fitted for business or professional life, there is no doubt that during that period the city offered better opportunities than the country, on the average. The foreigner, unless he were a man of unusual education and culture, had to take his choice between farming on the one hand, and some form of hand labor on the other. To him farming was frequently the only attractive opportunity. The reason the American farmer was willing to sell out at a price which the foreigner could pay was not altogether because the foreigner could make the farm pay better, but because the American had opportunities in the city which the foreigner did not have, not having yet become sufficiently adjusted to the conditions of American life. Now that agriculture is becoming more prosperous, so that the American-born farmer may have as good opportunities in the country as in the city, it remains to be seen whether he can be displaced by the foreigner, that is, whether he will generally be willing to sell out at a price which the foreigner can afford to pay, or whether he will not be willing and able to pay as much for land as the foreigner will. In the second place, a cheap standard of living is not necessarily an efficient one. A more expensive standard, provided it is rational, may be more efficient in competition than a cheaper one. An expensive standard of living, which includes forms of expenditure that minister to mere pride and ostentation, or to unwholesome appetites, and does not add to one's intelligence or working capacity, will handicap one in competition with men whose standards of living do not include these irrational forms of expenditure. But an expensive standard of living, which includes only such forms of expenditure as maintain strength and working capacity, stimulate mental energy and alertness, and minister to the higher intellectual, social, and æsthetic desires, will never handicap any one in competition with men of lower standards. One result of a competition among standards of living will be, in the long run, to rationalize the standards, eliminating those forms of expenditure which add nothing, and preserving those which add something, to efficiency. This will come about through the greater success of those families whose standards of living approach most nearly to rationality, and through the lesser success of those families whose standards of living depart most widely from rationality. When farming becomes sufficiently profitable to furnish opportunities approximately as good as those furnished by the businesses and professions of the city, there is no reason why farmers with a high standard of living should be displaced by those with a low standard, provided the high standard is rational, and not one which ministers to enervating appetites or mere vanity and ostentation.

Rural sports and recreations. Every hard-working student will easily understand how essential a reasonable amount of recreation is to the maintenance of a high state of mental and physical efficiency. He will then appreciate the statement that a rational standard of living must include a reasonable expenditure of time or money on recreations. Just what is a reasonable expenditure for this purpose may not be easy to determine, though there need be no disagreement as to the general principle that too little recreation, which produces dullness of body and mind, is as bad as too much, which is mere dissipation or waste of time, energy, and money. Nor need there be any disagreement as to the principle that the recreations should be such as to appeal to all members of the community. While economists generally approve a division of labor in industry, there are few who will approve a kind of division of labor which is too frequently found in rural communities, where most of the men work all the time and never play, while a few loafers amuse themselves all the time and never work.

Rural sports are the natural adjunct of rural festivals as a means of maintaining a wholesome and agreeable social life in the country. Owing to a natural excitability and tendency to excess, Americans have found it difficult to develop distinctive rural sports as a permanent and dignified institution of rural life, except in a few favored localities. Fox hunting and horse racing tend, in this country, to be spoiled as rural sports by their affectation by urban magnates in the one case and livery-stable toughs in the other. Nothing is finer and more dignified than for a group of neighboring, well-to-do farmers to unite for a day's hunting, when the purpose is to rid the country of vermin ; but when a group of townsmen, who have learned to ride under a roof in a professional riding school, proceed to the country and advertise their solvency by chasing a timid fox across the fields, the sight is not calculated to inspire admiration. Nor is there any sport more fitting than for a group of horse-breeding farmers to meet for the purpose of testing the speed of their colts in a fair and open competition. It is only by such open competition that successful horse breeding is made possible. But when horse racing degenerates into a mere vaudeville "stunt," or, as is more frequently the case, into a mere opportunity for a group of professional gamblers from the purlieus of the livery stables, who have been initiated into the mysteries of race-track management, to enrich themselves at the expense of the uninitiated, it is not too much to say that it has lost its virtue as the inspirer of a wholesome and agreeable social life in the country.

In view of the well-known excitability of the American temperament, and its tendency to excess, it is important that rural sport in this country should be of a character which does not lend itself readily to extreme specialization; otherwise it will tend to drift into the hands of specialists, who do the playing while the public looks on. This produces a spectacle rather than a sport. It is also important that there should be considerable variety in the forms of sport, in order that as many as possible should be able to participate. Of particular importance, however, is the requirement that these sports should fit into the seasonal character of rural work. City work is so uniform that the time for recreation can be evenly distributed throughout the year. Short hours with regular weekly, biweekly, or monthly half holidays give the city worker ample time for wholesome recreation. But since in every farming country there are rush seasons, when short hours and half holidays would mean a loss of crops, it is obvious that recreation time cannot be so evenly diffused. To make up for this, it is desirable that during the seasons when work is slack there should be regular periods of recreation, and games which need not be crowded into a single afternoon.

This suggests the need also of regular annual festival occasions, suited to each section of the country and its type of agriculture, when there can be a general relaxation from the strenuous toil of the rush seasons. In anticipation of such a period of jollity, the grinding fatigue of the busy season is borne with more patience, particularly by the young people, and the work is done more vigorously because more cheerfully. Again, there is the possibility of uniting social pleasure with rural work to a somewhat greater degree than is now done. If the spirit which showed itself among our ancestors in the barn raisings, logrollings, and similar occasions could be restored, it is possible that the present generation could get a great deal of social pleasure out of the threshing season and other occasions of a similar character. This would seem to be the natural time for the harvest home celebration, which has been so important an event in all old rural civilizations. In former days, however, as the writer can testify, threshing was such prodigiously hard work, and a great deal of it was so dusty and disagreeable, as to stifle any spirit of jollification which might otherwise have arisen. But with the more powerful engines and more highly improved machinery of the present, the hardest and most disagreeable part of the work of threshing has been eliminated. Under such conditions it is at least a theoretical possibility that the threshing season in any neighborhood might be made a festival occasion, to be participated in by women as well as by men — by priest, parson, and schoolma'am as well as by the farmers themselves. This, however, is only by way of suggestion.

The grange. Of all the organizations which are now contributing on a large scale to the social life of rural America, the grange is, at the present time, one of the most effective, partly, perhaps, because it is organized for the purpose. It is, however, somewhat exclusive, in that it serves the social needs of its own membership rather than those of the whole community. Even more exclusive in character are the lodges of the various secret and fraternal orders, which also serve the social needs of their own members. This brings us face to face with one of the most difficult problems in the whole field of rural social economy,— Is it possible to maintain a social life except through some agency of selection and exclusion? In aristocratic countries, where class distinctions are of ancient and historic standing, the social life runs pretty definitely within class lines, but within those boundaries it runs freely. In democratic America, where caste and hereditary class distinctions are not allowed, we have not yet become adjusted to the new situation, especially in the rural districts; and there is a strong tendency toward the formation of groups on the basis of likes and dislikes, and for the social life to run within these groups. This is clearly a long step in advance of the caste system, or of the stratification of society according to aristocratic principles, in that the grouping is based upon something besides the accident of birth ; but it falls short of a thoroughly democratic ideal, according to which social life ought to run freely without regard to the boundaries of class, creed, or fraternal order. This ideal, however, has not yet been realized, for those countries and communities where hereditary aristocracy is least in evidence are the places where secret societies and fraternal orders are most highly developed and most influential. Doubtless they furnish a protection against the disagreeable obtrusiveness of the mob element in our aggressive democracy; but there is danger that their very exclusiveness should breed a spirit of snobbishness.

Shall rural people set their own standards, or shall they imitate city people? But all the organizations and agencies which contribute to the social life of rural communities will fall short of their highest possibilities unless they make rural life socially self-supporting, and independent of the standards and fashions of the city; unless, in short, they give to the social life of the country a character and dignity of its own, instead of being a bad copy of city life. So long as country life lacks this distinctive character and dignity, so long as country people look to the cities for their standards of dress, their social habits, and their ideals of propriety, so long will rural social life remain unsatisfactory. The domination of the city over the country is, in last analysis, a mental or spiritual domination. It will end when country people are able to set their own standards, when they stop trying to be city people, or to be like city people. When they develop a reasonable pride in the fact that they are country people, and in their country dress, country habits, country customs ; and when this pride is justified by the inherent sanity and simple, unostentatious dignity of their lives,— then we shall have a rural civilization worthy of the name. Unless this result is achieved, many of the so-called rural improvements will merely serve to link the country to the city and still further increase the domination of the latter over the former. If rural free delivery does no more than to bring to the farmer the daily paper from the city, with its garish advertisements and its neurotic sensationalism, and if this should develop among country people a desire for those forms of excitement which city people seem to like and to be willing to pay for, the result will be not to diminish but to increase the lure of the city. When the quiet and serenity of country life are referred to in such terms as lonesomeness and monotony, and the rural free delivery is regarded merely as a means of relieving that lonesomeness and monotony, the symptoms are not favorable for the development of a wholesome rural life. But if rural free delivery, like the rural telephone, is a means of linking one country neighborhood with another, of exchanging ideas among country people as well as between city and country, if it results in the development of an *esprit de corps* among country people, and enables them to develop a social life of their own, all these things will help in the building of a worthy rural civilization, and in making country life satisfying and agreeable.

This is a factor of great financial as well as social importance. When the city contains everything which country people really want, then the city will be the place where country people will go to spend their money. If a farmer becomes prosperous enough to retire from work, he will go to town to live ; he will buy a lot and build a house in the town and spend his time and his money there. But if the country contains the things which country people want, then the country is the place where they will go to spend their money. If the farmers who wish to retire from active work would spend in the country, on their own farms, for example, the money which would be necessary to buy and maintain residences in the towns and cities, it would not take very long to make the country a most attractive place of residence. Schools, churches, library facilities, plumbing, and steam heat can all be had in the country as well as in the city. But if people cultivate a liking for the noises, the electric displays, the large billboards, and other similar delectations of the cities, the country can furnish few attractions of this kind to compete with the city. Country people will continue to move cityward, seeking a chance to spend their money for the things of their choice.

It may be supposed that if the country should furnish the things which city people really want and are willing to pay for, it would contribute to the financial prosperity of the country; but this conclusion must not be too hastily reached. It must not be imagined that a mere willingness on the part of certain townspeople to spend a part of their time and money in the country is in itself a mark of genuine appreciation of country life, or that it tends to make real farmers, who have to make their living at farming, more appreciative of rural enjoyments. It is one thing to go to the country once in a while to disburden one's self of an accumulation of surplus cash, and then return to the city to talk about it; it is quite another thing to appreciate the quiet and homely enjoyments which lie within the reach of the plain farmer, — enjoyments which do not require even an automobile as an accessory. Against the idea that the rural-life problem is to be solved by a few wealthy capitalists building themselves palatial residences in the country and spending a part of their surplus time there, Sir Horace Plunket uses the following weighty words:

I am not, so they tell me, up to date in my information; there is a marked reversion of feeling upon the town *versus* the country question; the tide of the rural exodus has really turned, as I might have observed without going far afield. At many a Long Island home I might see on Sunday, weather permitting, the horny-handed son of week-day toil in Wall Street, rustically attired, inspecting his Jersey cows and aristocratic fowls. These supply a select circle in New York with butter and eggs, at a price which leaves nothing to be desired, — unless it be some information as to cost of production. Full justice is done to the new country life when the Farmers' Club of New York fulfills its chief function, — the annual dinner at Delmonico's. Then agriculture is extolled in fine Virgilian style, the Hudson villa and the Newport cottage being permitted to divide the honors of the rural revival with the Long Island home. But to my bucolic intelligence it would seem that against the " back-to-the-land " movement of Saturday afternoon the captious critic might set the rural exodus of Monday morning.[1]

A few magnificent villas, where wealthy townsmen spend the money which they acquire in town, will not help to solve the problem of country life for those who have to make their living from the soil, except where wealth is combined with taste, tact, and sympathy. If these qualities are absent, the display of urban magnificence in the country tends rather to increase the discontent of the young men and women of the neighborhood. It helps to create the impression that the only satisfactory way to live in the country is to go to town and make a fortune, and then come back to the country to spend it. There were many magnificent villas owned by Roman magnates in Italy, even in the very worst period of rural decline under the Roman Empire. The dominance of the city was so complete that the country was never looked upon as a place in which to live unless one had a fortune to spend there. Aside from its function of furnishing pleasing sites for villas, the country was regarded merely as a place where the city could get supplies of food. People really *lived* in town. In fact, this dominance of the town over the country was one of the characteristics of ancient civilization, though that dominance was more complete at certain times than at others.

On this point the following passages are significant :

Rome was, in its origin, only a municipality, a corporation. The government of Rome was merely the aggregate of the institutions which were suited to a population confined within the walls of a city ; these were

[1] The Rural Life Problem in the United States (New York, 1910), p. 152.

municipal institutions, — that is their distinguishing character. This was not the case with Rome only. If we turn our attention to Italy at this period, we find around Rome nothing but towns. That which was then called a people was simply a confederation of towns. The Latin people was a confederation of towns. The Etruscans, the Samnites, the Sabines, the people of Græcia Magna, may all be described in the same terms.

There was at this time no country, — that is to say, the country was wholly unlike that which at present exists; it was cultivated, as was necessary, but it was uninhabited. The proprietors of lands were the inhabitants of the towns. They went forth to superintend their country properties, and often took with them a certain number of slaves; but that which we at present call the country, that thin population — sometimes in isolated habitations, sometimes in villages — which everywhere covers the soil, was a fact almost unknown in ancient Italy.

When Rome extended herself, what did she do? Follow history, and you will see that she conquered or founded towns; it was against towns that she fought, with towns that she contracted alliances; it was also into towns that she sent colonies. The history of the conquest of the world by Rome is the history of the conquest and foundation of a great number of towns. . . .

In Gaul, in Spain, you meet with nothing but towns. At a distance from the towns the territory is covered with marshes and forests. Examine the character of the Roman monuments, of the Roman roads. You have great roads, which reach from one city to another; the multiplicity of the minor roads, which now cross the country in all directions, was then unknown; you have nothing resembling that countless number of villages, country seats, and churches, which have been scattered over the country since the Middle Ages. Rome has left us nothing but immense monuments, stamped with the municipal character, and destined for a numerous population collected upon one spot. Under whatever point of view you consider the Roman world, you will find this almost exclusive preponderance of towns and the social nonexistence of the country.[1]

The establishment of the feudal system produced one of these modifications, of unmistakable importance; it altered the distribution of the population over the face of the land. Hitherto the masters of the soil, the sovereign population, had lived united in more or less numerous masses of men, whether sedentarily in cities, or wandering in bands through the country. In consequence of the feudal system these same men lived isolated, each in his own habitation, and at great distances from one another. You will

[1] Guizot, F., The History of Civilization (London, 1856), Vol. I, pp. 27–29.

immediately perceive how much influence this change was calculated to exercise upon the character and course of civilization. The social preponderance, the government of society, passed suddenly from the towns to the country; private property became of more importance than public property; private life than public life. Such was the first and purely material effect of the triumph of feudal society. The further we examine into it, the more will the consequence of this single fact be unfolded to our eyes.[1]

Elsewhere Guizot points out the well-known fact that the rise of modern civilization is again reversing the order and tending to concentrate population, wealth, and power in the cities, and to emphasize urban rather than rural ideals.

Farming *vs.* talking as a field for ambition. One striking evidence of the general dominance of urban over rural ideals in America is the almost total indifference of our people to agriculture as a field of distinguished achievement. Great efficiency in the practical application of science to agriculture, or in the organization of the factors of agricultural production, are recognized in the abstract by every thoughtful person as of the highest possible value to the country as a whole; but in the concrete we pay very little attention to it. The ancient remark about the value of the man who makes two blades of grass to grow where one had grown before, as compared with the politician (or the talker), we approve in a general way, but specifically we think a great deal more of the talker. The man who applies great executive ability and scientific knowledge to agriculture may get good crops and make profit for himself; he may also win local recognition, particularly among farmers; but unless he talks or writes about it, he does not gain general recognition among the people at large. In proof of this, let any one look through "Who's Who in America," which is supposed to contain the names of those who have achieved marked success in every large field of human endeavor. Judging by its pages, either

---

[1] Guizot, F., The History of Civilization (London, 1856), Vol. I, p. 68.

agriculture is not a large field of human endeavor, or else there are no markedly successful farmers. Choosing those states in which agriculture is commonly supposed to be a large field of endeavor, we find in the edition of 1908–1909 almost no farmers. The number of distinguished persons connected with agriculture and allied fields of work is as follows :

Maine, 1 farmer-manufacturer, 1 horticulturist (at the State University)
Ohio, 1 agricultural educator, 1 agriculturist
Indiana, 1 arboriculturist
Illinois, 1 farmer
Iowa, 1 forester, 1 horticulturist (both in the State College at Ames), 1 breeder, 1 farmer
Kansas, 1 stockman, 1 fruit grower
Nebraska, 1 agricultural educator, 1 forester, 1 farmer

This lack of recognition of the farmer is not, of course, the fault of the editors of " Who 's Who." They include in their publication only the names which are widely known or talked about. The fact that an eminently successful farmer is not widely known or talked about is due to the fact that our people have no interest in that kind of achievement.

Another proof of the same thing is the fact that almost no farmer has secured, in recent years, any political recognition. Even Mr. Roosevelt, with all his enthusiasm for rural uplift, consistently preferred the man who talked about farming to the man who did the work of farming. His Rural Life Commission, for example, was an excellent commission, but it was not made up of farmers, but of eminent men who had talked a great deal and very wisely about agriculture and the problems connected with it. This helps to explain why farmers were generally so skeptical as to the results of the commission's work.

So long as men are so constituted as to crave distinction and wide public esteem, so long will they tend to avoid an occupation which seems to furnish no opportunities in that direction. Until our esteem for the farmer ceases to be merely an approval of farming in the abstract, and begins to show itself in the form of an appreciation of the individual farmer and his particular achievement, we shall not accomplish very much in the way of checking the movement of the more ambitious youths toward the city.

Absentee landlordism.   Next to war, pestilence, and famine, the worst thing that can happen to a rural community is absentee landlordism.   In the first place, the rent is all collected and sent out of the neighborhood to be spent somewhere else ; but that is the least of the evils.   In the second place, there is no one in the neighborhood who has any permanent interest in it except as a source of income.   The tenants do not feel like spending any time or money in beautification, or in improving the moral or social surroundings.   Their one interest is to get as large an income from the land as they can in the immediate present. Because they do not live there, the landlords care nothing for the community, except as a source of rent, and they will not spend anything in local improvements unless they see that it will increase rent.   Therefore such a community looks bad, and possesses the legal minimum in the way of schools, churches, and other agencies for social improvement.   In the third place, and worst of all, the landlords and tenants live so far apart and see one another so infrequently as to furnish very little opportunity for mutual acquaintance and understanding.   Therefore class antagonism arises, and bitterness of feeling shows itself in a variety of ways.   Where the whole neighborhood is made up of a tenant class which feels hostile toward the absent-landlord class, evasions of all kinds are resorted to in order to beat the hated landlords.   On the other hand, the landlords are goaded to retaliation, and the rack-rent system prevails.   Sometimes the community feeling among tenants becomes so strong as to develop a kind of artificial "tenant right," which is in opposition to the laws of the land, and the laws of the land are then made more severe in order to control the "tenant right." [1]

Even where the class antagonism is not carried to this extreme, there is a wasteful expenditure of human energy in the efforts of one class to circumvent the other, and the attractiveness and dignity of rural life are destroyed by the jealousy and rancor thus created.

In this country we are accustomed to look with disfavor upon any system of tenancy; but whatever may be said of tenancy as such, there is not the slightest doubt that the worst possible system is that under which the landowner lives at a distance and maintains no connection with the land except as a receiver of rent. Where the landlord lives upon his own estate and takes an interest in it, the worst features of tenancy disappear. The landowner's interest in his own home creates in him an attitude toward the rural neighborhood which is quite different from that of the absentee.

The resident landlord as leader. Besides, there are some advantages in a system which gives the large landowner a chance to devote his time to broad schemes of improvement while his tenants are completely occupied with the immediate problem of growing crops. This is the one serious disadvantage of the American type of agriculture under which the land is owned by small- or medium-scale farmers who do their own work. No one has the time or the surplus capital to carry on elaborate experimenting, extensive drainage operations, or similar large-scale improvements. Under the English system the large landed proprietors have led in most of these progressive movements,

---

[1] In some parts of France, under the old régime, the tenants would combine to fix rents and to prevent newcomers from renting land. The tenant would even sell his "right," or bequeath it to his son, very much as though he owned the land. Any one else who would lease the land so bequeathed, or interfere with the son's possession, would be liable to injury or murder. The laws of the country were ineffective against this determined stand of the tenants.

without waiting for a general public awakening. In the United States, and other countries of small proprietors, these enterprises have been carried on either by the state or by coöperative enterprises. These methods are excellent in themselves, but they are necessarily slower than the English method, for the simple and sufficient reason that the general public is always slower than a few of its most intelligent individuals. At the present time, in the United States, the federal Department of Agriculture, the state agricultural colleges, and the experiment stations are carrying on this kind of work on a more elaborate scale than is possible for a group of individual proprietors, however large their estates, though much pioneer work was done on great English estates.

Another advantage of the tenancy system, as it exists in England, is that it furnishes a kind of organization of agricultural interests, — or at least a very good substitute for organization. A great landowner living on his estate, and interested in its prosperity, is a natural leader and organizer of the rural community consisting of his tenants. It is everywhere recognized in the United States that the great difficulty in the way of organization of rural communities is the lack of leaders. If this difficulty is still further accentuated by a feeling of jealousy, as is too frequently the case, among the farmers of a neighborhood, the problem of organization is well-nigh insoluble. Unless the country church can remove this feeling of jealousy and suspicion by the effective preaching of a gospel of brotherhood, it is difficult to see what can be done for such a neighborhood. With the well-known efficiency of our agricultural colleges and experiment stations, and of our national Department of Agriculture, we have done a great deal to remove the one disadvantage of the system of detached, one-family farming. If we can, in addition, bring about an effective organization of our rural interests, we shall have all the advantages and none of the disadvantages of the system of tenancy under large proprietors.

Organization for a purpose, or organization for its own sake.
It is extremely unlikely that any effective or permanent organization of rural interests can ever be brought about without some
pretty definite object to be accomplished. Organization for organization's sake is a poor program. Again, it is extremely unlikely that any single object, or group of objects, can be made
the basis of a national organization. Our agricultural interests
are too diverse for that. All attempts to form a general homogeneous organization of the farmers of the country will probably fail, as they have hitherto. This points unmistakably to
the organization of local interests for definite purposes. When
several farmers in a certain locality have a clear and definite
purpose to accomplish, they have no difficulty in organizing for
that purpose. One of the best examples of this is the California
Fruit Growers Exchange. A large number of fruit growers,
seeing that they must organize their marketing arrangements
or become bankrupt, had a sufficient motive. The question of
leadership solves itself under such conditions. The man who
knows how to do what everybody wants done is a leader by the
only kind of divine right, — namely, natural fitness. An illustration of the same principle on a smaller scale is furnished by
the farmers of a certain New Hampshire township, who needed
a market. They organized and opened a store in Cambridge,
Massachusetts, to which they sent their produce. In this case
the leader was a country pastor. A multitude of other examples,
large and small, could be named, all illustrating the same principle, namely, that the organization must be local to begin with,
and that it must have a clear and definite object to accomplish.

The organization of rural interests need not, however, remain
local and scattered. They may be federated. Those who are
interested in rural organization may well take lessons from
the organizers of the labor movement. The attempt to form
a general, homogeneous organization of all laboring men had a

promising beginning in the Knights of Labor, but it lacked the element of definiteness and of local unity. Its influence, therefore, waned rapidly, whereas the American Federation of Labor rose to great prominence, power, and influence. Organizing local unions among members of each separate trade, and then federating these unions, leaving to each a great deal of independence and local autonomy, this movement has proceeded on sound principles of organization. This points to the principle of federation as the correct one upon which to attempt the general organization of rural interests. A beginning is already made in the various local and special organizations scattered over the country. If these can be federated into state and national organizations, leaving each local body independent and autonomous, at least so far as its own special objects are concerned, a movement may be started which will do for farmers what the American Federation of Labor has done for wageworkers, though the active program need not be the same.

It cannot be too much emphasized, however, that any organization whose objects are not constructive, and designed to promote the welfare of the country as a whole, is foredoomed to ultimate failure, because it ought to fail. It is for the interest of the country as a whole that the supply of fruit should be adjusted to the demand, and that there should not be a glut in one market while there is a scarcity in another. A fruit-growers exchange, by organizing the shipping and selling of its fruit so as to bring about a more uniform and equal adjustment of the supply to the demand, is performing a productive function for the country as a whole, and deserves success. When it begins to abuse its power and, instead of adjusting the supply to the demand, undertakes merely to charge monopoly prices, it will deserve to fail, and will eventually fail. The same may be said of an organization of dairymen, market gardeners, cotton growers, etc. However, it is not necessary that such organizations should be philanthropic. On the contrary, it is probably better that they should be strictly self-interested; but it is essential that self-interest should be followed in economic rather than in uneconomic ways, as these terms were defined in Chapter I. To attempt to promote one's self-interest in a way which contributes to the productivity of the whole country is to deserve success; to attempt to promote it in any other way is to deserve failure. That is why coöperative enterprises, when actuated by mere jealousy of some storekeeper, or of any one else who is doing useful and honest work, usually fail. But coöperative enterprises which attempt something constructive, like the starting of a new industry, the opening of a new market, or the prevention of real waste, and are therefore actuated by a higher motive than hate or jealousy, are usually successful, and redound to the interest and profit of the participants.

This part of our discussion may be summed up by saying that until our rural interests become organized our rural life will continue to be dominated by urban interests, urban standards, urban ideals, and that this will leave rural life in a weak and undignified position. Furthermore, it will not be easy to organize rural interests in any single homogeneous organization, because our agricultural interests are too diverse and heterogeneous; but the organization must proceed through the formation of local associations having definite, tangible, and constructive aims, and the gradual federation of these local organizations into a general organization combining unity and solidarity with diversity and local autonomy.

INDEX

383

Tax, single, 302
Taxation, 215
Taylor, Henry C., 300
Tenancy, in England, growth of, 52;
   growth of, in America, 114; cash or
   share, 231
Thoroughbred, 61
Three-field system, 39
Thrift as a factor in prosperity, 213
Thwaites, Reuben G., 73 note
Tomatoes, price of, 332
Tompkins, Benjamin, 61
Townshend, "Turnip," 55
Turkeys, price of, 332
Twine binder, 99
Two-field system, 39

Uneconomic methods of getting a
   living, 2
Urban migrations toward wider markets, 127

Urban superiority, assumption of, 26

Value, law of, 290

Wages, 290
Waiting as related to interest, 309
War as a means of livelihood, 2
Warren, George F., 254
Waste labor, forms of, 184
Waste land, causes of, 132
Ways of economizing in the use of
   money, 211
Weeden, William B., 66, 67
Westward migration, 81
Wheat belt, migration of, 113
Wolff, Henry W., 280 note
Woods, Charles D., 161
Wright, C. W., 83 note

Young, Arthur, 57

ANNOUNCEMENTS

PRINCIPLES OF RURAL ECONOMICS

By Thomas Nixon Carver
David A. Wells Professor of Political Economy in Harvard University

8vo, cloth, 386 pages, $1.30

RURAL ECONOMICS is a new book on a phase of agriculture which has as yet been little exploited in textbook literature. It differs from other books on agriculture mainly in its discussion of every problem from the standpoint of national economy rather than from the standpoint of the individual farmer. Instead of explaining to the latter how to grow crops and make his farm pay, the author takes up such questions as the place of agriculture in national prosperity; the characteristics of rural life; the significance of rural as distinguished from urban civilization.

What is good agriculture — in its national significance; why rural migrations are from densely to sparsely populated areas, while urban migrations are in the opposite direction; why agriculture is necessarily an industry of small units; why rural people are more generally self-employed than urban people; why they are harder to organize and upon what principles rural organization can succeed; why, and under what conditions, agricultural coöperation is desirable and possible, — these and a number of other questions of tremendous practical importance in rural life are carefully worked out in the text, the emphasis being always upon the social rather than upon the business phase.

It is the purpose of the book to give to the rapidly increasing number of agricultural students a more definite idea of their place in the economy of modern civilization, and to others a knowledge of the dignity and honor of the most ancient and honorable of all occupations, — that of the farmer.

165 a

GINN AND COMPANY Publishers

COUNTRY LIFE EDUCATION SERIES

Edited by CHARLES WILLIAM BURKETT, recently Director of Experiment
Station, Kansas State Agricultural College; Editor
of *American Agriculture*

A SERIES of practical texts for the amateur and professional
farmer written by experts in their respective lines. These books
aim to give a thorough exposition of both the theory and the practice of the various branches of farming and breeding.

TYPES AND BREEDS OF FARM ANIMALS

By CHARLES S. PLUMB, Professor of Animal Husbandry in the College of Agriculture of the Ohio State University. 8vo, cloth, 563 pages, illustrated, $2.00.

PRINCIPLES OF BREEDING

By EUGENE DAVENPORT, Dean of the College of Agriculture, Director of the
Agricultural Experiment Station, and Professor of Thremmatology in the University of Illinois. 8vo, cloth, 727 pages, illustrated, $2.50.

FUNGOUS DISEASES OF PLANTS

By BENJAMIN MINGE DUGGAR, Professor of Plant Physiology in Cornell University. 8vo, cloth, 508 pages, illustrated, $2.00.

SOIL FERTILITY AND PERMANENT AGRICULTURE

By CYRIL GEORGE HOPKINS, Professor of Agronomy in the University of Illinois;
Chief in Agronomy and Chemistry and Vice Director in the Illinois Agricultural
Experiment Station. 8vo, cloth, xxiii + 653 pages, $2.25.

PRINCIPLES AND PRACTICE OF POULTRY CULTURE

By JOHN H. ROBINSON, Editor of *Farm Poultry*. 8vo, cloth, xvi + 611 pages,
illustrated, $2.50.

Other volumes in preparation

GINN AND COMPANY PUBLISHERS

BOOKS ON AGRICULTURE

SHEEP FEEDING AND FARM MANAGEMENT

By D. HOWARD DOANE, Assistant Agriculturist in the Office of Farm Management, United States Department of Agriculture, and Assistant Professor, in charge, of Farm Management in the University of Missouri. 12mo, cloth, 128 pages, illustrated, $1.00.

A PRACTICAL manual on the feeding of sheep for market, embodying the experience of successful sheep men and farmers throughout the country. As a textbook for classes in farm management, animal husbandry, and agronomy, the book contains much useful material.

SOIL PHYSICS LABORATORY MANUAL

By J. G. MOSIER, Professor of Soil Physics, and A. F. GUSTAFSON, Associate in Soil Physics, in the University of Illinois. 8vo, cloth, 71 pages, illustrated, 60 cents.

PRACTICES designed to give the student a knowledge of the physical principles that underlie the common agricultural operations. Many of these practices are here published for the first time. An appendix contains work for advanced students.

EXAMINING AND GRADING GRAINS

By THOMAS L. LYON, Professor of Soil Technology in the Federal Experimental Station, Cornell University, and EDWARD G. MONTGOMERY, recently Assistant Professor of Experimental Agronomy in the University of Nebraska. 12mo, cloth, 101 pages, illustrated, 60 cents.

TEXT and exercises providing a thorough drill in the study of the structure and quality of all cereals, in the identification of seeds of the common grasses, millets, and legumes, and in judging the quality of hay of these crops.

EXPERIMENTAL DAIRY BACTERIOLOGY

By H. L. RUSSELL, Dean of the College of Agriculture, and E. G. HASTINGS, Associate Professor of Agricultural Bacteriology in the University of Wisconsin. 12mo, cloth, 147 pages, illustrated, $1.00.

A STUDY of the bacteriological processes which must be understood before the relation of microörganisms to dairy processes can be appreciated. This guide will be found equally valuable for the student and for the practical worker.

PRINCIPLES OF RURAL ECONOMICS

By THOMAS NIXON CARVER, David A. Wells Professor of Political Economy in Harvard University. 8vo, cloth, xx + 386 pages, $1.30.

CHAPTERS on the history of agriculture, the factors of agricultural production, farm management, agricultural coöperation, the distribution of the agricultural income, and the problems of rural social life are among those included in this book.

GINN AND COMPANY PUBLISHERS

SOCIOLOGY AND SOCIAL PROGRESS

A HANDBOOK FOR STUDENTS OF SOCIOLOGY

By THOMAS NIXON CARVER

Professor of Political Economy in Harvard University

8vo, cloth, 810 pages, $2.75

SOCIOLOGY as a distinct science is new, yet society is one of the oldest subjects of human inquiry. The moralist, the metaphysician, the philosophic historian, and the man of science have all commented, more or less profoundly, upon the phenomena of society in general, upon the laws of social growth and decay, and upon the problems of social improvement. This book is published for the purpose of gathering together the more significant of these observations, found in the main outside of systematic treatises on sociology, and presenting them in convenient form for the student. The book may be used as a text-book or as the basis of a course in sociology, but it is the expectation of the author that it will be used more generally as a handbook or companion volume to one of the various text-books already in use. The selections are classified and arranged in logical sequence, so that the student may get a systematic view of the subject, through reading from a wide list of writers from Plato down to the present time.

The work is designed primarily for juniors and seniors in our colleges and universities ; but the general reader will find it thoroughly readable. Highly technical selections have been avoided, and the book contains none of the scientific jargon of many of the treatises on sociology.

GINN & COMPANY PUBLISHERS

Milligan College Library
Milligan College, Tennessee